THE PATHOLOGY
OF
LABORATORY ANIMALS

A conference sponsored by the Section on Microbiology of The New York Academy of Medicine and The New York Pathological Society

SECTION ON MICROBIOLOGY

THE NEW YORK ACADEMY OF MEDICINE

EDWARD E. FISCHEL, *Chairman*
ALAN W. BERNHEIMER, *Secretary*

THE NEW YORK PATHOLOGICAL SOCIETY

HANS POPPER, *President*
JAMES I. BERKMAN, *Secretary*

PROGRAM COMMITTEE

JOHN R. McCOY
WILLIAM E. RIBELIN

1

Conference on

THE PATHOLOGY

OF

LABORATORY ANIMALS

Compiled and Edited by

WILLIAM E. RIBELIN
Environmental Health Laboratory
American Cyanamid Company
Princeton, New Jersey

and

JOHN R. McCOY
Bureau of Biological Research
Rutgers University
New Brunswick, New Jersey

CHARLES C THOMAS · PUBLISHER
Springfield · Illinois · U.S.A.

Published and Distributed Throughout the World by
CHARLES C THOMAS • PUBLISHER
BANNERSTONE HOUSE
301-327 East Lawrence Avenue, Springfield, Illinois, U.S.A.
NATCHEZ PLANTATION HOUSE
735 North Atlantic Boulevard, Fort Lauderdale, Florida, U.S.A.

© *1965, by* CHARLES C THOMAS • PUBLISHER
Library of Congress Catalog Card Number: 65-15809

With THOMAS BOOKS careful attention is given to all details of manufacturing and design. It is the Publisher's desire to present books that are satisfactory as to their physical qualities and artistic possibilities and appropriate for their particular use. THOMAS BOOKS will be true to those laws of quality that assure a good name and good will.

Printed in the United States of America
N-1

CONTRIBUTORS

Frank Bloom: *Flushing, New York.*

Herman T. Blumenthal: *Veterans Administration Hospital, St. Louis, Missouri.*

Gerald E. Cosgrove: *Oak Ridge National Laboratory, Oak Ridge, Tennessee.*

Thelma B. Dunn: *National Cancer Institute, Bethesda, Maryland.*

Walter Fleischmann: *Veterans Administration Center, Mountain Home, Tennessee.*

Harry S. N. Greene: *Yale University School of Medicine, New Haven, Connecticut.*

A. H. Handler: *Childrens Medical Center, Boston, Massachusetts.*

J. R. M. Innes: *Bionetics Research Laboratory, Falls Church, Virginia.*

David Lehr: *New York Medical College, New York, New York.*

Phyllis G. Lemon: *Imperial Chemical Industries Limited, Alderly Park, Macclesfield, Cheshire, England. (Presently with Smith, Kline, and French Company, Welwyn Garden City, Hertfordshire, England.)*

J. Russell Lindsey: *The Johns Hopkins University School of Medicine, Baltimore, Maryland.*

Edward C. Melby: *The Johns Hopkins University School of Medicine, Baltimore, Maryland.*

A. A. Nelson: *Food and Drug Administration, Washington, D. C.*

G. E. Paget: *Imperial Chemical Industries Limited, Alderly Park, Macclesfield, Cheshire, England. (Presently with Smith, Kline, and French Company, Welwyn Garden City, Hertfordshire, England.)*

James B. Rogers: *University of Louisville School of Dentistry, Louisville, Kentucky.*

Boris H. Ruebner: *The Johns Hopkins University School of Medicine, Baltimore, Maryland.*

Katharine C. Snell: *National Cancer Institute, Bethesda, Maryland.*

Leon Sokoloff: *National Institute of Arthritis and Metabolic Diseases, Bethesda, Maryland.*

Arthur C. Upton: *Oak Ridge National Laboratory, Oak Ridge, Tennessee.*

Jean K. Weston: *Burroughs Wellcome and Company (U.S.A.), Inc., Tuckahoe, New York.*

PREFACE

T HIS PUBLICATION is a compilation of the papers and related discussions presented at the *Conference on the Pathology of Laboratory Animals* held at The New York Academy of Medicine. The conference was intended primarily for experimental pathologists, and dealt with problems which were felt to be of particular interest to individuals working in that field. This, also, is the reason for the inclusion of two papers on the interpretation of data in pathology and on the recording and reporting of such data.

Information on the lesions of the larger or domesticated laboratory animals such as the dog and cat is readily available in texts on veterinary pathology and so was not emphasized at the conference. For those persons seeking information on the lesions of the common smaller laboratory animals, it is our hope that this book will provide access to the present knowledge of this fast developing field, in which, to quote Sir William Osler, "To have patients without books is to sail uncharted seas."

We are grateful to the Trustees of the Brown-Hazen Fund of Research Corporation for the grant which made possible the invitation of distant colleagues, and to the Smith, Kline and French Foundation for underwriting the cost of preparing the manuscripts for publication. Special appreciation is given to Dr. Howard Reid Craig, Director of The New York Academy of Medicine, and to Dr. Aims C. McGuinness, Executive Secretary of the Academy's Committee on Medical Education and his staff, for guidance and administrative assistance throughout the conference.

We are particularly grateful to the late Doctor Erwin Jungherr for the excellently prepared discussion he presented following the paper on lesions of the monkey.

WILLIAM E. RIBELIN
JOHN R. McCOY

vii

CONTENTS

ix

THE PATHOLOGY
OF
LABORATORY ANIMALS

1

MUSCULOSKELETAL LESIONS IN EXPERIMENTAL ANIMALS

LEON SOKOLOFF

T HIS PAPER WILL survey briefly the non-neoplastic diseases of skeletal muscle, bone and joint in rats, mice, hamsters, guinea pigs, rabbits and monkeys. For purposes of simplicity, the disorders will be classified into two main groups: inflammatory and non-inflammatory.

SKELETAL MUSCLE

The general pathology of striated muscle in various animals has been the subject of a recent competent review by Hadlow (1). Focal areas of hyaline or Zenker's degeneration have long been recognized in animals with various infectious or debilitating diseases. The degeneration may result from many sorts of noxious agents that, it has been proposed, cause abnormal contraction and coagulation of sarcoplasm. The lesions are thus seen as non-specific by-products of many experiments. Two possible contributing mechanisms have been suggested by certain experiments. Circulating proteolytic enzymes have been shown to have a selective injurious effect on striated muscle in rabbits (2). Similar lesions have been induced by strenuous exercise in rats (3) and by large doses of cortisone in rabbits (4), and may conceivably have their counterpart in experimental stress. The degenerated fibers often provoke a severe phagocytic and inflammatory reaction even though the sarcoplasmic change is not inherently of inflammatory origin. It is, for this reason that the histologic differentiation of human myopathies including muscular dystrophies, from polymyositis remains a controversial matter even among experienced pathologists (5). By the same token, there is a certain monotony in the histologic character of muscle lesions of highly diverse origins in experimental animals. Calcification of necrotic muscle is encountered in some of these species with much greater frequency than in man.

Inflammatory Diseases of Muscle

The principal infectious diseases of skeletal muscle in laboratory animals have been of parasitic type (1). Most domestic and laboratory animals (less commonly dogs and white rats) may be affected by sarcosporidiosis and suffer little harm from it. In mice, *Sarcocystis muris* has been the commonest parasite of muscle; and in severe cases, may cause death. The infections are transmitted through cannibalism and, for this reason, appropriate isolation of mice readily brings the spread of the condition under control. Similar considerations prevent trichiniasis from being a serious problem in laboratory rats. Although a devastating myositis may be caused by *Trypanosoma cruzi,* and muscle involvement also develops in experimental infections with *Toxoplasma* and *Besnoitia,* they have not been reported as spontaneous problems.

Muscle of suckling mice is readily affected by various experimental viruses, particularly the Coxsackie type, but natural infections of this type have not been recognized.

An epizootic of acute myositis has been described in guinea pigs (6) in which there was some evidence for a transmissible causative agent. The central and peripheral nervous systems were normal. Hemorrhage and edema of the muscles were the conspicuous pathologic features of the disorder, but they were accompanied by some interstitial infiltration of acute and chronic inflammatory cells as well.

Skeletal muscle is sensitive to nutritional deficiencies of several sorts (7). Degenerative myopathy accompanied by severe inflammatory infiltration occurs in all laboratory animals, particularly herbivorous ones, receiving diets deficient in vitamin E. Although deficiency of selenium causes economically important myopathies in livestock and can do so in the experimental rats, comparable spontaneous lesions have not been recognized in laboratory animals. Degenerative myopathy also develops in scorbutic guinea pigs. The histologic features of the lesions are quite similar in the several deficiency states.

Non-inflammatory Diseases of Muscle

Considerable research has been carried out on an hereditary muscular dystrophy of an inbred strain of mouse (129, Bar Harbor) (8). The disorder becomes apparent clinically by two to three weeks of age and death usually occurs by ten weeks. It is transmitted by a single recessive autosomal gene, *Dy*. Histologically, there is considerable variation in the size of the muscle fibers within fascicles, compensatory hypertrophy accompanying atrophy in the early stages of the disease. Later in the course, there is a progression of the atrophy. Necrosis of individual fibers occurs, particularly between four and eight weeks of age. In the late lesions, there is condensation and probably some replacement fibrosis of the muscle; adipose tissue may also infiltrate to an extent. As in the human muscular dystrophies, a most conspicuous feature distinguishing the lesions from various types of myositis is a progressive diminution in regeneration of the muscle fibers that would otherwise be evidenced by hypertrophy and hyperplasia of sarcolemmal nuclei and basophilia of the sarcoplasm. Many chemical abnormalities have been described in these mice, including diminished content of myofibrillar proteins, increased rate of creatine turnover, and various abnormalities of enzyme activities in the muscle and serum. Nevertheless, the initial or basic defect in the muscle has not yet been identified.

A polymyopathy, affecting every member of an inbred line of Syrian hamsters, designated BIO 1.50, has been described (9). Histological changes were detected as early as the twentieth day of life, but clinical manifestations, in the form of muscle weakness and edema, did not appear until the sixtieth day. Death supervened five months later. The histologic changes in the skeletal muscle consisted of loss of cross-striations, pycnosis of sarcolemmal nuclei with phagocytic infiltration, and, finally, reparative phenomena. The condition did not respond to the administration of vitamin E. The disorder in hamsters differed from the dystrophy of mice in several respects—in its association with cardiac necrosis and calcification, in its greater evidences of muscle regeneration and less progressive character.

A muscular dystrophy, manifested by a progressive, and ultimately fatal weakness of the hind extremities in old Sprague-Dawley rats, has been described by Berg (10). After the second year of life, the animals displayed thoracolumbar kyphosis and several other lesions of "senescence." Histologically, the muscle lesions resembled somewhat the myopathy caused by deficiency of vitamin E and other nutrients; they did not respond, however, to the administration of the vitamin. Neural lesions, consisting chiefly of myelin degeneration of the spinal roots and peripheral nerves, were present in these animals (11), but were not believed to account for the muscle changes. Spinal paraplegia was not present as evidenced by the fact that the spinal cord was rarely demyelinated and the urinary bladders were not enlarged. We have reported thoracolumbar kyphosis of older rats associated with aseptic necrosis of vertebral epiphyses (12). At these sites, prominent osteophytes develop with frequency, and we have observed instances of spinal cord demyelinization and paraplegia associated with this vertebral condition.

Widespread calcification of soft tissues occurs frequently in old mice; it has been most common, in our experience, in the DBA/2 strain. The lesions have been recognized most often in the myocardium (13) and kidney, but may also affect skeletal muscle to some extent (Fig. 1). The lesions have been precipitated by certain diets (14), but develop spontaneously in others. In decalcified sections stained with hematoxylin and eosin, the calcific material may appear as pale blue and variably curled bodies in the muscle. They may be accompanied by a few giant cells and cause confusion with unidentified parasites.

SKELETON

There are two principal structural differences between bones of small laboratory rodents and those of larger species, that must be kept in mind in comparisons of bone diseases in laboratory animals to those found in man: 1. In rodents, many of the epiphyses of the bones remain open past the onset of sexual maturity and, in some instances, throughout the life span of the animals. The distribution and rate of epiphyseal maturation vary not only between species, but also among various inbred strains of the same species (15). 2. In many small mammals, including the laboratory mouse and rat, there is no osteone or Haversian system in the compact bone, as there is in man and other large species (16).

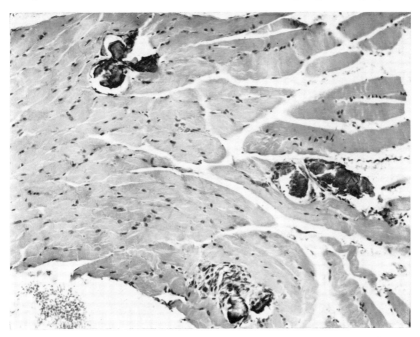

FIGURE 1. Spontaneous pathologic calcification of levator ani muscle, fifteen-month-old DBA/2 JN mouse. (Hematoxylin and eosin, x 155.)

Inflammatory Diseases of Bone

Hematogenous osteomyelitis is not a common spontaneous condition, but may occur with several types of bacteremia and be an integral part of infectious arthritis. In old rats housed in hanging cages with wire mesh bottoms, decubitus ulceration of the hind paws occurs with some frequency. Extension into the tarsometatarsal bones may result. Maceration of the skin of the paws by moist wood-shaving litter may also lead to destructive mycotic infections (17). Swelling of the paws is a feature of the chronic cutaneous form of infectious ectromelia in mice (18). Necrosis of underlying soft tissue and bone may develop. Histologically, the large intracytoplasmic inclusion bodies in the epidermis are quite characteristic in this condition.

Non-inflammatory Diseases of Bone

Inherited anomalies of the axial and appendicular skeleton, as well as the skull and tail are exceedingly common and have been the subject of numerous genetic studies in mice (19), and, to a lesser extent, in rats and rabbits. Some of the variation is caused by single genes, some by multiple ones. Occasionally there are variations in the apparent inheritance patterns, e.g., in the configuration of the sacrum in mice (20), that defy genetic interpretation. Mild asymmetry of the skeleton is fairly frequent both with respect to epiphyseal maturation and the length of the bones in mice.

Nutritional disorders of the skeleton are readily produced in small laboratory animals, but contemporary commercial laboratory chows have largely done away with the well-recognized patterns of rickets and scorbutic osteoarthropathy (21). Skeletal disease, once the rule rather than the exception in captive monkeys, has also largely disappeared since the improvement of the dietary regimens in these species. Considerable interest was evinced at one time in certain peculiar forms of hyperostosis of the facial bones in primates, resulting in tumor-like enlargements (so-called pseudogoundou (22)). These lesions still occur from time to time and it is uncertain whether they represent a specific nosologic entity of unknown etiology, or are a peculiar form of simian rickets. We have studied two cases from the National Zoological Park in Washington, D. C., through the courtesy of Dr. W. H. Eyestone. In both animals (a golden baboon and a capuchin monkey), the disorder was not confined to the face but affected the limbs as well. The epiphyseal plates were greatly thickened and irregular (Fig. 2) and there was much new formation of osteoid tissue. The picture thus closely resembled rickets although there was an unusually severe osteoclastic reaction associated with proliferation of fibroblasts in the adjacent marrow.

Arrest of growth and sealing off of the epiphyseal plates accompanies inanition in animals with ununited epiphyses and later

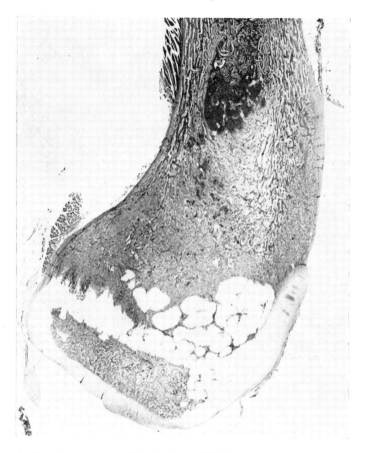

FIGURE 2. Pseudogoundou, golden baboon. This is a sagittal section of the distal end of the femur. The epiphyseal plate is greatly enlarged and irregular. There is a great increase of disorderly trabeculae in the metaphysis and epiphysis. (Hematoxylin and eosin, x 3.)

leads to a reduction in the amount of bone in the cortex. It is common usage to speak of induced hypoplastic or atrophic bone in experimental animals as osteoporosis. The objection has sometimes been raised that since mice and rats normally have no Haversian system, the analogy to human osteoporosis is inaccurate. The latter condition is a fairly complex process involving excessive resorption of bone about Haversian canals. In this regard, it is appropriate to note that secondary osteone formation has at times been produced in rats by several means, including certain regimens of calcium deprivation (16). Senescent atrophy of bone has been described in mice. In addition, a pattern of vascular resorption of bone, regarded as analagous to human osteoporosis, was present in some animals (23). We have at times observed similar lesions in old mice that were associated with osteoclastic activity. This appearance suggests the possibility of early osteitis fibrosa resulting from coexisting renal disease in these mice.

Aseptic necrosis of bone occurs with some frequency in laboratory rodents, particularly in epiphyses (12). In many instances, they appear to be silent clinically, but they may result in one of three syndromes at times: 1. fracture of the neck of the femur in old females of certain strains of mice; 2. osteophytosis and occasionally transverse myelopathy in old rats with thoracolumbar kyphosis; and 3. rarely, collapse of an epiphysis with secondary arthropathy. In some instances, there is evidence of arterial obliteration as basis for the bone necrosis; in most, however, the cause of the infarcts is unknown.

Fractures occur with some frequency and have certain sites of predilection in various species. In rats and mice, the lesions are most often found in the tibia and fibula. They heal spontaneously, usually with marked anterior bowing (17) and are detected only when specifically sought for at autopsy. We have recently observed such fractures in 10 per cent of a large group of mice housed in hanging cages with wide-meshed screen floors. In other mice, housed in shoebox type of cages having solid plastic floors covered with wood shavings, such fractures occurred only in approximately 1 per cent of the groups. In rabbits, fractures of the spine may occur if the animals struggle in restraining boxes, and lead to transection of the spinal cord with paraplegia. Fractures of the bones are common in primates taken in the wild.

Osteopetrosis has been observed as a form of lethal hereditary disease of rabbits (24), transmitted by a single recessive gene. The serum of affected animals had low concentrations of calcium, elevated phosphorus and alkaline phosphatase activity. The pathological mechanisms involved were uncertain, but hypertrophy of the parathyroid glands suggested primary hyperparathyroidism to the author.

A form of osteosclerosis also occurs in an inbred strain of rat, in which the trait is inherited as a simple Mendelian recessive. The condition is characterized by deficient resorption of bone, and disappears between thirty and 100 days of age. Osteoclasts are normal as is parathyroid function. A defect in the oxidative metabolism of citrate that could account for much of the pathologic process has recently been found (25).

JOINTS

Inflammatory agents may gain access to joints either by direct penetration, by extension from adjacent bone or by seeding from the blood stream (26). The patterns of reaction that they induce are quite similar to those produced in other tissues, but are modified by the pluripotentiality of granulation tissue in this area. Whereas in other sites, this tissue eventuates only in scar formation, in joints it may also mature into hyaline or fibrous cartilage, bone and synovial tissue. This capacity for multiple development of proliferating fibroblasts also causes variable composition of reactive changes in joints affected by degenerative and traumatic diseases.

Inflammatory Diseases of Joints

Three principal sorts of histologic process may be distinguished in hematogenous infections of joints in laboratory animals:

1. Bacteremias of many sorts result in embolic seeding of the bone marrow and development, within twenty-four to forty-eight hours, of focal osteomyelitis. In young animals of any sort or in older rodents with open epiphyses, the metaphysis rather than the epiphysis is the usual site of localization. Extension into the joint space usually occurs by way of the periosteal ring, i.e., the soft tissue gap in the cortex of the bone at the metaphysis. This is the common pattern of sporadic suppurative infectious joint disease encountered in laboratory animals. Large joints—elbow, knee, wrist and ankle—are involved.

2. Under experimental conditions in rabbits and more commonly as a spontaneous finding in larger animals, including livestock, chronic synovitis with villous hypertrophy of the soft tissues of the joint and pannus formation develops after repeated intravenous injections of bacteria, or hematogenous infections following intravenous introduction of homologous vaccines.

3. In rats, infection with *Mycoplasma arthritidis* (pleuropneumonia-like organisms, PPLO) is the commonest cause of spontaneous inflammatory joint disease. The PPLO are filtrable agents that frequently reside in various tissues without causing a detectable inflammatory response. They are, however, at times evoked from a dormant into a virulent state resulting in severe sporadic or epizootic disease. This group of organisms was first discovered during studies of the infectivity of tumors in rats (Woglom's pyogenic virus). They are difficult to culture but are still readily transmitted for experimental purposes by inoculation of rats with contaminated tumors, e.g., Murphy-Sturm lymphosarcoma. The organisms also appear to be activated by other manipulations of the host. This probably accounts for much of the "arthritis" that has been reported to be induced by a variety of non-specific means and makes difficult the interpretation of experimental arthritis in this species.

The principal site of involvement is the periarticular soft tissue of the wrist and ankle regions and the caudal vertebrae. In one careful study of experimentally induced PPLO infection, the earliest lesions were found in the synovial tissue of the joints. The inflammatory reaction then rapidly extended to the periarticular soft tissues (27). In one unpublished outbreak of the condition in young JR rats inoculated with Yoshida sarcoma, that we have studied through the courtesy of Dr. Morris Belkin, the major lesions were found in the tendon sheaths rather than the joints (Fig. 3). Small suppurative foci were present but areas of infiltration by lymphocytes and mononuclear cells also could be found even in the early lesions.

The end results of the inflammation caused by PPLO vary from apparent resolution to massive bony ankylosis of the affected regions. Much of the bony deformity in such instances is due to exuberant periosteal new bone formation. Although the skeletal lesions are the principal manifestations of the infection, conjunctivitis and urethritis also may be present. Partial protection from the disorder has been obtained by pretreatment of rats with tumor exudate in which the PPLO contaminant had been destroyed by ultra-violet light (28). A vaccine has, however, not been developed for systematic control of the infection. It does respond to broad spectrum antibiotics.

Streptobacillus moniliformis, a common relatively benign in-

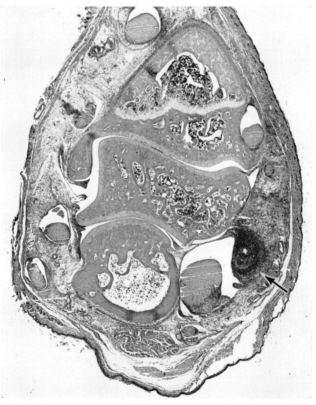

FIGURE 3. Early *Mycoplasma arthritidis* infection, ankle of young JR rat inoculated with Yoshida sarcoma. A small abscess is present in the wall of the tendon sheath of the flexor digitorum profundus muscle *(arrow)*. There is a massive cellulitis with swelling of the periarticular soft tissues of the ankle and leg, including periosteum, subcutaneous tissue, and synovium. No exudate is present in the joint spaces and the bone and cartilage are intact. (Hematoxylin and eosin, x 13.)

habitant of the upper respiratory tract of laboratory rats, has caused several epizootics in mice (29). The disease has been transmitted by housing the mice in the proximity of rats, and apparently also by contaminated litter and food of the mice shared with the rats. The infection is a severe one in mice, most of the animals dying of fulminant bacteremia. Polyarthritis develops early in approximately one of five surviving animals. One of the peculiarities of this organism is that it quite readily undergoes transformation into a minute, filtrable form (so-called L form) that retains a capacity for virulence. It has thus, a superficial similarity to the PPLO, but the latter is a fixed species rather than a variant form of another bacterium. In mice, the histologic appearance of the lesions reported has varied in different laboratories. One strain of *S. moniliformis,* infective for the joints of rats, caused the first pattern of hematogenous arthritis noted above: the primary change occurred in the bone marrow (30). In another account of the lesions in mice (27), bone, joint and periarticular tissue were affected in a suppurative process but the earliest changes was not studied. Although most bacterial joint diseases, including those due to *M. arthritidis* and *S. moniliformis,* become apparent grossly within a few days of infection, the appearance of the lesions may be delayed as long as thirty days when the mice are infected with the L form organisms.

Another type of epizootic polyarthritis, caused by a filtrable agent, has been described in young albino mice. The joint disorder was associated with pneumonia. Although the causative agent was filtrable, PPLO could not be recovered (31).

Arthritis of mice also is caused by *Corynebacterium kutscheri* (32, 33). It is particularly likely to occur in debilitated, tumor-bearing animals. The tibiotarsal region is the site of predilection. Histologically, the lesions are characterized by coagulation necrosis and accumulation of masses of Gram-positive diphtheroids.

It has been a frequent, although not often reported or appropriately investigated experience of many laboratories, to have spontaneous sporadic arthritis appear in old rats. The wrist and ankle regions are the principal sites affected. Whether these represent infection by PPLO or other agent is presently unknown.

Non-inflammatory Diseases of Joints

Congenital dysplasia of the hip and shoulder, analagous in many ways to the lesions common in certain breeds of dogs, man and certain other mammals, has been described under the name "splayleg" in rabbits (34). The contours of the joint are poorly formed in the earliest stages of the condition: The acetabulum is shallow and the head of the femur subluxated for this reason. As in other subluxated hips, secondary osteoarthritis may supervene in surviving animals. The lesion has an hereditary basis, and, in one study, was apparently transmitted by a single recessive autosomal gene (35).

Achondroplasia of the hip in rabbits was described by Crary and Sawin (36) as a recessive chondrodystrophy affecting not only the head of the femur but also the cartilage of the ear. Others have observed osteoarthritis developing as a later phenomenon in these abnormal hips (34).

Osteoarthritis, having many of the characteristics of degenerative joint disease, occurs in old individuals of each of the laboratory animal species, although it has been least studied in primates. The lesions are comparable to the human counterpart in all respects except that focal necrosis of chondrocytes is a conspicuous feature of the degenerated cartilage in small animals. The genetic nature of the lesions has been demonstrated in mice, in which its inheritance is polygenic, recessive and not sex-linked (20). Rats are relatively resistant to degenerative joint disease, in contrast to mice. In most species, the knee is most often affected, although in rats, the ankle is more often involved than in other rodents. Male mice have more frequent and more severe osteoarthritis than do females.

Minute cystic areas of chondromucoid degeneration appear in small numbers in the articular cartilage of older rats, but do not progress to erosion and osteoarthritis (17).

Recently, an hereditary abnormality of the intervertebral discs has been reported in mice having the Pintail (*Pt*) trait (38). This mutation results in reduction of the size of the nucleus pulposus in adults and accelerates fibrous degeneration of the disc. Partial ossification of the annulus fibrosus also was observed.

REFERENCES

1. HADLOW, W. J.: Diseases of skeletal muscle. In, *Comparative Neuropathology*. J. R. M. Innes, and L. Z. Saunders, eds. New York, Academic Press 1962, p. 147.
2. KELLNER, A., and ROBERTSON, T.: Selective necrosis of cardiac and skeletal muscle induced experimentally by means of proteolytic enzyme solutions given intravenously. *J. Exp. Med. 99*:387, 1954.
3. HIGHMAN, B., and ALTLAND, P. D.: Effects of exercise and training on serum enzyme and tissue changes in rats. *Amer. J. Physiol., 205*:162, 1963.
4. ELLIS, J. T.: Necrosis and regeneration of skeletal muscle in cortisone treated rabbits. *Arch. Path., 52*:221, 1951.
5. GREENFIELD, J. G., SHY, G. M., ALVORD, E. C., JR., and BERG, L.: *An Atlas of Muscle Pathology in Neuromuscular Diseases*. Edinburgh, Livingstone, 1957.
6. SAUNDERS, L. Z.: Myositis in guinea pigs, *J. Nat. Cancer Inst., 20:* 899, 1958.
7. MASON, K. E.: Effect of nutritional deficiencies upon muscle. In, *The Structure and Function of Muscle*. G. H. Bourne, ed. New York, Acad. Press, 1960. Vol. 3, p. 171.
8. HARMAN, P. J., TASSONI, J. P., CURTIS, R. L., and HOLLINSHEAD, M. B.: Muscular dystrophy in the mouse. In, *Muscular Dystrophy in Man and Animals*. G. H. Bourne, and N. Gollarz, eds. New York, Hafner, 1963, p. 407.
9. HOMBURGER, F., BAKER, J. R., NIXON, C. W., and WHITNEY, R.: Primary generalized polymyopathy and cardiac necrosis in an inbred line of Syrian hamsters. *Med. Exp., 6*:339, 1962.
10. BERG, B. N.: Muscular dystrophy in aging rats. *J. Geront., 11*:134, 1956.
11. BERG, B. N., WOLF, A., and SIMMS, H. S.: Degenerative lesions of spinal roots and peripheral nerves in aging rats. *Gerontologia, 6*:72, 1962.
12. SOKOLOFF, L., and HABERMANN, R. T.: Idiopathic necrosis of bone in small laboratory animals. *Arch. Path., 65*:323, 1958.
13. VAN DER SCHOOT, H. C. M.: *Cardopathia Calcificans in Mice.* Amsterdam, Thesis, University of Leiden, Rototype 1962. An abbreviated translation by Dr. V. Swaen may be obtained from Dr. T. B. Dunn, National Cancer Institute, Bethesda, Maryland.

14. HIGHMAN, B., and DAFT, F. S.: Calcified lesions in C₃H mice given purified low protein diets. Tissues involved: heart, skeletal muscle, arteries and lungs. *Arch. Path., 52:*221, 1951.

15. SOKOLOFF, L., JAY G. E., JR., and RANDOLPH, L. K.: Variation in epiphyseal maturation of medial epicondyle of humerus in inbred strains of mice. *Proc. Soc. Exp. Biol. Med., 103:*491, 1960.

16. ENLOW, D. H.: Functions of the Haversian system. *Amer. J. Anat., 110:*269, 1962.

17. SOKOLOFF, L.: Joint diseases of laboratory animals. *J. Nat. Cancer Inst., 20:*965, 1958.

18. SAUNDERS, L. Z.: Mouse pox (infectious ectromelia). *J. Nat. Cancer Inst., 20:*875, 1958.

19. GRÜNEBERG, H.: *The Genetics of the Mouse.* The Hague, Nijhoff, 1952. 2nd ed.

20. SOKOLOFF, L., CRITTENDEN, L. B., YAMAMOTO, R. S., and JAY, G. E., JR.: The genetics of degenerative joint disease in mice. *Arthritis Rheum., 5:*531, 1962.

21. PIRANI, C. L., BLY, C. G., and SUTHERLAND, K.: Scorbutic arthropathy in the guinea pig. *Arch. Path., 49:*710, 1950.

22. RUCH, T. C.: *Diseases of Laboratory Primates.* Philadelphia, Saunders, 1959. Chapt. 12, p. 472.

23. SILBERBERG, M., and SILBERBERG, R.: Osteoarthrosis and osteoporosis in senile mice. *Gerontologia (Basel), 6:*91, 1962.

24. PEARCE, L.: Hereditary osteopetrosis of the rabbit. 3. Pathologic observations; skeletal abnormalities. *J. Exp. Med., 92:*591, 1950.

25. VAES, G. M., and NICHOLS, G., JR.: Bone metabolism in a mutant strain of rats which lack bone resorption. *Amer. J. Physiol., 205:*461, 1963.

26. SOKOLOFF, L.: Comparative pathology of arthritis. *Advance Vet. Sci., 6:*193, 1960.

27. WARD, J. R., and JONES, R. S.: The pathogenesis of mycoplasmal (PPLO) arthritis in rats. *Arth. Rheum., 5:*163, 1962.

28. HERSHBERGER, L. G., HANSEN, L. M., and CALHOUN, D. W.: Immunization to experimental arthritis in rats. *Arth. Rheum., 3:*387, 1960.

29. FREUNDT, E. A.: Arthritis caused by Streptobacillus moniliformis and pleuropneumonialike organisms in small rodents. *Lab. Invest., 8:*1358, 1959.

30. LERNER, E. M., II., and SOKOLOFF, L.: The pathogenesis of bone and joint infection produced in rats by Streptobacillus moniliformis. *Arch. Path., 67:*364, 1959.

31. COLLIER, W. A.: Über eine Pneumonie—und Arthritis Epizootie bei weissen Mäusen. *Schweiz. Z. allg. Path., 11:*133, 1948.

32. FISCHL, V., KOECH, M., and KUSSAT, E.: Infektartinritis bei Muriden *Z. Hyg. Infektionskr., 112:*421, 1931.

33. WOLFF, H. L.: On some spontaneous infections observed in mice; *C. kutscheri,* and *C. pseudo-tuberculosis. Antonie van Leeuwenhoek. J. Microbiol. Serol., 16:*105, 1950.

34. INNES, J. R. M.: Inherited dysplasia of the hip joint in dogs and rabbits. *Lab. Invest., 8:*1170, 1959.

35. DA ROSA, F. M.: Uma nova mutação, luxação congénita da anca no coelho. *Rev. Med. Vet., 40:*103, 1945.

36. CRARY, D. D., and SAWIN, P. B.: A second recessive achondroplasia in the domestic rabbit. *J. Hered., 43:*255, 1952.

37. BERRY, R. J.: Genetically controlled degeneration of the nucleus pulposus in the mouse. *J. Bone Joint Surg., 43B:*387, 1961.

DISCUSSION

Dr. Ronald D. Hunt: About your comment on skeletal muscle calcification: I have seen this in mouse and it is frequently associated with the calcification of epicardium and myocardium. We can increase the incidence by feeding high calcium diets. The greatest incidence has occurred in female mice and not just the male mice.

Dr. Sokoloff: Our experience is largely confined to male mice because we want to avoid the endocrine contributions of pregnancy in our arthritis experiments.

So far as diet is concerned, I think the first time the muscle calcification was reported was in connection with a low protein diet that Dr. Highman and Dr. Daft used in C_3H mice years ago. The contribution of different calcium diets to this lesion seems an obvious sort of thing to study. Dr. Dunn was good enough to let me have a copy of a translation of a recent Netherland monograph dealing with this cardiopathy, and certain experiments were carried out with steroid hormones. Dr. Dunn would be willing to supply mimeographed copies of the translation to any interested parties (see Reference 13).

Question: Is there any particular relation between ossification of the muscle and its incidence in calcification of the heart? Do you distinguish the various segments or site of the heart such as the pericardium or myocardium, and what is the incidence? Is it related to vascular insufficiency or metabolic factors?

Dr. Sokoloff: This has been reported a little differently, as I gather it, in various studies. It is my recollection that it was described as calcific pericarditis in the studies of DBA mice by Dr. Hare and Dr. Stewart some years ago. I have been more impressed with the calcification of the myocardium in our animals. Occasionally this occurs in the epicardium as well. I think one sees most of this in the left ventricle and interventricular system.

The difference between this lesion in the striated muscle and the one in the heart is that, although in the heart there is considerable fibrosis, in the striated muscle one does not find fibrosis but an inflammatory reaction. There is a local phagocytic response that one doesn't see in the myocardium. I don't recall seeing dying cells of this sort in the myocardial calcification.

Question: Dr. Sokoloff, I would like to ask a question and you may want to refer it to Dr. A. A. Nelson or someone else, but in the course of chronic toxicity studies we routinely examine bone. After looking at a great many bones from a great many studies I have yet to see any lesions induced by the feeding of chemicals or drugs. I wonder how common drug-induced changes in bone are.

Dr. Sokoloff: I would just as soon defer the answer to Dr. Nelson. Growth arrest is very common with many forms of toxicity, such as that due to selenium and malnutrition.

Dr. A. A. Nelson: Disease of the bone are rare in our experience, but in the Sept. 1963 issue of *Toxicology and Applied Pharmacology* there is a paper by Webb and Hansen where they are dealing with 2 per cent of methylsalicylate which caused in young rats a quite pronounced excess of spongy bone.

Dr. T. C. Jones: I wonder if I might comment on the fibrocystic state in the monkeys with "big jaw disease." Although most of the evidence in monkeys is indirect, there is some evidence in other species that this actually can result from a calcium-phosphorus imbalance. A one-to-one dietary ratio between phosphorus and calcium is common and this is too much phosphorus. This might well be an explanation for this lesion. We still see it in pet monkeys as well as some laboratory ones.

Dr. Sokoloff: Do you see the same changes in the epiphyseal plates that our monkeys have?

Dr. Jones: Yes, we do, but the lesions in the jaw are most prominent.

Dr. Sokoloff: Then why isn't this rickets?

Dr. Delwin Bokelman: In the past year Dr. Krook, at Cornell, did some work with this bone disease of monkeys (*Cornell Veterinarian, 52:*469–492, 1962). He has found that there is parathyroid hyperplasia associated with this condition and that this bone change was a secondary condition.

Dr. Sokoloff: It is my recollection that secondary parathyroid hyperplasia in rickets was demonstrated by Dr. Pappenheimer thirty odd years ago; so I would anticipate this sort of finding.

Question: Some time ago Dr. Leon Saunders described a spontaneous myositis in guinea pigs (*J. Nat. Cancer Inst., 20:*899–901, 1958) which we have likewise encountered. Are you familiar with this? Do you know anything about the incidence of it?

Dr. Sokoloff: It appears to be relatively infrequent. Histologically it was hard to tell from a viral or nutritional myositis, but it is my recollection that Dr. Saunders was able in the preliminary experiments to transmit an agent from the muscle of these guinea pigs to others, but in follow-up subcultures it was not possible to get it back. Whether it is of an infectious or other type has not been established.

Question: In our laboratory we do not have a sledge type microtome, so routinely for studies of bone we decalcify the bone and then study it. I have often wondered if we might be missing some bone resorption by this continual use of demineralized bone. Do you think that this could be so?

Dr. Sokoloff: Oh yes. I don't think you need a sledge type microtome to get this information. You can get it by using an ordinary microtome, but, of course, keep the knife separate from your soft tissue knife. A satisfactory sectioning machine has been developed by the Bronwill Company, Rochester, New York. It costs about $1,600. It works on a diamond wheel over which water flows. The bones are embedded in one of a number of plastics.

2

PATHOLOGY OF THE
RETICULOENDOTHELIAL SYSTEM

G. E. COSGROVE AND A. C. UPTON

INTRODUCTION

THE LESIONS of the RES to be described here are those we encounter frequently in the laboratory mice of our own colony,
which are used chiefly in short-term and long-term survival experiments on the study of radiation injury and repair. We will not attempt to review comprehensively the pathology of the reticuloendothelial system (RES) of the laboratory animal. This subject,
involving diverse lesions of many organs and species, is too broad
and complex to fall within the scope of the present survey. Those
seeking detailed discussions of specific aspects of this topic are referred to earlier reviews; i.e., on the pathologic anatomy of reticular tissue of the mouse (Dunn, 1954), the diseases of hemic and
lymphatic systems of the rat (Ratcliffe, 1942) and larger animals
(Smith and Jones, 1958), and the leukoses of fowl (Jungherr,
1943), cats (Holzworth, 1960a, b), and other animals (Engle-
breth-Holm, 1942; Moulton, 1961).

RETICULOENDOTHELIAL SYSTEM

The RES is composed of a series of interrelated cells and their
cellular and fibrillar derivatives. Some idea of the variety of the cell
types is gained by studying the diagrams of Doan (Fig. 1) and of
Rebuck and LoGrippo (Fig. 2); however, the precise interrela-
tion among the various types of cells remains speculative.

The important organs of the RES are the spleen, liver, bone
marrow, lymph nodes, Peyer's patches, and thymus. To these may
be added the tonsils and lymphoid aggregates in the lung and
elsewhere. It should be noted, however, that the RES is scattered

---

*Operated by Union Carbide Corporation for the U.S. Atomic Energy Commission.

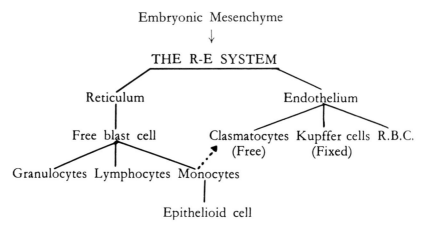

FIGURE 1. The genealogy of the RES. From Doan (1957).

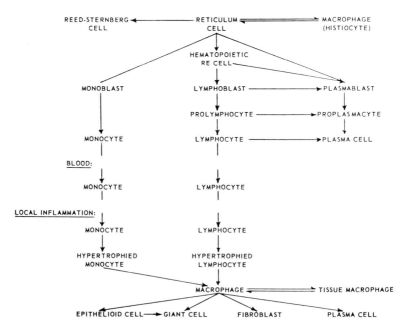

FIGURE 2. Interrelationships of cells in the RE, macrophage, lymphocyte, and plasma cell series in man. From Rebuck and LoGrippo (1961).

throughout the body, no organ being completely devoid of reticuloendothelial elements. The essentially ubiquitous distribution of the RES is exemplified by the demonstration that pluripotent precursors of hemic and lymphoid cells circulate in the peripheral blood (Popp, 1960; Goodman and Hodgson, 1962) and are present in appreciable numbers within the peritoneal cavity (Cole, 1963; Goodman, 1963).

CLASSIFICATION OF RETICULOENDOTHELIAL DISEASES

Diseases of the RES and its derived cells are usually classified in two major categories, neoplastic and non-neoplastic. A classification of the neoplasms of the mouse (Table I) was developed by Dunn (1954), since classification based on human diseases of the RES, such as that of Marshall (Table II), are not completely applicable to rodents. The major neoplastic diseases we will discuss include lymphomas and leukemias derived from lymphocyte and granulocyte precursors and from the reticulum cell.

Non-neoplastic diseases fall into many categories (Table III). Because our experience with some of these categories is limited, we will confine our remarks to the major non-neoplastic lesions encountered in our own mice.

TABLE I
CLASSIFICATION OF NEOPLASTIC AND RELATED CONDITIONS OF THE
RETICULAR SYSTEM OF THE MOUSE
From Dunn (1954)

Cell of Origin	*Neoplastic condition*
1) Undifferentiated	Stem-cell leukemia
2) Lymphocyte	Lymphocytic neoplasm - localized (lymphosarcoma)
	Lymphocytic neoplasm - generalized (lymphocytic leukemia)
3) Granulocyte	Granulocytic leukemia (rarely a chloroleukemia)
4) Reticulum cell	Type A
	Reticulum-cell sarcoma - localized
	Monocytic leukemia - generalized
	Type B
	Hodgkin's-like lesion
	Type C
	Potter lesion - (doubtfully neoplastic)
5) Plasmacyte	Plasmacytoma - localized
	Plasmacytic leukemia - generalized
6) Tissue mast cell	Mastocytoma - localized
	Mast-cell leukemia - generalized
7) Miscellaneous and unclassified	

TABLE II
NEOPLASMS OF THE RETICULAR TISSUE
Modified from Marshall (1956)

Group I	Unifocal benign neoplasms - (little or no tendency to extension)
	1. Benign lymphoma of rectum
	2. Primary solitary plasmacytoma
	3. Possibly some "stroma reticulosa" of thyroid
Group II	Multifocal benign neoplasms - (progressive extension, without evidence of true malignancy)
	1. Lymphoid follicular reticulosis
	2. Hodgkin's disease
	3. Multiple myelomatosis
	4. Acute leukemia
	5. Polycythemia vera
	6. Chronic leukemia
	(and others)
Group III	Malignant neoplasms
	1. Lymphosarcoma
	2. Reticulum cell sarcoma
	3. "Hodgkin's Sarcoma"
	4. Plasmacytic sarcoma

TABLE III
NON-NEOPLASTIC ALTERATIONS OF RES
Modified from Dunn (1954)

A. Functional responses
　　1. Stress reactions and adrenal cortical hormone
　　2. Other endocrine effects
B. Hyperplasia of particular cell types
　　1. Reticulum cells
　　2. Plasma cells
　　3. Mast cell
C. Aging and degenerative changes
　　1. Aging
　　2. Hemosiderosis
　　3. Amyloidosis
　　4. Cyst formation
　　5. "Mesenteric disease"
D. Reactions to injury
　　1. Inflammation
　　2. Degeneration
　　3. Necrosis
　　4. Atrophy
　　5. Hypertrophy
　　6. Hyperplasia

Reticuloendothelial Neoplasms

The principal RES neoplasms (Table IV) of the strains of mice in greatest use in our colony are: (1) thymic lymphoma, with varying degrees of dissemination, from involvement of the thymus alone to generalized lymphomatosis; (2) myeloid (granulocytic) leukemia, and (3) reticulum cell sarcoma.

Neoplasms of vascular origin, including hemangioendothelio-mas and hemangiosarcomas, plasma cell tumors, and mast cell neo-plasms are seen comparatively rarely in our material.

TABLE IV

INCIDENCE OF SPONTANEOUS LEUKEMIA AND LYMPHOMA IN VARIOUS STRAINS OF MICE

Mouse Strain	Sex	Number Studied	Thymic Lymphoma	Mean Age at Death (Days)	Myeloid Leukemia	Mean Age at Death (Days)	Other[a]	Mean Age at Death (Days)	Total
LAF	♀	437	3[b]	771	1[b]	730	35[b]	850	39
	♂	391	1	942	0.5	840	22	832	24
RF	♀	1081	10	544	3	590	38	617	51
	♂	267	3	376	4	464	31	599	38
1C₃F₁	♀	415	1	769	1	881	10	861	12
	♂	233	1	787	0.5	823	2	945	4

[a]Predominantly reticulum cell sarcoma.
[b]% incidence.

Clinical Signs

We have associated certain clinical features with each of our three major types of mouse leukemia and lymphoma, as follows:

THYMIC LYMPHOMA: This is a rapidly progressive disease. The course from the first outward signs of illness to death is a matter of a few days or weeks, and the mouse often appears well-nourished at the time of death. The precipitating cause of death frequently is respiratory embarrassment from a greatly enlarged thymus. Breathing is labored, and the blood is poorly oxygenated. This is observed most easily in albino mice, whose eyes and lips appear conspicuously darker than normal (cyanotic). The respiratory diffi-culty may be due in part to compression of the trachea and in part to filling of the thorax by the large thymus. When the disease spreads beyond the thymus, the mouse usually shows enlargement of lymph nodes in the neck. In the absence of generalized dissemi-nation, abdominal palpation is negative and may fatally aggravate respiratory distress by increasing the pressure on the neck and chest.

MYELOID LEUKEMIA: This is a disease of short clinical course. The affected mouse shows weight loss while the abdomen appears enlarged. Anemia is conspicuous, especially in albino mice, being manifested by pallor of the eyes, lips, and skin of the ears and tail.

There is no associated respiratory difficulty. Enlargement of lymph nodes usually is not externally discernible. On abdominal palpation the spleen and liver feel smooth and large, with discrete edges.

RETICULUM CELL SARCOMA: The clinical features of this disease are variable since the sites of predilection are so varied. This neoplasm is typically of several months' duration, with a slowly progressive enlargement of the involved group of lymph nodes, which may become massive. The resulting enlargement of nodes and visceral organs masks any weight loss, so that the mice usually appear outwardly well-nourished, or even abnormally large. The extent of abdominal enlargement may be extreme. Palpation of the abdomen reveals firm nodules of uncertain origin. On internal examination, these large nodules are usually found in the liver, spleen, and mesenteric lymph node. Sudden increase in the size of tumor masses, whether peripheral or visceral, usually indicates hemorrhage and/or infarction. Such hemorrhage may be massive in organs or in cavities. Respiratory difficulty and cyanosis are not common.

Hemogram

The peripheral blood contains abnormal cells in the leukemic forms of these diseases; that is, in the presence of generalized thymic lymphoma, there may be lymphoblastic cells in the blood, but a minority of thymic neoplasms show this degree of lymphomatosis.

In myeloid leukemia, abnormal cells of the granulocytic series are almost always present and the leucocyte count may be extremely high. The abnormal cells are principally at the myelocyte and metamyelocyte stages of maturation, but some promyelocytes and a few myeloblasts are usually seen. The packed red cell volume decreases rapidly in myeloid leukemia, reaching levels as low as 18-20 per cent terminally.

Reticulum cell neoplasms are not usually accompanied by leukemic manifestations, but when present such manifestations are those of monocytic leukemia. A sudden fall in packed red cell volume may be observed as a complication of extensive hemorrhage in reticulum cell tumors.

Gross and Microscopic Pathology

THYMIC LYMPHOMA: The thymus is enlarged to varying degrees, often filling the anterior mediastinum, and is pale and friable. The remaining viscera may show no gross involvement, or these may be variable enlargement of lymph nodes, liver, spleen, kidney, ovary, and uterus. Infiltration of darkly colored organs, such as the liver, is associated with change to a lighter color, toward grey or white.

If the spleen is cut longitudinally, white nodules and cords of neoplastic tissue are seen centrally; that is, in the white pulp. The enlarged lymph nodes are pale and friable. The involved ovary is whiter than is typical for a granulosa cell tumor or other neoplasm of ovarian origin. There may be a frosting-like coating of neoplastic cells over pleura and pericardium.

Histological preparations from involved organs show extensive infiltration by monomorphous, immature, lymphoid cells. Cuffs of these cells are commonly found along pulmonary vessels and bronchi.

Further details of the pathology of this neoplasm have been described and illustrated by Dunn (1954).

MYELOID LEUKEMIA: The organs principally involved are the bone marrow, spleen, and liver. The latter maintain their usual form but are enlarged, pale red, and not nodular. Transection of the spleen reveals diffuse involvement without the nodularity characteristic of the lymphomas. The lymph nodes vary in size from normal to somewhat enlarged. In some cases, the infiltrate has a greenish color (chloroleukemia). Punctate hemorrhagic infarcts of the lung are commonly present.

In histologic sections, the infiltrating cells in our mice have always been of the neutrophilic series. Myelocytes and promyelocytes are numerous. Rarely, megakaryocytes are encountered, but foci of erythropoiesis are lacking. Ischemic necrosis of the leukemic bone marrow is common in the long bones and sternum (Upton and Furth, 1954).

RETICULUM CELL SARCOMA: Nodules are predominant in this disease. The neoplastic nodules are yellowish-white and tend to be large. There are several patterns of gross involvement. One common pattern consists of nodules throughout the lymph nodes, spleen, liver, kidneys, and Peyer's patches of the intestine, but not in the thymus. Another common form does not involve the peripheral lymph nodes to any degree but is characterized by marked involvement of the mesenteric lymph node, liver, spleen, and kidney, as well as Peyer's patches. The third form is more highly localized, consisting of one or only a few nodules in one or more organs. When only one nodule is found it may be in a lymph node, a Peyer's patch, the spleen, or occasionally, in the uterus. The large nodules in this disease are prone to coalesce and to undergo degeneration, infarction, and hemorrhage. These complications may be associated with extra-neoplastic hemorrhage in tissues or cavities. Chylous ascites is a frequent result of abdominal involvement. Infarcted nodules may develop into abscesses, particularly in the wall of the intestinal tract.

We have not tried to separate these lesions histologically into the types A, B, and C of Dunn (1954), although most of them fall into one of these categories. The infiltrations are composed predominantly of large polymorphous reticulum cells with abundant, somewhat eosinophilic cytoplasm, although their microscopic appearance is irregular. Phagocytic activity by these cells is variable. The reticulum cells tend to be present in poorly bounded masses and may or may not be accompanied by intermingling lymphocytes and granulocytes. Sometimes the neoplastic lesions contain multinucleate giant cells and resemble Hodgkin's Disease. Other cases are even more granulomatous or epithelioid. The histologic pattern often varies at different sites in the same mouse. The bone marrow usually appears relatively normal.

Incidence of Neoplasms in Relation to Strain, Sex, Age, Irradiation, and Other Factors

There are marked strain and sex differences in the frequency of spontaneous and induced leukemias and lymphomas, as discussed earlier (see Upton and Furth, 1957). A good example of this is seen in our strains AKR and RF, and in the hybrids derived from them (Table V). A high incidence of spontaneous thymic lymphoma and a low incidence of myeloid leukemia is seen in

AKR, while in RF there is a much lower incidence of spontaneous thymic lymphoma and a slightly higher incidence of myeloid leukemia than the AKR. After moderate doses of irradiation, the incidence of the two diseases varies with strain and sex, not necessarily increasing with irradiation (Table V). The incidence of neoplasms in irradiated mice is accompanied in each case by a shift to a younger mean age at death with the disease in question.

TABLE V
SPONTANEOUS AND RADIOGENIC LEUKAEMIAS IN RF, AKR, AND F1 HYBRID MICE

Strain	Sex	X-ray Dose (r)[a]	No. of Mice	Median Age at Death (Months)	Thymic Lymphoma %	Thymic Lymphoma Median Age at Death (Months)	Myeloid Leukaemia %	Myeloid Leukaemia Median Age at Death (Months)
AKR	F	0	92	10	85	8	2	18
	F	300	84	10	79	9	0	—
	M	0	79	10	69	10	0	—
	M	300	93	12	52	10	3	10
(AKR x RF) F1	F	0	86	21	24	12	3	13
	F	300	97	12	43	8	3	16
	M	.0	78	20	17	18	1	10
	M	300	88	14	24	8	16	13
(RF x AKR) F1	F	J	94	22	27	23	0	—
	F	300	85	15	40	8	12	15
	M	.0	83	24	7	19	0	—
	M	300	95	18	22	9	9	17
RF	F	0	603	19	8	17	2	19
	F	300	193	12	32	10	20	13
	M	0	512	19	5	16	3	16
	M	300	201	12	12	10	30	11

[a]Whole-body 250 kVp x-rays administered at a dose-rate of 80-90 r/min. Mice were irradiated at ten weeks of ag.
After Upton (1963).

In any one strain, the relation between leukemia incidence and radiation dose is complex. For example, in RF mice exposed to a single dose of high intensity whole-body x-radiation, there is a several-fold increase in the incidence of myeloid leukemia following a 100 rad exposure, a further increase at 200-300 rad, and a declining incidence following higher doses (Fig. 3). The incidence of thymic lymphoma, on the other hand, increases with increasing exposure in the sublethal range (Fig. 4). The incidence of non-thymic lymphomas and reticulum cell sarcomas decreases with increasing dose (Upon *et al.*, 1958). Reticulum cell sarcomas are, likewise, apparently not induced by large amounts of colloidal radiogold, despite the selective uptake of the radioisotope in macrophages of the RES (Upton *et al.*, 1956).

The dose rate and quality of radiation also influence the leukemia incidence at any given level of dose, leukemogenesis generally increasing with the dose rate and with the linear energy transfer (Figs. 3 and 4).

The age of the animal at the time of exposure is another factor affecting the incidence of radiation-induced leukemia and lymphoma. Myeloid leukemia induction is minimal when exposure is

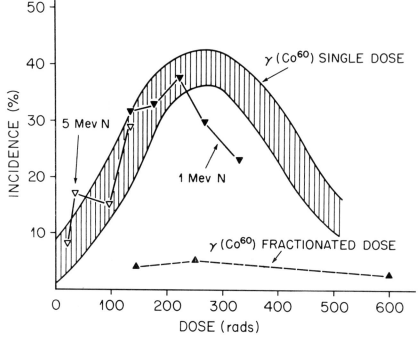

FIGURE 3. Incidence of myeloid leukemia in RF male mice exposed to various types of whole-body radiation, beginning at eight-ten weeks of age.

Shaded area indicates results of a single exposure to whole-body x-or γ rays (7-80 rads/min.), with 95 percent confidence limits.

▲ CO⁶⁰ γ-rays, 23 hrs. daily (0.00072-0.0036 r/min).

△ Cyclotron fast neutrons (∼ 1.0 Mev avg. energy), single exposure (50-210 rad/min.).

△ Po-Be fast neutrons (∼ 5.0 Mev avg. energy). 23 hrs. daily (0.00058-0.0056 rad/min.).

prenatal or immediately postnatal, rises to a peak with exposure at seventy days of age, and declines gradually, if at all, thereafter. Thymic lymphoma induction, on the other hand, is minimal when exposure is prenatal, maximum when shortly after birth, and declines with thymus involution (Upton, *et al.*, 1960).

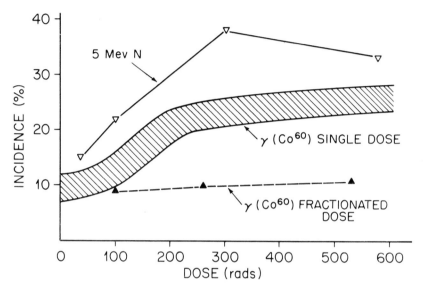

FIGURE 4. Incidence of thymic lymphomas in RF female mice exposed to various types of whole-body radiation, beginning at ten weeks of age.
Shaded area indicates results of a single exposure to CO⁶⁰ γ rays (7-50 rads/min.), with 95 per cent confidence limits.
▲CO⁶⁰ γ rays, 23 hrs. daily (0.00036-0.0036 rad/min.).
Δ Po-Be fast neutrons (~5.0 Mev. avg. energy).
23 hrs. daily (0.00058-0.0012 rad/min.).

That these leukemogenic effects are not specific for radiation, is indicated by the similar leukemogenic action of radiomimetic chemicals (Table VI). It is noteworthy, however, that cortisone, which resembles radiation in its lymphocytic effects on lymphatic and thymic lymphocytes, is not comparably leukemogenic and may even inhibit the development of spontaneous and radiogenic leukemia under certain conditions (see Upton and Furth, 1954; Kaplan *et al.*, 1954; Kirschbaum, 1957).

TABLE VI
INFLUENCE OF TREATMENT ON OCCURRENCE OF LEUKEMIA*
From Conklin et al. (1963)

Agent	Dose	No. Mice	Thymic Lymphoma		Myeloid Leukemia		Other Leukemias	
			Incidence	Mean Age	Incidence	Mean Age	Incidence	Mean Age
HN2	3.7-4.5 mg./kg.	158	5	402	9	511	28	581
TEM	3.0-4.0 mg./kg.	146	16	360	6	557	31	563
X ray	500-600 r	242	26	307	7	320	16	446
Control	-	114	5	605	3	615	39	646

The involvement of leukemogenic viruses in the pathogenesis of spontaneous and induced leukemias has been suggested by independent studies in several laboratories (see Gross, 1961; Parsons *et al.*, 1962). It is of interest that a broad spectrum of hematologic types of leukemias and lymphomas may be transmitted by viruses and that a single virus may conceivably cause more than one form of reticular neoplasm, depending on the physiologic constitution of the host (see Gross, 1961).

NON-NEOPLASTIC DISEASES OF THE RETICULOENDOTHELIAL SYSTEM

Leukemoid Reaction

Non-malignant proliferation of RES elements is found occasionally in our mice in the leukemoid reaction. This is characterized by an increased production of one or more lines of reticular cells, usually neutrophilic granulocytes. It commonly appears as a reaction to inflammation or necrosis associated with large neoplasms, abscesses, or infarcts. The blood leukocyte count is markedly elevated and the cells are relatively mature, which helps to distinguish it from myeloid leukemia. Increased granulocytopoietic tissue is evident histologically in the splenic red pulp, medullary portions of lymph nodes, liver sinusoids, and perirenal connective tissue (nonmalignant extramedullary myelopoiesis). Although the hemopoiesis in these sites may suggest the possibility of leukemia, the degree of maturation of the granulocytic elements and the presence of megakaryocytes, lymphocytes, plasma cells, and erythropoietic foci characteristically enable the differential diagnosis (Barnes and Sisman, 1939).

Erythroblastosis

In this form of apparently benign extramedullary hyperplasia of hemopoietic cells, the erythrocyte precursors are predominantly involved although the sites of formation are the same as those in the leukemoid reaction. On gross inspection, the spleen is much enlarged, smooth, and has a characteristic purplish color. The liver may be slightly enlarged and brown. The lymph nodes and thymus appear normal. The hemogram indicates macrocytic anemia, with normoblasts and polychromatic forms in varying numbers. On histologic examination, the most striking and consistent finding is erythropoietic hyperplasia in the spleen, which may be so marked as to obliterate the normal splenic architecture. Foci of erythropoiesis, and to a lesser extent granulocytopoiesis, are usually present in the liver and in lymph nodes. In advanced stages of the disease, hemosiderosis is found in the liver. Sections of the bone marrow usually reveal erythropoietic hyperplasia, although atrophy and fibrosis have been noted in a few advanced cases. Attempts to transmit the disease have been successful in one instance, serial transmission being carried out by injection of spleen cells or cell-free filtrates (Upton and Furth, 1955).

Amyloidosis

Amyloidosis is uncommon ($<$ 1 per cent) in our mice. When noted, it is commonly associated with severe chronic pyelonephritis in aged mice, appearing within the kidney in glomeruli and in areas of cortical scarring. Related papillonephritis, as described by Dunn (1944), has not often been encountered in our material. Outside the kidney, the amyloid is deposited in perivascular locations; in the liver along sinusoids, in the spleen at the junction of white and red pulp, in the adrenal around capillaries, in the stroma of intestinal villi, and occasionally in myocardial connective tissue. Less frequent sites include the interstitial connective tissue of the salivary gland and pancreas. It has been seen in association with chronic infections, such as abscesses, suppurative otitis media and otitis externa, and chronic ulcerative dermatitis. It has also been noted in the absence of detectable predisposing inflammation, presumably as a spontaneous manifestation of aging, in keeping with observations by others (see Dunn, 1949; Thung, 1957).

Mesenteric Disease

In aging C3H/Anf mice and hybrids derived from this strain, we occasionally find the mesenteric lymph node markedly enlarged and dark red. On section, it is bloody. Histologically, the node is filled with congested hemangiomatous or hemangiectatic spaces. Other details of the lesion are as reported previously (see Dunn,

1954). Its restriction to mice of C3H derivation in our laboratory supports earlier suggestions that its occurrence is strongly dependent on genetic factors.

Effects of Ionizing Radiation

Although hemopoietic and antibody-forming elements have long been recognized to be highly radiosensitive (see Jacobson, 1954), newly developed techniques have helped to identify the cells primarily affected in these systems and to define their injury in quantitative terms. With the exception of the small lymphocyte, mature, non-dividing cells of the RES appear relatively radioresistant, effects of radiation being largely attributable to impaired renewal of such cells, with resulting hemeostatic changes (see Patt and Quastler, 1963).

Immediately after irradiation, reduced mitotic activity and degenerative changes are evident in primitive cells throughout lymphatic and blood-forming tissues. These effects are accompanied by prompt fall in the lymphocyte count in the circulating blood. If the whole body has been exposed to a lethal dose of penetrating radiation, the lymphopenia becomes extreme within the first twenty-four to forty-eight hours. Other cells in the peripheral blood decline more gradually, depending on the species and radiation dose. In most laboratory rodents, maximal depression of circulating leukocytes and platelets occurs one week or more after a mid-lethal radiation exposure. In the absence of hemorrhage the erythrocyte count drops more gradually. Underlying the development of these changes in the peripheral blood are necrosis and aplasia of lymphoid and hemopoietic cells in lymphatic tissues, thymus, spleen, and marrow.

If the affected individual survives for one month or longer, regeneration of blood-forming elements ensues, leading eventually to repopulation of the depleted tissues. This can be facilitated by shielding blood-forming cells in the marrow or spleen or by transplantation of intact, isologous, hemopoietic cells (see Smith and Congdon, 1960; van Bekkum, 1960). Residual damage may persist, however, as indicated by lasting impairment of hemopoietic reserve (Baum and Alpen, 1959), increased propensity to development of leukemia (see Upton, 1961), and persistence of circulating blood cells with chromosomal aberrations (Bender and Gooch, 1963).

Depression of immunity by whole-body irradiation is dramatic and prompt (Makinodan and Gengozian, 1960). There is a difference, however, between the radiosensitivity of the primary response and that of the anamnestic reaction, the latter being several times less vulnerable than the former. Moreover, the depression of the primary response varies in severity, depending on the time-sequence of irradiation and exposure to the antigen; that is, depression is greatest when irradiation precedes exposure to the antigen by one to fourteen days (Makinodan and Gengozian, 1960; Stoner and Hale, 1962). This indicates the existence of a radioresistant phase during antibody production, presumably following "recognition" of the antigen and initiation of antibody synthesis. It also indicates that preformed antibody itself is radioresistant. The nature of the radiation injury to the immune mechanism is revealed, in part, by the observation that it can be repaired by transfusion of intact lymphoid cells from a nonirradiated donor (see Makinodan and Gengozian, 1960).

The phagocytic activity of the RES is relatively radioresistant (DiLuzio *et al.*, 1957), although its functional and proliferative reserve are impaired by lethal whole-body x-radiation (see Benacerraf *et al.*, 1959; Wooles *et al.*, 1962). The ability of induced peritoneal macrophages to destroy engulfed bacteria is moderately radiosensitive, perhaps as a result of depression of systemic immunity and of opsonins (Donaldson, 1962).

Radiomimetic and cytotoxic chemicals induce some of the RES effects of radiation (see Asano *et al.*, 1963); however, data on the effects of chemicals are for the most part fragmentary by comparison with those on radiation. One noteworthy difference between the two is the differential selectivity of various chemicals for different types of cells in the RES, as opposed to the more general toxicity of radiation to all undifferentiated cells.

Transplantation ("Runt") Disease

Administration of foreign lymphoid or hemopoietic cells to an immature (prenatal or neonatal) recipient mouse may give rise to a syndrome called "runt disease." If the recipient mouse is beyond the neonatal period, depression of the immune mechanism (e.g., by radiation or chemicals) will facilitate the occurrence of a comparable syndrome on transplantation of foreign lymphoid or hemopoietic cells. Changes in the RES are pronounced under these circumstances. These are considered to be the manifestations of an immune reaction resulting from the presence of incompatible populations of immunologically competent cells. The sequence of changes (Cosgrove *et al.*, 1962) is as follows:

About five days after injection the mouse begins to appear ill. The activity is reduced, the fur becomes ruffled, and the food intake decreases. These symptoms become more severe, marked hunching of the back occurs, and the weight loss is rapidly progressive. In severe cases, death ensues in two to three weeks. In non-fatal cases, clinical recovery occurs.

Gross examination of tissues at the peak of the reaction reveals enlargement of lymph nodes and spleen, scattered hemorrhages, and occasionally necrosis of bone marrow. Later, there is atrophy of lymph nodes and spleen, followed by partial or complete recovery if the mouse survives. The rate of mortality and severity of clinical and pathologic findings are correlated with several variables, including the genetic relationship between donor and host, the age of recipient, the radiation dose, and the number and immunological competence of injected hemopoietic cells. The histologic changes in lymphoid organs consist of marked hyperplasia of stromal reticular cells, proliferation of large basophilic mononuclear (antibody-forming?) cells, obliteration of the normal follicular architecture, and interference with repopulation or regeneration of lymphocytes. The lesions often progress to necrosis, followed by fibrosis and scarring. If the host survives, regeneration of hemopoietic tissues may ultimately occur. The thymus does not ordinarily react in the above manner. The time for these changes to run their course is 30-120 days. At the peak of the reaction, there is often necrosis of bone marrow and atrophy of the thymic cortex. The periportal areas of the liver commonly show leukocytic infiltration during the reaction. The severely affected animals frequently die. In immature animals, growth is inhibited; hence, the designation "runt disease."

The pathogenesis of these changes is not fully known, although graft-anti-host and host-anti-graft reactions are postulated (Gengozian, 1962). Similar changes have been noted in a variety of species (Porter, 1960; Solomon, 1961), including man (Mathé, 1960).

The implications of these changes for our understanding of autoimmune phenomena and immunological tolerance are attracting wide attention among experimental biologists, and related studies are helping to elucidate problems concerning hemopoiesis and immunity. It has been observed, for example, that the distribution of donor reticular cells in various organs of a recipient depends markedly on the anatomical origin of such cells and the genetic and physiologic constitution of the recipient. Although spleen and marrow cells may eventually repopulate all hemopoietic and lymphoid tissues in irradiated adult mice, donor cells from thymus and lymph nodes concentrate preferentially in the lymph nodes of the recipient (see Ford and Micklem, 1963). These and other observations point to the existence of pluripotential stem cells in the marrow and to the differentiation of such cells in other reticular organs. Although it is not yet clear whether a common stem cell may give rise to all types of reticular elements in adult life, this problem would seem to be nearing solution. Existing evidence favors the speculation that such a cell does exist in the marrow and is morphologically similar to the small lymphocyte (Harris *et al.*, 1963; Cudkowicz *et al.*, 1963).

Antigen-Antibody Reaction

Congdon and Goodman (1962) have re-evaluated the composition and relationships of the germinal centers in various lymphoid organs, which they believe to be important in the antigen-antibody reaction. Active germinal centers, wherever located, have two major portions. In histologic preparations there is a dark-staining, densely populated mass of primitive reticular cells, which they postulate to be the cell formative area. Adjacent to one side of the dark cell mass is a larger, less densely populated, lighter-staining cell mass. This usually oriented toward the direction of antigenic stimulation and is inferred to be the reactive portion of the germinal center. The accompanying diagrams show this relationship for spleen, lymph node, and Peyer's patches (Fig. 5).

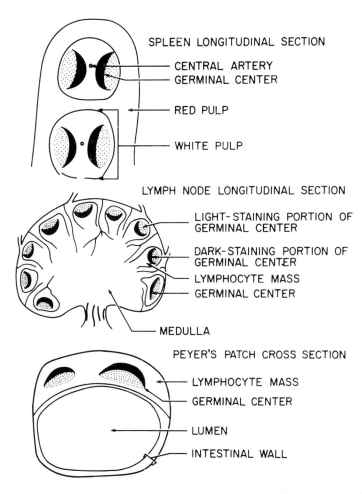

FIGURE 5. Schematic representation of the architecture and orientation of the germinal centers in the spleen, lymph node, and Peyer's patch of the mouse. Modified from Congdon and Goodman (1962).

Morphologic changes have been described in these structures following injection of various antigens, including suspensions of foreign nucleated cells, foreign erythrocytes, bovine serum albumin, and horse serum (Congdon and Goodman, 1962). When large doses of these materials are given intravenously to a mouse, a sequence of cell changes is promptly initiated, which are followed most easily in the white pulp of the spleen. First, there is swelling of the white pulp, with edema around the central artery of the follicle. The cells of the darkly staining area of the germinal center proliferate markedly and are thought to migrate outward and fill the white pulp. Lymphocytes disappear from the germinal center, and the architecture of the germinal center becomes obliterated. The newly formed cells are postulated to be antibody-forming cells. They are large, hyperchromatic, and pyroninophilic. This phase of the reaction runs its course in three days. After this time, newly formed germinal centers appear, and these are hyperplastic for three more days. Congdon and Goodman use the terms "proliferation of dissociated germinal centers" for the first phase and "restitution of germinal centers" for the second.

The relation between germinal center cells and plasma cells in antibody formation remains to be determined, although these appear to be two classes of immunologically competent cells which may function differently (Mellors and Korngold, 1963). Likewise, whether the recently discovered role of the thymus in immunity involves these cells is yet to be elucidated, but if so it may depend on the action of a diffusible thymic substance which can circulate in the blood to all parts of the body (Osoba and Miller, 1963; Levey et al., 1963).

Colloid Storage Disease

In rats subjected to heavy loading of the RES by colloids, hypersplenism and hemolytic anemia may ensue. Throughout the RES in this condition there is marked hyperplasia of reticulum cells, erythrophagocytosis, hemasiderosis, and lymphoid atrophy (see DiLuzio et al., 1957).

Loading the phagocytes of the RES with colloidal material (zymosan) impairs the survival of lethally irradiated mice injected with heterologous or homologous marrow, but not of mice injected with isologous marrow (Wooles and DiLuzio, 1962). This exemplifies the complexity of the RES and ostensibly the extent to which one of its functions appears to influence other physiological parameters.

SUMMARY

Although the reticuloendothelial system (RES) is concentrated principally in the liver, spleen, bone marrow, and lymphoid organs, cells derived from the system are widespread as fixed and circulating forms and carry out diverse functions.

In many common laboratory rodents, neoplastic diseases of the RES are encountered frequently. In mice, leukemias and lymphomas of three major types are seen: thymic lymphoma, myeloid leukemia, and reticulum cell sarcoma. Each has characteristic cellular, morphologic, and clinical features. The incidence of these diseases varies according to a complex interaction of many influences, including host factors (such as species, strain, age, sex, endocrine status) and environmental factors (such as viruses, radiation, cytotoxic and carcinogenic chemicals). The precise role of these factors remains, however, to be determined.

Non-neoplastic alterations of the RES are likewise common in certain laboratory animals. Some of the lesions more frequently encountered in mice are leukemoid reactions, amyloidosis, and mesenteric disease.

Among the most important functions of the RES are its roles in phagocytosis, immunity, and resistance to infection. Investigation of the effects of radiation, thymectomy, and of transplantation of RES cells on these functions has provided new insight into the physiology of the RES and into the kinetics of cell maturation and cell renewal in this system.

REFERENCES

Asano, M., Odell, T. T. Jr., McDonald, T. P., and Upton, A. C.: Radiomimetic agents and x rays in mice and AET protectiveness. *Arch. Path., 75:*250, 1963.

Barnes, W. A., and Sisman, I. E.: Myeloid leukemia and nonmalignant extramedullary myelopoiesis in mice. *Cancer, 37:*1, 1939.

Baum, S. J., and Alpen, E. L.: Residual injury induced in the erythropoietic system of the rat by periodic exposures to x-radiation. *Radiat. Res., 11:*844, 1959.

Benacerraf, B., Kivy-Rosenberg, E., Sebestyen, M. M., and Zweifach, B. W.: The effect of high doses of x-radiation on the phagocytic, proliferative, and metabolic properties of the reticulo-endothelial system. *J. Exp. Med., 110*:49, 1959.

BENDER, M. A., and GOOCH, P. C.: Persistent chromosome aberrations in irradiated human subjects. II. Three and one-half year year investigation. *Radiat. Res., 18*:389, 1963.

COLE, L. J.: Hemopoietic restoration in lethally x-irradiated mice injected with peritoneal cells. *Amer. J. Physiol., 204*:265, 1963.

CONGDON, C. C., and GOODMAN, J. W.: Changes in lymphatic tissues during foreign tissue transplantation. In, *Proceedings International Symposium on Tissue Transplantation,* ed. A. P. Cristoffanini, and G. Hoecker, Univ. of Chile, Santiago, pp. 181-207, 1962.

CONKLIN, J. W., UPTON, A. C., CHRISTENBERRY, K. W., and McDONALD, T. P.: Comparative late somatic effects of some radiomimetic agents and x rays. *Radiat. Res., 19*:156, 1963.

COSGROVE, G. E., UPTON, A. C., and CONGDON, C. C.: A histologic study of the foreign spleen reaction in sublethally irradiated F_1 hybrid mice. *Amer. J. Path., 40*:455, 1962.

CUDKOWICZ, G., UPTON, A. C., SHEARER, G. M., and HUGHES, W. L.: Lymphocyte content and proliferative capacity of serially transplanted mouse bone marrow. Abstract for 6th Annual Meeting of the American Society of Hematology. *Nature, 201*:165-167, 1964.

DiLUZIO, N. R., SIMON, K. A., and UPTON, A. C.: Effects of x rays and trypan blue on reticuloendothelial cells. *Arch. Path., 64*:649, 1957.

DOAN, C. A.: The reticulo-endothelial cells in health and disease. In *Physiopathology of Reticulo-Endothelial System,* ed. B. N. Halpern, B. Benacerraf, and J. F. Delafresnaye. Springfield, Thomas, 1957, pp. 290-311.

DONALDSON, D. M.: Responses of diseased animals to ionizing radiation. In *The Effects of Ionizing Radiations on Immune Processes,* ed. C. A. Leone. New York, Gordon and Breach, 1962, pp. 245-268.

DUNN, T. B.: Relationship of amyloid infiltration and renal disease in mice. *J. Nat. Cancer Inst., 5*:17, 1944.

DUNN, T. B.: Some observations on the normal and pathologic anatomy of the kidney of the mouse. *J. Nat. Cancer Inst., 9*:285, 1949.

DUNN, T. B.: Normal and pathologic anatomy of the reticular tissue in laboratory mice, with a classification and discussion of neoplasms. *J. Nat. Cancer Inst., 14*:1281, 1954.

ENGELBRETH-HOLM, J.: *Spontaneous and Experimental Leukemia in Animals.* Edinburgh, Oliver & Boyd, Ltd., 1942.

FORD, C. E., and MICKLEM, H. S.: The thymus and lymph-nodes in radiation chimaeras. *Lancet, 1*:359, 1963.

GENGOZIAN, N.: Radiation immunology: Effects of hematopoietic tissue transplantation. In *The Effects of Ionizing Radiations on Immune Processes,* ed. C. A. Leone. New York, Gordon and Breach, 1962, pp. 403-454.

GOODMAN, J. W.: Transplantation of peritoneal fluid cells. *Transplant. Bull., 1:*334, 1963.

GOODMAN, J. W., and HODGSON, G. S.: Evidence for stem cells in the peripheral blood of mice. *Blood, 19:*702, 1962.

GROSS, L.: *Oncogenic Viruses.* New York, Pergamon, 1961.

HARRIS, P. F., HAIGH, G., and KUGLER, J. H.: Observations on the accumulation of mononuclear cells and the activities of reticulum cells in bone marrow of guinea-pigs recovering from whole body gamma irradiation. *Acta Haemat., 29:*166, 1963.

HOLZWORTH, J.: Leukemia and related neoplasms in the cat. I. Lymphoid malignancies. *J. Amer. Vet. Med. Ass., 136:*47, 1960a.

HOLZWORTH, J.: Leukemia and related neoplasms in the cat. II. Malignancies other than lymphoid. *J. Amer. Vet. Med. Ass., 136:*107, 1960b.

JACOBSON, L. O.: The hematologic effects of ionizing radiation. In, *Radiation Biology,* ed. A. Hollaender, Vol. I. New York, Grune & Stratton, 1954, pp. 311-317.

JUNGHERR, E.: The avian leukosis complex. In, *Diseases of Poultry,* ed. H. E. Biester, and L. H. Schwarte. Ames, Univ. Iowa Press, 1943, pp. 393-442.

KIRSCHBAUM, A.: The role of hormones in cancer: Laboratory animals. *Cancer Res. 17:*432, 1957.

LEVEY, R. H., TRAININ, N., and LAW, L. W.: Evidence for function of thymic tissue in diffusion chambers implanted in neonatally thymectomized mice. Preliminary report. *J. Nat. Cancer Inst., 31:*199, 1963.

MAKINODAN, T., and GENGOZIAN, N.: Effect of radiation on antibody formation. In, *Radiation Protection and Recovery,* ed. A. Hollaender. New York, Pergamon, 1960, pp. 316-351.

MARSHALL, A. H. E.: *An Outline of the Cytology and Pathology of the Reticular Tissue.* Springfield, Thomas, 1956.

MATHÉ, G.: Application of hematopoietic cell grafts to the treatment of leukemias and allied diseases. A critical review. *Blood, 16:*1073, 1960.

MELLORS, R. C., and KORNGOLD, L.: The cellular origin of human immunoglobulins (γz, $\gamma 1M$, $\gamma 1A$). *J. Exp. Med., 118:*387, 1963.

MOULTON, J. E.: Tumors in domestic animals (Chap. 4). In, *Tumors of the Vascular, Hemopoietic, and Lymphoid Tissues.* Berkeley, Univ. California Press, 1961, pp. 75-114.

Osoba, D., and Miller, J. F. A. P.: Evidence for a humoral thymus factor responsible for the maturation of immunological faculty. *Nature, 199:*653, 1963.

Parsons, D. F., Upton, A. C., Bender, M. A., Jenkins, V. K., Nelson, E. S., and Johnson, R. R.: Electron microscopic observations on primary and serially passaged radiation-induced myeloid leukemias of the RF mouse. *Cancer Res., 22:*728, 1962.

Patt, H M., and Quastler, H.: Radiation effects on cell renewal and related systems. *Physiol. Rev., 43:*357, 1963.

Popp, R. A.: Erythrocyte repopulation in x-irradiated recipients of nucleated peripheral blood cells of normal mice. *Proc. Soc. Exp. Biol Med., 104:*722, 1960.

Porter, K. A.: Graft-versus-host reactions in the rabbit. *Brit. J. Cancer, 14:*66, 1960.

Ratcliffe, H. L.: Spontaneous diseases of laboratory rats (Chap. 22). In, *The Rat in Laboratory Investigation,* ed. J. G. Griffith, Jr., and E. J. Farris. Philadelphia, Lippincott, 1942, pp. 443-455.

Rebuck, J. W., and LoGrippo, G. A.: Characteristics and interrelationships of the various cells in the RE cell macrophage, lymphocyte, and plasma cell series in man. *Lab. Invest., 10:*1068, 1961.

Smith, H. A., and Jones, T. C.: *Veterinary Pathology.* Philadelphia, Lea, 1958, pp. 225-230, 724-739.

Smith, L. H., and Congdon, C. C.: Experimental treatment of acute whole-body radiation injury in mammals. In, *Radiation Protection and Recovery,* ed. A. Hollaender. New York, Pergamon, 1960, pp. 242-302.

Solomon, J. B.: The onset and maturation of the graft versus host reactions in chickens. *J. Embryol. Exp. Morph., 9:*355, 1961.

Stoner, R. D., and Hale, W. M.: Radiation effects on primary and secondary antibody responses. In, *The Effects of Ionizing Radiations on Immune Processes,* ed. C. A. Leone. New York, Gordon and Breach, 1962, pp. 183-219.

Thung, P. J.: Senile amyloidosis in mice. *Gerontologia, 1:*259, 1957.

Upton, A. C.: The dose-response relation in radiation-induced cancer. *Cancer Res., 21:*717, 1961.

Upton, A. C.: Leukaemogenesis: Role of viruses and cytological aspects. In, *Cellular Basis and Aetiology of Late Somatic Effects of Ionizing Radiation,* ed. R. J. C. Harris. London and New York, Acad., Press 1963, pp. 67-82.

Upton, A. C., and Furth, J.: The effects of cortisone on the development of spontaneous leukemia in mice on its induction by irradiation. *Blood, 9:*686, 1954.

UPTON, A. C., and FURTH, J.: A transmissible disease of mice characterized by anemia, leukopenia, splenomegaly, and myelosclerosis. *Acta Haemat., 13:*65, 1955.

UPTON, A. C., FURTH, J., and BURNETT, W. T., JR.: Liver damage and hepatomas in mice produced by radioactive colloidal gold. *Cancer Res., 16:*211, 1956.

UPTON, A. C., and FURTH, J.: Host factors in the pathogenesis of leukemia in animals and in man. In, *Proc. 3rd Natl. Cancer Conf.,* Philadelphia, Lippincott, 1957, pp. 312-324.

UPTON, A. C., WOLFF, F. F., FURTH, J., and KIMBALL, A. W.: A comparison of the induction of myeloid and lymphoid leukemias in x-radiated RF mice. *Cancer Res., 18:*842, 1958.

UPTON, A. C., ODELL, T. T., JR., and SNIFFEN, E. P.: Influence of age at time of irradiation on induction of leukemia and ovarian tumors in RF mice. *Proc. Soc. Exp. Biol. Med., 104:*769, 1960.

VAN BEKKUM, D. A.: Recovery and therapy of the irradiated organism. In, *Mechanisms in Radiobiology, Vol. II. Multicellular Organisms,* ed. M. Errera, and A. Forssberg. New York, Acad. Press 1960, pp. 297-360.

WOOLES, W. R., and DiLUZIO, N. R.: Influence of reticulo endothelial hyperfunction on bone marrow. *Amer. J. Physiol., 203:*404, 1962.

WOOLES, W. R., ELKO, E. E., and DiLUZIO, N. R.: Influence of Pre- and Post- x-irradiation zymosan administration on reticulo endothelial function. *Radiat. Res., 16:*546, 1962.

DISCUSSION

Dr. Thelma B. Dunn: I am very much interested in the parasites you demonstrated in the mesenteric lymph nodes of mice. I consulted Dr. Conklin about this just recently because I have had the experience of looking at what appeared to be a high and a low leukemia line. The high line is the line which has been affected adversely by a virus which is continuously transplanted. Now, within that high line we have seen numerous of these parasites, whereas we have never seen them, so far as I recall, in any other mice that I have examined. I wonder if you have any comment upon this, how frequently you do find these parasites, and are they particularly associated with any special group of mice.

Dr. Cosgrove: They are associated with certain strains which also seem to run a higher incidence of the intestinal tapeworm. I can't remember exactly which of the strains in our colony are so affected but one time we made a little table of eight or ten strains and there were marked differences. The animals were derived from the same source, namely, Cumberland View Farms, in Clinton, Tennessee, where we buy many of our mice. They were maintained in exactly the same conditions in the same animal room and theoretically should have roughly leveled out on their parasitic incidence, but they were different, both for the incidence of tapeworms and for the two pinworm species of mice. The ones that had the highest incidence of the tapeworm also had the highest incidence of the metastasis, you might say, of the immature form of the worm. This is probably the cysticercoid, or last larval stage, of the tapeworm and it usually develops in the intestinal villus but apparently gets into the lymphatics occasionally—burrows its way in—it is actively motile—and is filtered out in the mesenteric node.

I have never attempted to correlate the presence of this with the incidence of leukemia in those various strains of mice.

Dr. Walter Fleischmann: I would like to ask Dr. Cosgrove whether in distinguishing between a true leukemia or a leukemoid reaction in rodents, he ever uses alkaline phosphatase. We have found that in human leukemia we have reactions which are extremely satisfactory.

Dr. Cosgrove: No, we haven't used that reaction in mice.

Dr. Fleischmann: The alkaline phosphatase is very low in true leukemias and in leukemoid reactions it is very high.

Dr. Cosgrove: This is one way of telling whether transplanted leucocytes are derived from mice or from rats. In this sense we use it in the way Dr. Fleischmann mentioned. The mouse has very low alkaline phosphatase levels in normal leucocytes whereas the rat has high levels, so this is one method of determining whether you have a chimera after transplantation of these cells.

Herman T. Blumenthal: Amyloidosis has been described as a sort of aging process in certain strains of mice. I wonder if the so-called spontaneous amyloid occurs in older mice?

Dr. Cosgrove: I would say that most of our amyloid occurs in older mice. It usually has an associated major lesion in the mouse and we have tended to blame the presence of that lesion for the first appearance of amyloid. This may be wrong. We have a few mice where amyloid has appeared spontaneously with ageing, as described by Thung and Dunn and others, but, as I say, we have such a small incidence of amyloid I really haven't been able to determine its true inter-relationships with other diseases.

Question: Would you enumerate amyloid sites in the order that they occur?

Dr. Cosgrove: The liver and spleen are about equal in occurrence and the kidney is not far behind. The adrenal and intestines are considerably less involved. Of one hundred animals with amyloid, practically all of them will have it in liver and spleen, lesser numbers in the other organs such as the salivary gland, pancreas and other perivascular locations, in connective tissue, subcutaneous, heart, and so forth. Spleen, liver and kidney are certainly the most common sites.

Dr. Innes: Just two points: I would like to recommend a book by Hans Cottier *Strahlenbedingte Lebensverkurzung.* Springer, Berlin, 1958, which contains a tremendous mass of information on diseases of mice and is beautifully illustrated.

The second point concerns amyloid degeneration. Probably twenty or thirty years ago Twort and Twort examined about 50,000 mice in connection with cancer studies and they discussed this degeneration. From then on there has been a lot written on this degeneration but I think with a good deal of confusion.

I am rather interested in this because there is an inbred mouse colony run by Dr. Anna Goldfeder in New York which for years has remained cancer-free. A study of the adrenal glands of these mice showed an incidence of ceroid degeneration (not amyloid) of nearly 50 per cent.

Question: I want to ask for comment on an occasional incidental finding in lymph nodes in which the node is enlarged, the internal structures are broken down, and the content is fluid. The condition resembles a cystic degeneration of the node. This is an occasional finding in an older rat.

Have you any remarks on this condition? It is not always restricted to a particular node, in my observation.

Dr. Cosgrove: I don't look at many rats. Can anybody answer that?

Katharine C. Snell: It is quite common in old rats. We call it cystic degeneration.

Chairman: Is it restricted to any particular node?

Dr. Snell: No, it is often in the pancreatic node but often you see it in the cervical nodes. I think I see it more often in the cervical than any other.

3

LESIONS OF THE RESPIRATORY TRACT OF SMALL LABORATORY ANIMALS

J. R. M. INNES

T HE ORIGINAL LITERATURE on studies of the pathology of diseases of laboratory animals is immense. It dates back for over fifty years, but unfortunately is scattered in a widely diverse variety of medical and veterinary journals. No attempt has ever been made to consolidate all of this valuable information into a textbook in the English language, and some of the bibliographies produced have been rather puerile. The only worthwhile, fully-documented, illustrated, composite account is the two volume treatise in German by Cohrs *et al.* (1958) with 1602 pages and thousands of references. This work is a revised and enlarged version of the book by Jaffé, first published in 1931. This chapter is restricted to a consideration of certain types of respiratory disease but is based on original observations which have been published. References to these, and to a large selected bibliography on diseases of rats and mice, will be found in Tuffery and Innes (1963). The latter also contains the most important references to the work of Dr. J. B. Nelson (Rockefeller Institute) on diseases of rats and mice dating back for nearly twenty years. Some of his earlier papers are essential reading upon the subject of the etiology of respiratory diseases of both rats and mice.

A listing, in categories, of respiratory diseases and lesions which affect small laboratory animals is presented herein. This is followed by a number of illustrative examples. Full descriptions of these conditions are omitted for there is no use treading over old ground representing work which is adequately covered elsewhere in the references cited. This approach should be a sufficient lead to pathologists for information when they are faced with the problem of diagnosis of pathological conditions seen in any part of the respiratory tract. Neoplastic diseases are not included for these are dealt with in other chapters. For information on anomalies, malformations, and inherited diseases, reference can be made to Nachtsheim in Cohrs *et al.*, and in the case of mice to Grüneberg (1952).

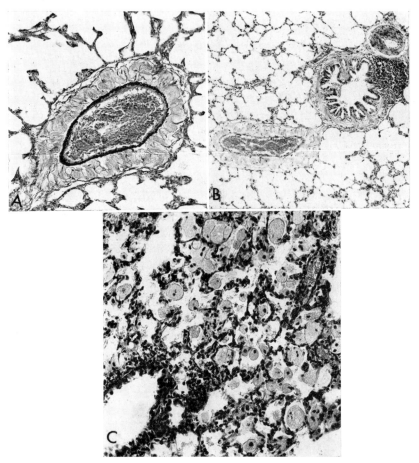

Figure 1A. High power view of a vein as in 1 B. Elastic tissue and Van Gieson stains.

Figure 1B. Lung, rat. Low power. Showing bronchiole, small artery, and vein with mantle of cardiac muscle which penetrates deeply into the lungs of rats and mice. Hematoxylin and eosin stain.

Figure 1C. A common picture in otherwise normal lungs of rats and mice. Foci of alveolar phagocytes, origin and causation unknown. They may also be seen as part of the cellular exudate in other stages of chronic pneumonia. Hematoxylin and eosin.

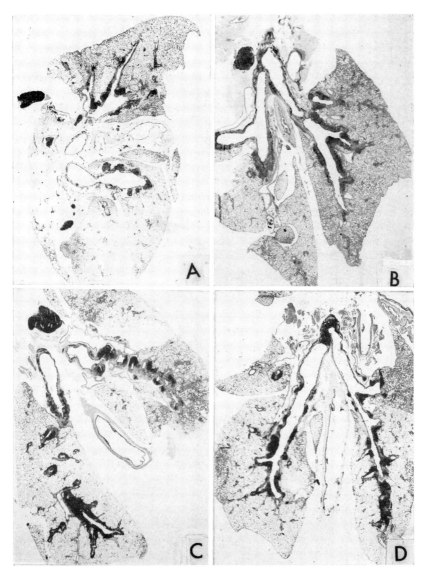

FIGURES 2-6. Evolution of chronic murine pneumonia, rats (Innes *et al.,* 1956).
FIGURE 2A-D. Four separate pictures of the lungs of rats showing grades of peribronchial lymphoid hyperplasia in the absence of any of the late stages of chronic murine pneumona. Hematoxylin and eosin.

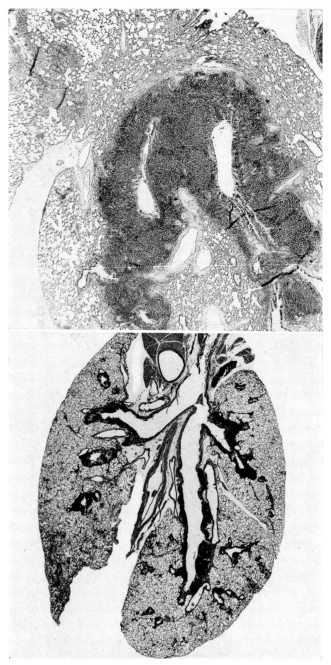

FIGURE 3. Severe degrees of peribronchial lymphoid hyperplasia without chronic pneumonia. Hematoxylin and eosin.

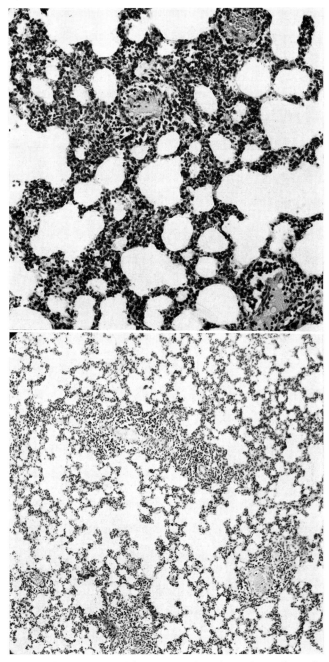

FIGURE 4. Interstitial pneumonitis (*top*) and perivascular cuffing (*bottom*) of a rat lung before the onset of bronchiectasis. Hematoxylin and eosin. Courtesy of *The American Journal of Pathology*.

In any consideration of the diseases of any organ, it is essential for the pathologist to know of the great differences in anatomical and histological structures among the different species. In each chapter of Cohrs *et al.*, as an introduction to discussion of diseases, there is a brief synopsis of normal structure and function. If more details on histological structure are required, recourse can be made to original papers and to the many volumes of the *Handbuch der mikroskopischen Anatomie des Menschen*, edited by W. von

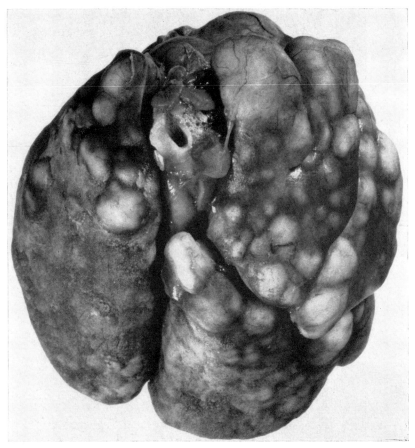

FIGURE 5. Chronic murine pneumonia in a rat over sixteen months of age. Typical naked eye appearance. All right lobes are affected. A cobbled bosselated surface with yellowish to gray areas superficially resembling abscesses. Part of the caudal surface of the left lobe is normal. Hematoxylin and eosin.

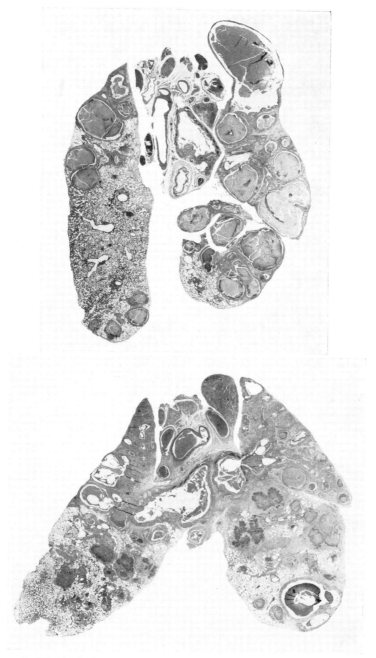

FIGURE 6. Histological appearance (low power view) of two cases of the type illustrated in Figure 5, showing the full development of bronchiectasis. Some areas of normal lung tissue are present. Hematoxylin and eosin.

Möllendorff (Springer, Berlin) in which there are usually some references to comparative studies.

LISTS OF DISEASES AND LESIONS

Infections

Contagious diplococcal pleuritis and catarrhal or suppurative pneumonia of guinea pigs. *Contagious rhinitis* of rabbits. *Fibrinous inflammation of the serous membranes and lungs* in guinea pigs. *Salmonellosis* in rabbits, guinea pigs, rats, hamsters, and mice with suppurative pulmonary phlebothrombosis in the last two species. *Pseudotuberculosis,* with occasional lung lesions, in all species. *Tularemia* in rabbits and rats, with occasional involvement of the lungs. *Tuberculosis* in rabbits and guinea pigs. As a spontaneous disease this is extremely rare but has been recorded. *Aspergillosis* in rabbits, with occasional pulmonary complications. *Pasteurellosis* in all species, with acute fibrinous or suppurative pleuropneumonia. *Acute pneumonia* in rats which is frequently caused by pneumococci. *Pulmonary phlebitis* with *myocarditis* and associated with rickettsial-like bodies, in mice.

Chronic viral murine pneumonia, complicated by secondary bacterial infection in rats and mice, *Mycoplasma infection* and *infectious catarrh* of the upper respiratory tract of rats and mice. *Viral pneumonia* of guinea pigs. *Influenza-like virus pneumonia* of hamsters. *Virus pneumonia* and *canine distemper* in ferrets. At least three different *viral pneumonias* in mice are caused, respectively, by an influenza-like agent, one of the psittacosis group, and grey lung virus. *Rabbit pox* may include occasional involvement of the lungs.

Clinically Silent or Occult Lesions

Foreign bodies in the nasal cavities. Adenomatosis in aged rats and mice, as distinguished from alveologenic carcinoma. Granu-

--→

FIGURE 7. Chronic murine pneumonia in a rat. Late stage showing the typical appearance of advanced bronchiectasis; cavitation of thickened bronchi and brochioles which in the fresh state are filled with detritus, caseous material and mucin; atelectasis in some parts of lungs. Fibrosis is more prominent in the picture at the bottom. Hematoxylin and eosin. Courtesy of *The American Journal of Pathology.*

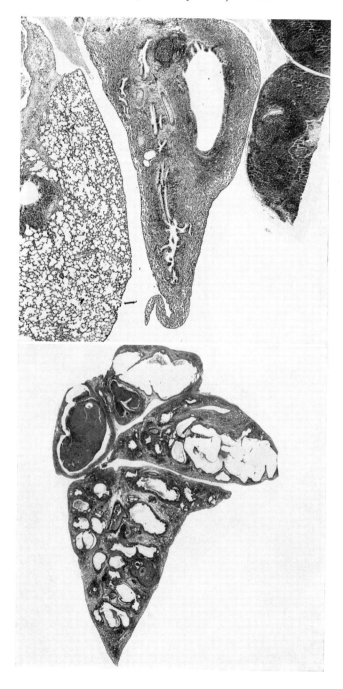

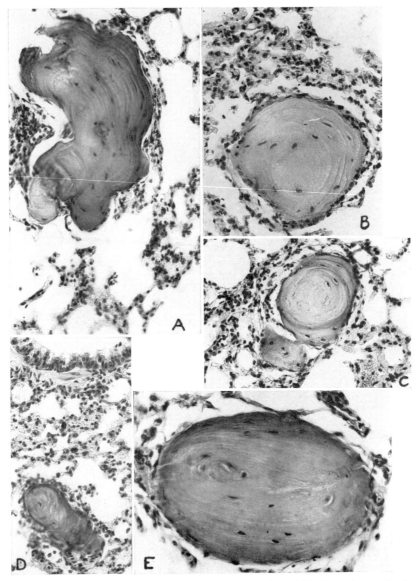

Figure 8. Spicules of bone in the lungs of rat A, rabbit B, guinea pig C, hamster D, and dog E. Lodgement in alveolar spaces without inflammatory reaction. These are believed to be aspirated fragments of bone from fish meal used in preparation of food pellets. (See Innes *et al.,* 1956.) Hematoxylin and eosin. Courtesy of the *Archives of Pathology.*

lomas due to foreign bodies, e.g., aspirated vegetable matter. Fragments of hair and epidermal scales introduced accidentally during intravenous inoculations. Unidentified crystals in mouse lung. Spicules of aspirated bone. Hemosiderosis. Megakaryocytic emboli in mice. Medial hypertrophy or calcification of the pulmonary arteries in rats.

REFERENCES

COHRS, P., JAFFÉ, R., and MEESSEN, M.: *Pathologie der Laboratoriumstiere.* Springer, Berlin, 1958.

GRÜNEBERG, HANS.: The Genetics of the Mouse. 2nd ed. *Bibliographia Genetica., 15:*1-650, 1952.

INNES, J. R. M., MCADAMS, A. J., and YEVICH, P. P.: Pulmonary disease in rats. A survey with comments on chronic murine pneumonia. *Amer. J. Path., 32:*141-159, 1956.

INNES, J. R. M., YEVICH, P. P., and DONATI, E. J.: Note on origin of some fragments of bone in lungs of laboratory animals. *Arch. Path., 61:*401-406, 1956.

TUFFERY, A. A., and INNES, J. R. M.: *Diseases of Laboratory Mice and Rats.* Chapter 3, in Animals for Research. Principles of Breeding and Management. W. Lane-Petter, Ed., London, 1963. Acad. Press

4

SPONTANEOUS ENDOCRINE DISEASES IN LABORATORY ANIMALS

WALTER FLEISCHMANN

INTRODUCTION

ENDOCRINE DISEASES in laboratory animals are rare. However we have to bear in mind that their incidence in human beings is low also. Endocrine disorders, exclusive of diabetes mellitus, constituted approximately 1.3 per cent of the population of The Johns Hopkins Hospital according to statistics compiled by Dr. E. L. Crosby.

PRIMATES

In a survey on neoplasms in monkeys (Macaca mulatta) Kent and Pickering (1958) write: "The incidence of tumors reported in primates from zoological gardens is very low when compared with the incidence in man and other species. Fox (1923) reported all tumors found in animals autopsied at the Philadelphia Zoological Gardens. The incidence was 0.5 per cent in primates, the lowest incidence of all groups studied.

"Ratcliffe in 1933, presenting the tumors found up to that time in the Philadelphia Zoological Gardens, reported eight tumors in 971 primate autopsies. The incidence of 0.8 per cent was the lowest of all mammalian orders."

Fairbrother and Hurst (1932), who performed 600 autopsies, and Kennard (1941), who performed 246 autopsies on monkeys, failed to find a single neoplasm. Before concluding that monkeys are resistant to the spontaneous development of neoplasms, several factors must be considered. First, the age of the animals at the time of death is important. Most of the animals were relatively young. For example, Fairbrother and Hurst's monkeys were usually killed for experimental purposes before puberty. The life span of monkeys in captivity is considerably shortened because of

60

exposure to human diseases to which they are quite susceptible. The shortening of the life span would have a profound effect on the incidence of spontaneous neoplasms noted at autopsy. Also, the number of tumors found at autopsy would be related, at least to some extent, to the care with which the autopsies were done. This is especially true of animals in which the observed clinical signs and symptoms, which often direct the pathologist's attention to the site of neoplasms in humans, are limited. During an epidemic of tuberculosis in Kent's monkey colony in 1953, often only a cursory examination was made at time of autopsy because of a shortage of personnel and the large number of animals coming to autopsy. A neoplasm in one of these animals could easily have been overlooked (Kent and Pickering, 1958). It is of great interest, however, that experimental attempts to produce malignant neoplasms in monkeys have been largely unsuccessful.

From a colony of monkeys (Macaca mulatta) maintained by the U. S. Air Force School of Aviation Medicine at Randolph Air Force Base, Texas, and by the Radiobiological Laboratory of the University of Texas, six spontaneous neoplasms were collected from more than 450 autopsies (Kent and Pickering, 1958). Two of these are tumors of the endocrine glands, which will be reported in detail.

The first was a male monkey killed as a part of the tuberculosis control program of the laboratory; the animal had a positive skin test for tuberculosis. It had received 400 r of total body x-irradiation, seventy-five days before death. Lesions characteristic of tuberculosis were found in the lungs and in the mesenteric lymph nodes, but not in other organs. The thyroid gland was atrophic; the right lobe was completely absent and the left was much smaller than usual. The pituitary gland appeared to be slightly enlarged, but it was not weighed. On microscopic examination, most of the anterior pituitary was replaced by large tumor cells. The nuclei of these cells were large and vesicular with prominent nucleoli (Fig. 1). The cytoplasm was abundant and contained basophilic granules, but not as many as seen in normal basophils. The cytoplasm was periodic acid-Schiff (PAS) positive and stained blue with the Martin-Mallory stain. This tumor resembled the amphophil adenomas of the pituitary described in thyroid aplasia. As the thyroid gland was hypoplastic in this case, this aplasia presumably was the cause of the pituitary adenoma. The cause of the hypoplasia of the thyroid was not evident. It was probably not due to irradiation, as many of the monkeys in Kent's autopsy series have received as much or more external irradiation without showing atrophy of the thyroid.

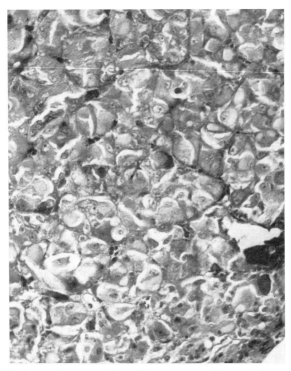

FIGURE 1. Pituitary, rhesus monkey. Note tumor cells replacing normal tissue (from Kent and Pickering).

The second male monkey was also killed because of a positive skin test for tuberculosis. At autopsy a number of caseous lesions, characteristic of tuberculosis, were found in the lungs and in the hilar lymph nodes, but not in the other organs. In addition, a well circumscribed, firm, rubbery, grayish-white mass, measuring 1.5 cm. in greatest diameter, was noted in the right adrenal. This mass largely replaced the adrenal medulla and appeared to be compressing the cortex. Microscopically, the mass was seen to be well circumscribed although not encapsulated. It was composed of dense interwoven bundles of collagen. Only an occasional fibroblast was found. A few small capillaries and venous channels were found in the tumor. On serial sectioning of the lesion, no evidence of inflammation or necrosis was noted. A diagnosis of fibroma was made (Fig. 2).

Two interesting cases of pituitary disease were described in detail by Fox (1923). In a capuchin monkey (Cebus capucinus) without generalized bone disease, the floor of the sella was missing, and bone absorption and erosion were evident in histologic sections. Blood had collected between the gland and the bone. The infundibular portion of the gland was large and irregularly distributed around the pars nervosa. The histological picture suggested an adenoma. In the second case, a cystic enlargement of the pituitary body was found in a *Macaca sinica,* which had lived eight years in captivity and had died of respiratory disease. The cyst,

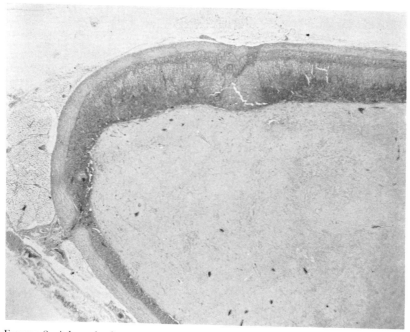

FIGURE 2. Adrenal, rhesus monkey. Fibroma and atrophy of cortex and medulla (from Kent and Pickering).

2 mm. in diameter, arose from the pituitary stalk and lay between the anterior lobe and the optic chiasm. Otherwise, the gland appeared normal.

Another interesting case of pituitary disease was found in the Berlin Zoological Garden. Koch (1937) found a pituitary cyst in a gorilla, and thought that this condition was responsible for the incomplete union of the epiphyses in the long bones and for the underdevelopment of the testes.

Parathyroid disease in monkeys has been reported from Russia. Hypoglycemia and tetany can be results of hypoparathyroidism, and Voronin *et al.* (1948) thought their experience and investigations at Sukhumi justified a diagnosis of parathyroprival tetany for most of the convulsive seizures which had occurred in that colony between 1927 and 1945. Both the clinical signs and presence of hypocalcemia during attacks were typical of tetany. Although several species of macaques and baboons were kept in the colony, tetany occurred only in sacred baboons *(Comopithecus hamadryas)*. This restricted incidence, combined with appearance of chronic tetany in weaned offspring of affected animals, led Voronin and his coworkers to postulate that a recessive hereditary predisposition to hypoparathyroidism was involved and to calculate from a genetic formula the number of cases to be expected among fifty-six colony-born baboons whose parents were free of the disorder. The predicted number was four and the actual number was five. Parathyroids from three baboons with histories of tetany were examined histologically. Tissues from one animal were normal, but pathologic changes, principally in the stroma, were found in the parathyroids of the other two animals.

DOG

In 1932, Tom Hare of the Royal Veterinary College, London, reported an adenoma of the pituitary gland associated with "dystrophia adiposogenitalis" in a mongrel terrier maiden bitch, aged nine years. This tumor was associated with depression of sexual function for two years, atrophy of the ovaries and vulva, gross adiposity and subsequent progressive emaciation. No abnormality was found in the skin and skeleton. Histologically the tumor was a chromophobe-cell adenoma.

A similar tumor was reported by Frankhauser and Wyler (1954) from Switzerland. The clinical signs were: obesity, polydipsia, loss of sexual activity, muscular atrophy and alopecia. In the last months of life apathy and circular walking to the left were noted. The cerebrospinal fluid showed xanthochromia with positive Nonne and Pandy tests and slightly increased cell count. At autopsy, a chromophobe adenoma of the anterior lobe of the pituitary gland was found. It protruded into the diencephalon and the third ventricle. It caused compression, displacement and diminished function of the anterior lobe and of the diencephalon. Other neurological signs (e.g., circular movements and disorientation) were most likely caused by general injury of the brain and meningitis.

Adenomata of the acidophil cells of the pituitary are apparently rare in dogs and in the few cases reported there has been no evidence of classic acromegaly. Hyperglycemia and glycosuria have been observed in dogs with acidophil adenomata. Small, well differentiated adenomata may produce these metabolic changes, whereas larger, more rapidly growing tumors will produce manifest local signs. A tumor of the latter type is shown in Figure 3 (from Innes and Saunders, 1962). This is an adenoma of the pituitary in a ten-year-old Boston terrier female. Figure A presents the ventral view. The optic chiasm is obscured and displaced forward so that the optic nerves turn back and down in their course to the foramina. The oculomotor nerves are displaced laterally. *B* is the midsagittal view. There is expansion of the tumor into the third ventricle with caudad displacement of the mammillary body and invasion of the optic nerve. Histologically the degree of the typical acidophil granulation varies as does the size both of the cells and their nuclei (Fig. 4).

Cushing's syndrome in dogs was first described by Coffin and Munson in 1953. "This condition occurs in dogs of middle age or beyond (six to sixteen years). It predominates in Boston Terriers. The onset is insidious, being marked by gradual enlargement of the belly and roughness of the coat. As the disease progresses, the belly continues to enlarge and, as the flesh is lost elsewhere, tends to have a pendulous appearance. Concomitantly, the hair-loss sequence progresses in a typical, bilateral pattern. The legs develop bare areas sooner than in the two previously mentioned conditions (Sertoli tumor of the testes, hypothyroidism). The remaining hair is rough, dry, often broken, and may easily be pulled from the follicles. Muscular weakness appears, being marked by the dog's trembling and by the assumption of a straight-legged, skeletal-braced posture. Muscular relaxation contributes to the pot-bellied appearance. The skin is often rough and scaly because of the presence of minute blackened projections. Small pustules or blisters

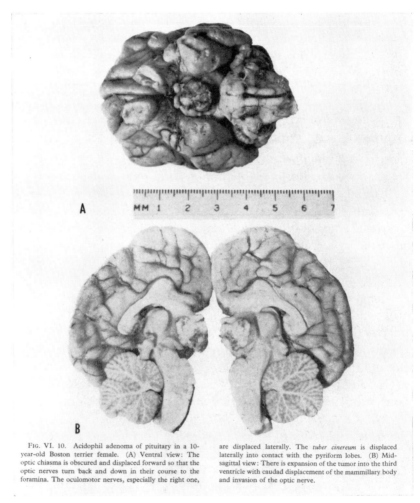

FIG. VI. 10. Acidophil adenoma of pituitary in a 10-year-old Boston terrier female. (A) Ventral view: The optic chiasma is obscured and displaced forward so that the optic nerves turn back and down in their course to the foramina. The oculomotor nerves, especially the right one, are displaced laterally. The *tuber cinereum* is displaced laterally into contact with the pyriform lobes. (B) Mid-sagittal view: There is expansion of the tumor into the third ventricle with caudad displacement of the mammillary body and invasion of the optic nerve.

FIGURE 3. Pituitary, dog, acidophil adenoma (from Innes and Saunders).

are seen frequently, especially on the belly. When these evacuate, the site is subsequently marked by ragged rims of desquamating epidermis. Characteristically, the centers of these areas become blackened, due to an accumulation of melanin pigment. The surface of the skin in such dogs is often cool."

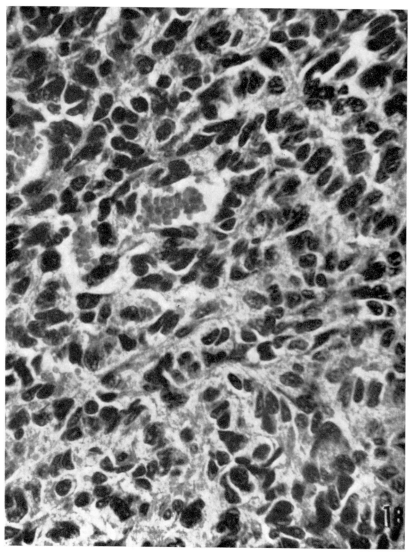

FIGURE 4. Pituitary, dog, acidophil adenoma (from Innes and Saunders).

In the majority of cases, polydipsia and polyuria occur to a degree compatible with diabetes insipidus. The specific gravity of the urine may range as low as 1.002 to 1.005. Marked lymphopenia and eosinopenia are of diagnostic value when other symptoms are suggestive.

The disease in dogs is caused by a disturbance of the pituitary-adrenal mechanism, in which basophil tumors of the pituitary gland and secondary bilateral cortical hyperplasia of the adrenal glands are found. Increased production of corticosteroids produces the diagnostic reduction of the lymphocytes and eosinophils, as well as changes in the skin and hair.

The essential pathologic findings in Coffin and Munson's cases were: (1) enlargement of the pituitary with adenomatous growth of the basophil cells, and frequently multiple cysts, leading to secondary atrophy of the posterior lobe; diminished production of the antidiuretic hormone explains the diabetes insipidus; (2) symmetrical hyperplasia of both adrenal cortices with an increased weight of the adrenals to from four to eight times the normal weight; (3) atrophy of the hair follicles, sebaceous glands and epidermis, and (4) loss of dermal fat, condensation of the collagenous and elastic fibers, and hyperkeratosis.

K. Dämmrich (1962) found five cases of "canine Cushing's disease" among 1700 autopsies of dogs. The microscopic findings in these five dogs were focal hyperplasia or adenoma of the basophil cells of the anterior lobe of the pituitary associated with hyperplasia of the adrenal cortical tissue. In varying degree the following signs were observed: alopecia, pyoderma, hyperkeratosis, adiposity, osteoporosis, atrophy of the testes (3 cases) and ovaries (2 cases), hyperglycemia with atrophy of the Langerhans islets of the pancreas, and calcium calculi in the kidneys. In two cases a large adenoma of the anterior pituitary was seen with destruction of the anterior and posterior lobe, in two cases a small adenoma caused atrophy through compression of the anterior and posterior lobe and in one case a small hyperplastic focus of basophil cells in the anterior hypophysis occurred.

Figure 5 illustrates large cells with basophil granulation from a large adenoma of the pituitary gland, Figure 6 large basophil cells accompanied by pleomorphic cells from the mixed cell aden-

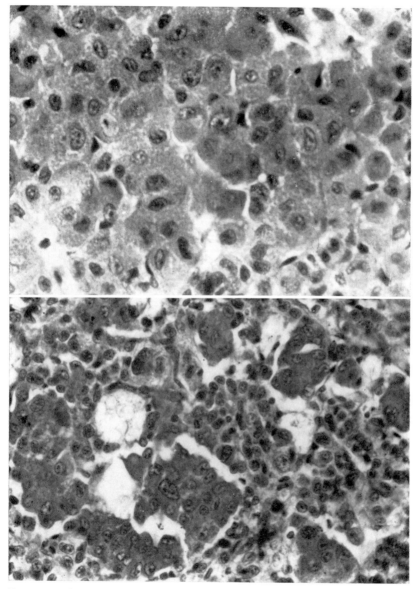

FIGURE 5. Pituitary, dog, large cells with basophil granulations (from Dämmrich).

FIGURE 6. Pituitary, dog, mixed cell adenoma (from Dämmrich).

oma, Figures 7 and 8 groups of pleomorphic cells with Crooke's changes.

In an earlier study, Dämmrich (1960) examined the adrenals of 100 autopsied dogs with chronic or acute diseases. He recorded the weight of the adrenals, gross and microscopic changes and interpreted them in terms of the adaptation syndrome of Selye. The frequent occurrence of nodules in the capsule and cortex is described. This was interpreted as a sign of increased functional activity. The results of these studies suggest that the effects of "stress" on the adrenals of the dog are similar to those in other species. Dämmrich distinguishes between hyperplasia and cortical adenoma on the basis of the histological picture.

Pheochromocytoma is found occasionally in older dogs. There is no breed or sex disposition. Noradrenalin was extracted from pheochromocytoma in several dogs. Clinically, tachycardia was the most striking sign. Unfortunately, no blood pressures were recorded. Figures 9 and 10 from Moulton (1961) show chromaffin cells from pheochromocytomata containing cytoplasmic granules.

In areas of the world where goiter is endemic, not only human beings but also dogs show enlargement of the thyroid gland. In the days before iodized salt was used goiters were as common in dogs as in man in many areas of Switzerland and Austria. I well remember having owned a puppy in Vienna fifty years ago who had a large goiter. Very frequently goiter in dogs became malignant. Carcinomata of the thyroid often occupy and replace the entire thyroid and extend into the neighboring structures. Histologically there is a marked variation in pattern (Figs. 11 and 12, Moulton, 1961).

A histological survey of the thyroid glands from dogs necropsied over a ten-year period at the Angell Memorial Animals Hospital indicates a high incidence of thyroid lesions. Alterations were associated with senescence, formation of goiters, tumors, and degeneration and inflammation. Degenerative and inflammatory lesions were rare as compared with goiters and tumors, the incidence of which increased with age. The wide variety of goitrous lesions was reflected in the patterns of the tumors, the goiters probably preceding the tumor growth. Thyroid lesions can only be considered absent after a complete gross and histological examination

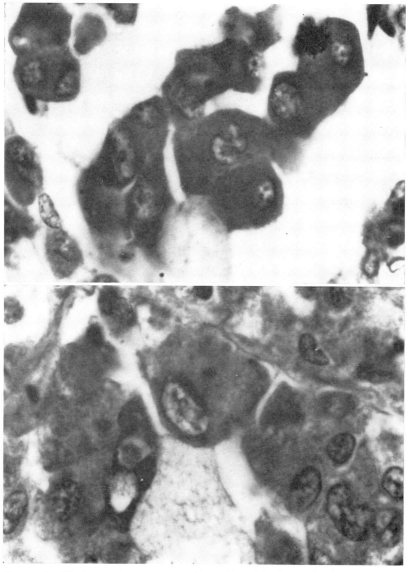

FIGURE 7. Pituitary, dog, pleomorphic cells with Crooke's changes (from Dämmrich).

FIGURE 8. Pituitary, dog, pleomorphic cells with Crooke's changes (from Dämmrich).

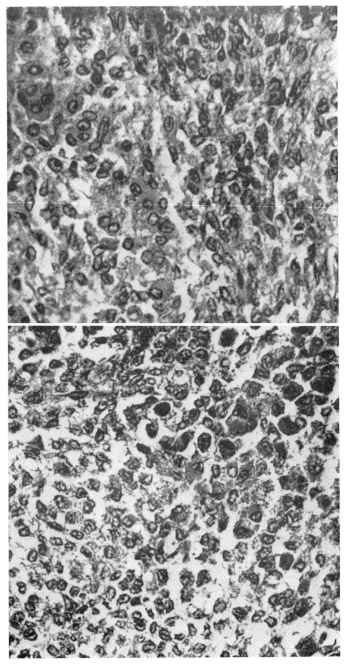

FIGURE 9. Adrenal, dog, phaeochromocytoma (from Moulton).
FIGURE 10. Adrenal, dog, phaeochromocytoma (from Moulton).

is carried out, since enlargement of the glands suggesting thyroid disease occurs in only a very low percentage of cases (Clark and Meier, 1958). In view of these pathological findings, thyroid disease has to be considered. Dysfunction of the thyroid may manifest itself as sluggishness, low pulse rate, bilateral symmetrical alopecia and hypercholesterolemia. Meier and Clark (1958) found the cholesterol levels extremely helpful in determining the effects of thyroid administration in hypothyroid dogs. They found an inverse correlation between the basal metabolic rate and the serum cholesterol level. These findings on serum cholesterol in dogs parallel ours in hypothyroid children (Wilkins and Fleischmann, 1941).

Secondary hyperplasia of the parathyroid gland due to chronic nephritis is common in dogs. It is often associated with osteodystrophia fibrosa, which occurs primarily in the flat bones of the head. There is no reported case of this bone change in domestic animals resulting from primary parathyroid hyperplasia. The bones of affected dogs exhibit decalcification, resorption, and replacement by fibrous connective tissue. The enlarged parathyroids are particularly noticeable at the anterior poles of the thyroids. Histologically, the hyperplastic parathyroid is indistinguishable from normal parathyroid (Moulton, 1961).

Multiple adenomata of the endocrine glands occur occasionally in man; the simultaneous occurrence of an eosinophilic adenoma of the pituitary gland and of four parathyroid tumors has been described in a mongrel dog (Wermer, 1963).

RAT

Tamaschke (1955) reviewed the literature on spontaneous tumors seen in rats; she found 173 such tumors reported. Twenty-four of these involved the endocrine system. Of these twenty-four tumors, twenty-one were thyroid tumors; in the other three rats carcinomata of the pituitary gland associated with tubular adenomata of the thyroid were reported. However, Miss Tamaschke apparently did not include reports on chromophobe adenoma-like lesions of the pituitary in her review. I would like to discuss these in some detail.

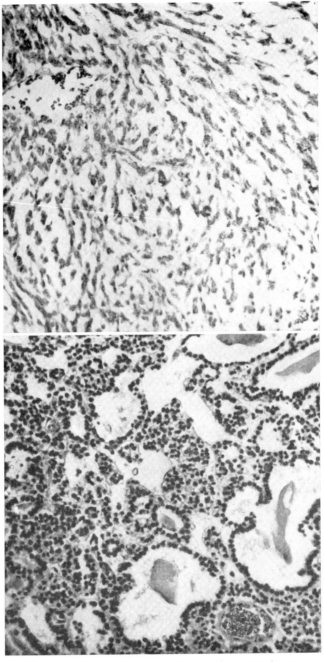

FIGURE 11. Thyroid, dog, carcinoma (from Moulton).
FIGURE 12. Thyroid, dog, carcinoma (from Moulton).

According to Saxton and Graham (1944) chromophobe adenoma-like lesions of the hypophysis were found in ninety-two of 362 albino rats of the Yale strain. Two lesions only were observed in rats less than one year of age. The lesions increased in frequency with advancing age, and were present in 60 per cent of male rats and in 30 per cent of female rats 600 and more days old. The lesions varied in size from small nodules seen only in microscopic sections to large masses, the largest weighing 367 mg. The majority of lesions were composed of cells with vacuolated chromophobic cytoplasm and large oval nuclei in which the chromatin was usually in the form of coarse granules. Chromophobe adenoma-like lesions were found in the hypophyses of three of eighty-three male rats of the Sherman strain, aged between one and three years, and of one of nine male rats of a stock derived from the Wistar strain, of comparable age.

Homologous intraocular transplants were done with adenoma-like tissue from two spontaneous lesions in male rats of the Yale strain, and these were carried in males into second and third serial intraocular generations respectively. Including all generations, growth of transplants occurred in twenty-one of forty-two recipients. The transplants grew at an extremely slow rate, requiring from eleven to nineteen months to reach a size suitable for serial transfer, and there was frequently a latent period of several months before growth was manifest. All transplants that grew became vascularized. The growth rate was not accelerated in subsequent transfers and the morphology did not change. Although the spontaneous lesions developed only at an advanced age, intraocular transplants grew as well in young as in old male rats. The strain of the recipient was found not to be a factor in either the percentage of successful transplants or their growth rate. The presence of spontaneous adenoma-like lesions in the pituitaries of the hosts did not influence the fate of transplants of adenoma-like tissue. Normal pituitary tissue persisted for a considerable period after intraocular transplantation, but did not grow in a manner comparable to adenoma-like tissue.

Chromophobe adenoma-like lesions of the rat's hypophysis probably are true neoplasms (Saxton and Graham, 1944). On the basis of the behavior of transplants the larger adenoma-like lesions are considered to be true neoplasms because the growth rate of transplants, while characteristically slow, is independent of the growth rate of tissues of the recipient. Furthermore, the ability of transplants to grow is independent of constitutional factors associated with age and strain of the host.

The findings confirm an earlier report by Wolfe *et al.* (1938) who found that adenomatous changes occur frequently in the pituitaries of old rats of the Wistar strain, particularly in females. The age of these rats was more than eighteen months. Hemorrhagic adenomata, a chromophobe adenoma, and adenomatous nodules believed to be precursors of true adenomata were described. More recently Furth (1955) stated that chromophobe pituitary adenomas are common in the Wistar strain of rats studied by him. They are not associated with an enlargement of the thyroid gland. Transplantation of these spontaneous pituitary tumors caused no secondary changes in the hosts with the possible exception of mammary gland hyperplasia.

A comprehensive study of spontaneous tumors in the Rochester strain of the Wistar rat was made recently by Crain (1958). In 786 albino rats of the Wistar strain, eighteen to twenty-four months old, eleven adenomata of the pituitary were noted. Not all of them showed the same degree of vascularity. The tumors were composed of cords of plump basophilic cells separated by a delicate reticulum and congested vascular spaces. The cytoplasm was scant and poorly defined. Nuclei were large, oval or round, and had prominent nuclear membranes with a light sprinkling of chromatin. Many nuclei contained a prominent central nucleolus. Deposits of brown pigment resembling hemosiderin were present in the cytoplasm of some of the cells and within vascular sinusoids. There was no invasion of adjacent structures. Mann's stain showed no chromophilic element in these adenomata (Fig. 13).

Ten tumors of the adrenal medulla were found among Crain's Wistar rats. In most cases the tumor was not recognized on gross examination. The frequency with which the adrenals of old rats were enlarged, cystic, and sometimes hemorrhagic made size a dubious criterion in detecting small adenomata. The smallest adenomata appeared as small clusters of intensively basophilic cells in the medulla. The sparse cytoplasm and marked basophilic

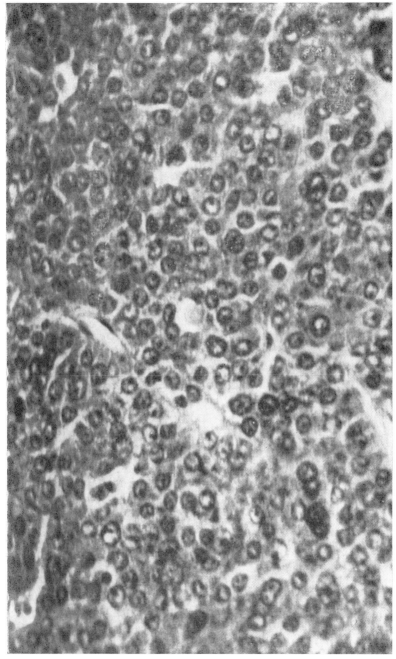

FIGURE 13. Pituitary, rat, adenoma (from Crain).

staining of the nuclei were in distinct contrast to the medullary elements. The larger tumors formed nodular clusters about sinusoids. Occasionally there were multiple clusters in separate portions of the medulla. The largest medullary tumors caused compression and narrowing of the cortex. The largest tumor in this series, measuring 1 cm. in diameter, had penetrated the cortex and capsule invading the perirenal fat. In this tumor the nuclei were larger, vesicular and less basophilic, and the cytoplasm more abundant and more clearly demarcated. The difference in cell type was not a regular feature and considerable variation was encountered. The cells of the small adenomata were arranged in solid cords separated by a delicate capillary network, whereas in the larger tumors the vascular network consisted of large sinusoids and venous lakes. Frank invasion was not observed. The heart weight:body weight ratios of the rats in this series were analyzed in an effort to establish a correlation between possible pressor substance secretion by the adrenal tumors and cardiovascular alterations. In all but two rats the heart weight:body weight ratios were within or below the normal range; in the two rats in which this range was exceeded, only microscopic adenomata were present and there were no other necropsy findings to indicate either an endocrinopathy or cardiovascular disease. Crain included an unusual adrenal tumor seen in a rat under six months of age in his report. This tumor most nearly resembled a neuroblastoma. It originated in the left adrenal medulla and invaded the spleen and adjacent peritoneum. The splenic metastases consisted of several nodules of friable gray-white tissue which varied from 0.6 to 1.8 cm. in diameter. The largest nodule was hemorrhagic and necrotic and accounted for the presence of free blood in the peritoneal cavity. The tumor was cellular and its nuclei were variable in size and shape. In a few areas, tumor cells were arranged in rosettelike fashion.

In earlier work Yeakel (1947) examined the adrenal glands of sixteen female and fifteen male albino rats and of three female and three male gray Norway rats, 700 days or older. Hyperplasia was observed in three of the female rats (16 per cent) and in thirteen of the male rats (72 per cent). Various degrees of hyperplasia were seen. The minimal stage consisted of a knot of hyperchromatic cells within the normal medulla. Sinusoidal dilatation was usually present, separating the strands of the medullary cords of the nodule. Similar but larger nodules surrounded enlarged blood channels. More advanced growths, suggesting an adenoma, were made up either of relatively solid hyperplastic tissue or of tissue separated into cords by greatly dilated sinusoids or of both. In the most advanced stages the cortex was compressed to a narrow rim or was completely obliterated, with no normal medullary tissue being identified. In two instances, invasion of the capsule was observed.

Gillman *et al.* (1953) made an extensive study of the adrenals in Wistar rats. Histological examination of the adrenal glands of 167 male and 189 female rats ranging in age from one month to over thirty months of age revealed a high incidence of pheochromocytoma. Only two tumors were found in rats under the age of one year. The incidence of tumors increased steadily after the age of one year and between the ages of thirteen and eighteen months adrenal tumors were found in 50 per cent of the female and in 82 per cent of the male rats. The tumor of the medulla had local malignant properties as it frequently eroded the adrenal capsule, invading the neighboring soft tissues or spreading along the adrenal vein and forming thrombi in the vena cava. The kidney itself was never involved even when the periadrenal tissues had been widely infiltrated. Emboli of tumor cells were found in the lung, although the tumor seemed incapable to establish itself beyond the region of local growth. The tumors were transplantable into very young rats. Subcutaneous transplants grew slowly. Histologically the transplants resembled the original tumor, however chromaffin material was very scanty in the transplants in comparison to the original tumor. From the fact that these tumors grew on transplantation and from their locally invasive nature the authors conclude that the pheochromocytoma in the rat possesses a low grade of malignancy.

The lesions associated with pheochromocytoma in rats included a high incidence of necrosis of the liver, of chronic myocarditis, and of nephrosclerosis. Gillman *et al.* were impressed by the frequency of tumors, benign and malignant, of other endocrine glands. In 327 rats, about half of them male, fourteen carcinomata of the thyroid, ten adenomata of the islets of Langerhans, and thirty-one interstitial cell tumors of the testes were found. For an analysis of spontaneous tumors in rats, see Gilbert and Gillman (1958).

Two thyroid adenomata encountered in Crain's material may not accurately reflect the incidence of thyroid neoplasm since sections of thyroid were made in only 24 per cent (188) of the necropsies. One adenoma consisted of solid cords and tubes of uniform large cells separated by delicate strands of connective tissue. The abundant cytoplasm was granular and stained pink, the nuclei were large and vesicular. Small amounts of colloid were present in portions of the adenoma (Fig. 14). A second well circumscribed adenoma of similar histologic pattern revealed marked compression of the acini in a narrow rim of thyroid around the periphery of the nodule.

According to Lindsay *et al.* (1951) spontaneously occurring alveolar carcinomata of the thyroid have a very high incidence (30 to 35 per cent) in normal rats of the Long-Evans strain. These spontaneous neoplasms of low-grade malignancy are characterized by their tendency to invade thyroid follicles, their alveolar pattern, their cellular uniformity, and lack of tendency to invade into extrathyroidal tissue (Figs. 15, 16, and 17). In these respects the spontaneous neoplasms differ from those induced by I^{131}. The thyroid carcinoma induced by I^{131} in rats has a greater similarity to human carcinoma of the thyroid than the spontaneous carcinoma found in rats.

MOUSE

Thyrotropic pituitary tumors can be induced in mice by sustained thyroid deficiency brought about by any of the following: radiothyroidectomy, surgical thyroidectomy, antithyroidal compounds, and low iodine diet. The effect is accomplished by interference with the physiological feedback mechanism and sustained stimulation of thyrotropes. This sequence of events appears to follow thyroidectomy in every strain of mice and in every individual. Occasionally spontaneous thyrotropic tumors of the pituitary gland are found in mice. Transplants of these tumors are hormone responsive. They grow very slowly in normal hosts. Their growth

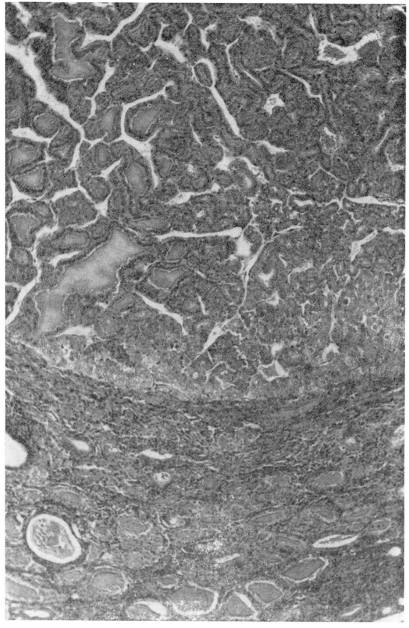

FIGURE 14. Thyroid, rat, adenoma (from Crain).

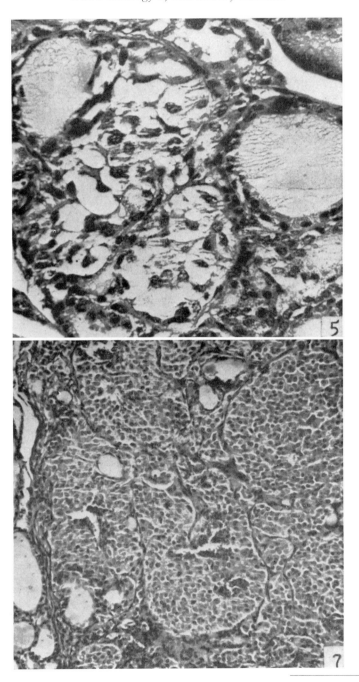

can be greatly enhanced by administration of propylthiouracil to the host. Cessation of conditioning with propylthiouracil markedly reduces their growth rate (Furth and Clifton, 1958).

Adenomata of the adrenal cortex occur spontaneously with high incidence in old female mice of the NH strain. They are similar to the adrenal tumors appearing following gonadectomy (Frantz *et al.*, 1948).

J. Furth (1955) reported the finding of a transplantable chromaffin cell tumor in a mouse. Adrenalin and noradrenalin were found in this tumor in slightly lesser amounts than in the normal adrenal medulla. Surprisingly enough the hosts of this transplantable adrenal tumor did not show the usual effects of spontaneous adrenal tumors, e.g., cardiac hypertrophy and hypertension. The adrenals of the tumor hosts were of normal size and color. The sex organs of the hosts showed no change. The hosts appeared to be in good health. Unfortunately the urine was not assayed for metabolites of adrenal hormones. Some homeostatic adjustment must have existed in these hosts or else the adrenalin was bound to the tumors; this conclusion is drawn from the fact that tumor tissue injected into normal mice caused immediate shock and death. Unfortunately the tumor became highly malignant and chromaffinity vanished.

Kühl (1958) autopsied 3065 white mice of the strain "Riems" and found changes in the thyroid in seventy-six animals.

Table I gives a summary of her findings. Fifteen mice showed hyperplastic microfollicular changes in the thyroid tissue. In twenty-nine mice adenomata were found; most of the adenomata were solitary nodules, but a few multiple nodules were also seen. Thirty-two mice showed diffuse colloid struma. In one case a papillary adenocarcinoma with pulmonary metastases was observed. The primary tumor showed a microfollicular, papillary, and tabular structure. In the metastases large follicles and cysts with formation of colloid were observed.

FIGURE 15. Thyroid, rat, early alveolar carcinoma. Age of rat: twenty-seven months (from Lindsay *et al.*).

FIGURE 16. Thyroid, rat, early alveolar carcinoma. Age of rat: twenty-eight months (from Lindsay *et al.*).

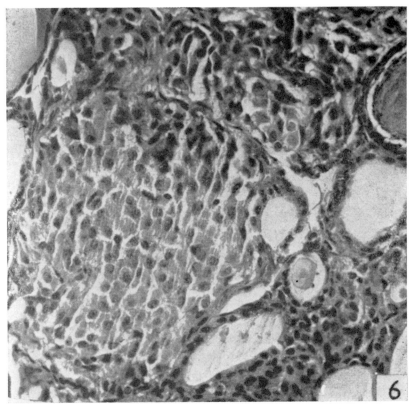

FIGURE 17. Thyroid, rat, extensive alveolar carcinoma. Age of rat: twenty-eight months (from Lindsay *et al.*) .

TABLE I
THYROID DISEASE IN WHITE MICE (KÜHL)

Number autopsied	3065
Hyperplasia	15
Adenoma	29
Adenocarcinoma	1
Colloid struma	32
Normal thyroid	2988

CONCLUSION

Spontaneous hyperthyroidism is exceedingly rare in animals. Only in wild rabbits have signs and symptoms closely resembling thyrotoxicosis (Graves' disease) in humans been observed. Wild rabbits usually die within a few weeks of captivity with symptoms of hyperthyroidism (muscle weakness, emaciation, tachycardia, tremor, and exophthalmus) (Eickhoff, 1949; Kracht, 1952, 1954). We know that in human beings the onset of Graves' disease is often preceded by psychic trauma. The parallelism of the "fright-thyrotoxicosis" in wild rabbits and the onset of Graves' disease in human beings precipitated by emotional upset is of great interest to every worker in the field of neuroendocrinology.

REFERENCES

CLARK, S. T., and MEIER, H.: A clinico-pathological study of thyroid disease in the dog and cat. Part I.: Thyroid pathology. *Zbl. Vet. Med., 5:*17, 1958.

COFFIN, D. L., and MUNSON, T. O.: Endocrine diseases of the dog associated with hair loss: Sertoli-cell tumor of testis, hypothyroidism and Cushing's Syndrome. *J. Amer. Vet. Med. Ass., 123:*402, 1953.

CRAIN, R. C.: Spontaneous tumors in the Rochester strain of the Wistar rat. *Amer. J. Path., 34:*311, 1958.

CROSBY, E. L.: Frequency of diagnosis of endocrine disease. Quoted from Grollman, A. *Essentials of Endocrinology*, 2nd Ed. Philadelphia, Lippincott, 1946.

DÄMMRICH, K.: Beiträge zur Morphologic der Nebennierenrinde bei Spontanerkrankungen des Hundes. *Zentralbl. Veterinärmed., 7:* 553, 1960.

DÄMMRICH, K.: Die Beeinflussung des Skeletts durch die Hormone der Nebennierenrinde unter besonderer Berücksichtigung des Morbus Cushing beim Hund. *Berlin. Münch. Tierärztl. Wschr., 75:*331, 1962.

EICKHOFF, W.: *Schilddrüse und Basedow.* Stuttgart, Thieme, 1949.

FAIRBROTHER, R. W., and HURST, E. W.: Spontaneous diseases observed in 600 monkeys. *J. Path. Bact., 35:*867, 1932.

FANKHAUSER, R., and WYLER, R.: Chromophobes Adenom der hypophyse bei einem Hund. *Schweiz. Arch. Tierheilk., 96:*181, 1954.

FOX, H.: *Disease of Captive Wild Mammals and Birds. Incidence, Description, Comparison.* Philadelphia, Lippincott, 1923. Quoted from Ruch.

FRANTZ, M. J., KIRSCHBAUM, A., and CASAS, C.: Endocrine interrelationship and spontaneous tumors of the adrenal cortex in NH mice. *Proc. Soc. Exp. Biol. Med., 66:*645, 1948.

FURTH, J.: Experimental pituitary tumors in *Recent Progress in Hormone Research* ed. G. Pincus, Vol. XI. New York, Acad. Press, 1955.

FURTH, J.: in *Ciba Foundation Colloquia on Endocrinology*, Vol. XII. Boston, Little, Brown and Company, 1958.

FURTH, J., and CLIFTON, K. H.: in *Ciba Foundation Colloquia on Endocrinology*, Vol. XII. Boston, Little, Brown and Co., 1958.

GILBERT, C., and GILLMAN, J.: Spontaneous neoplasms in the albino rat. *S. Afr. J. Med. Sci., 23*:257, 1958.

GILLMAN, J., GILBERT, C., and SPENCE, I.: Phaeochromocytoma in the rat: Pathogenesis and collateral reactions and its relation to comparable tumours in man. *Cancer, 6*:494, 1953.

HARE, T.: Chromophobe-cell adenoma of the pituitary gland, associated with dystrophia adiposo-genitalis in a maiden bitch. *Proc. Roy. Soc. Med., 25*:1493, 1932.

INNES, J. R. M., and SAUNDERS, L. Z.: *Comparative Neuropathology.* New York and London, Acad. Press, 1962.

KENNARD, M. A.: Abnormal findings in 246 consecutive autopsies on monkeys. *Yale J. Biol. Med., 13*:701, 1941.

KENT, S. P., and PICKERING, J. E.: Neoplasms in monkey (Macaca mulatta): Spontaneous and irradiation induced. *Cancer, 11*:138, 1958.

KOCH, W.: Bericht über das Ergebnis der Obduktion des Gorilla Bobby des Zoologischen Gartens in Berlin. *Veröff. Konst. und Wehr. Path.,* 1937. Quoted from Ruch.

KRACHT, J.: Fright-thyrotoxicosis in the wild rabbit, a model of thyrotropic alarm reaction. *Acta Endocr., 15*:355, 1954.

KRACHT, J., and KRACHT, U.: Zur Hisopathologie und Therapie der Schreckthyreose des Wildkaninchens. *Virchow Arch. Path. Anat., 321*:238, 1952.

KÜHL, I.: In Fischer, W., and Kühl, I. *Geschwülste der Laboratoriumsnagetiere.* Dresden and Leipzig, Steinkopff, T., 1958.

LINDSAY, S., POTTER, G. D., and CHAIKOFF, I. L.: Thyroid neoplasms in the rat: A comparison of naturally occurring and I^{131} induced tumors. *Cancer Res., 17*:183, 1957.

MEIER, H., and CLARK, S. T.: The Clinico-Pathological aspect of thyroid disease in the dog and cat. *Zbl. Vet. Med., 5*:120, 1958.

MOULTON, J. E.: *Tumors in Domestic Animals.* Berkeley and Los Angeles, Univ. California Press, 1961.

RATCLIFFE, H. L.: Incidence and nature of tumors in captive wild mammals and birds. *Cancer, 17*:116, 1933.

RUCH, T. C.: *Diseases of Laboratory Primates.* Philadelphia and London, Saunders, 1959.

SAXTON, J. A., JR., and GRAHAM, J. B.: Chromophobe adenoma-like lesions of rat hypophysis. *Cancer Res.*, *4:*168, 1944.

TAMASCHKE, C.: Die Spontantumoren der kleinen Laboratoriumssäuger in ihrer Bedeutung für die experimentelle Onkologie. *Strahlentherapie*, *96:*150, 1955.

VORONIN, L. G., KANFOR, I. S., LAKIN, G. F., and TIKH, N. H.: Spontaneous diseases of lower monkey, their prophylaxis, diagnosis and treatment. In, *Exp. on the Keeping and Raising of Monkeys at Sukhumi.* Moscow, Acad. of Sciences, 1948.

WERMER, P.: Endocrine adenomatosis and peptic ulcer in a large kindred. *Amer. J. Med.*, *35:*205, 1963.

WILKINS, L., and FLEISCHMANN, W.: Hypothyroidism in childhood. III. The effect of withdrawal of thyroid therapy upon the serum cholesterol. Relationship of cholesterol, basal metabolic rate, weight and clinical symptoms. *J. Clin. Endocr.*, *1:*91, 1941.

WOLFE, J. M., BRYAN, W. R., and WRIGHT, A. W.: Histologic observations on the anterior pituitaries of old rats with particular reference to the spontaneous appearance of pituitary adenomata. *Cancer, 34:*352, 1938.

YEAKEL, E. H.: Medullary hyperplasia of the adrenal gland in aged Wistar Albino and Gray Norway Rats. *Arch. Path.*, *44:*71, 1947.

ACKNOWLEDGMENTS

I wish to thank the following for permission to use their illustrative material: Drs. S. P. Kent and J. E. Pickering and the publishers of *Cancer* for Figures 1 and 2; Academic Press for Figures 3 and 4; Dr. K. Dämmrich and Verlag Paul Parey for Figures 5, 6, 7 and 8; the University of California Press for Figures 7, 8, 9, 10, 11 and 12; Dr. R. C. Crain and the publishers of the *Am. J. Path.* for Figures 13 and 14; and Dr. S. Lindsay and the publishers of *Cancer Research* for Figures 15, 16, and 17.

DISCUSSION

Dr. C. H. Eades: I wish to comment on the cholesterol and thyroid relationship in a rat. I want to say that I think many, many things besides thyroid have something to do with the cholesterol level and if one uses that as a gauge or measure of thyroid function without delineating all the other conditions that the rat is under, like age and blood pressure and diet and all that, it is a risk just to say thyroid all the time when speaking of cholesterol level changes.

Dr. Fleischmann: I was talking about the dog and not the rat.

Dr. Eades: The same thing is true about the dog.

Dr. Fleischmann: I think I didn't make myself clear. Our paper describes the procedure followed by us in hypothyroid patients. If a patient is started on thyroid extract and this medication is discontinued later his serum cholesterol curve will reflect the changes in treatment. Of course, the patient has to be on a fixed diet.

I agree with you on your point. In the rat the cholesterol level is not regulated by the thyroid only. I didn't mean to imply that this was otherwise—so I think we are in agreement.

Dr. J. R. M. Innes: I would like to point out that rats with pituitary tumors are frequently paralyzed. When one sees the rat, paralyzed in the hind quarters, with loss of sphincter control and stained tail, that is the limit of his neurologic examination, but rats with these clinical signs may suffer from pituitary tumors, from spinal cord tumors, from middle ear disease and some can suffer from encephalitozoonosis of rats and mice. It is extremely rare to find encephalitozoonosis in rats or mice, but I have encountered it.

Dr. Hunt: I just want to make one comment. I would just like to comment on hyperplasia of thyroid epithelium.

There are apparently two epithelial cell types in the rat thyroid, the normal follicular epithelium and then that which is referred to as the "light cell." In an older rat hyperplasia or adenomas of these light cells—referred to as light cell adenoma—are quite common, but tumors of epithelial cells are quite rare. The function of the light cell is obscure. It does not concentrate radioiodine nor does this type of epithelium respond to either deficient diet or to antithyroid drugs.

Chairman: Is it still thyroid epithelium if it doesn't?

Dr. Hunt: These are cells, epithelial in nature, first described, I believe, by Dr. Long.

Chairman: I will raise this question with you, Dr. Fleischmann: if one has an adenocarcinoma that won't concentrate iodine, is it still a thyroid gland?

Dr. Fleischmann: Yes, I would consider it such if it originated from the thyroid.

Chairman: Even though it lost its function?

Dr. Fleischmann: Even if it lost its function, if it is growing wild and anaplastic, I would still consider it so.

Chairman: Adrenal cortical tumors have been mentioned. What is the corticoid production of these adrenal cortical tumors? Dr. Dunn?

Dr. Thelma Dunn: I think it varies a great deal. Each tumor seems to be quite individual and we practically need to study each one. There is a distinct hormone effect produced by most of them. There is one that has considerable effect on the mammary gland and others have varied effects, so it is hard to make a general statement.

Chairman: In other words, you haven't really been able to correlate the pathology with the physiological steroid production.

Dr. Dunn: No.

Dr. John King: Dr. Fleischmann, you had a comment dealing with the malignancy of phaeochromocytoma in rats.

Dr. Fleischmann: That was Inman's finding.

Dr. John King: My observation is that in about 1,000 rats autopsied by ourselves in this last year only three or four of them had malignant neoplasms. Three of those were of phaeochromocytomas. Three were in the adrenal gland and the other in some other structure.

And one question regarding chronic thyroiditis, or struma lymphomatosa. We have recently had 26 per cent in a group of forty-some dogs. Dr. Hürthle's original paper says that they found it in 13 or 14 per cent. I found it in 26 per cent and I am just wondering if anybody has opinions on the marked lymphoid infiltration, some with Hürthle cell hypertrophy, in the thyroid of mature dogs, not necessarily old dogs. It seems to be very common.

Dr. Fleischmann: You mentioned the Hürthle cells and if you look at Hürthle's original paper, this cell was originally described in the dog, not in the human.

I went through the literature and I expected to find that Hürthle cells were normal in dogs and were a normal constituent of the dog thyroid. I didn't find anything on it and I can't remember having seen it elsewhere.

Dr. Wm. Ribelin: I would appreciate Dr. Fleischmann's comments on tumors of the adrenal medulla.

In the medulla of the adrenal gland of the rat there are two types of cells that take a chromaffin stain, the large open type and the small more densely packed type with dark but scanty cytoplasm. Each of these cells gives rise to a very characteristic type of neoplasm, both in the adrenal medulla, both arising from chromaffin positive cells. In theory they should probably be called pheochromocytoma but they are distinctly different types of tumors.

This dark, compact cell forms a very dense, compact, typically adenoma-type tumor and following the lead, I believe, first of Dr. Crain, at Rochester, we have been calling these medullary adenomas. Dr. Snell tells me she doesn't approve of this, that these are obviously of neurogenic origin and should have a different name.

These other tumors, composed of the more open type larger cells with abundant pale cytoplasm we have been applying the usual term pheochromocytoma.

I wonder if Dr. Fleischmann could distinguish between these two cells and tell me what we ought to call the tumors?

Dr. Fleischmann: I am afraid I didn't know too much about these two types of cells. I have talked to Dr. Crain who is now in Knoxville, and he still sticks to his original classification. I think that each is a distinct type of cell and a distinct type of tumor, as he proposed in his paper (*Amer. J. Path., 34:*311-335, 1958).

Dr. Ribelin: I have noticed a number of publications listing adrenal tumors in the rat and most authors call them pheochromocytomas, but I have seen distinct specimens of each of the two groups of tumors. I suspect that authors, by combining the two types, will create problems for the reader who wishes to know the incidence of each tumor in the various strains of rats.

Dr. Thelma Dunn: May I make a comment? We have, with Dr. Hans Pfeiffer, been able to identify certain iron-containing bodies in adrenal tumor cells and we have found that these are true pheochromocytomas in rats. I would be interested in knowing whether there is any difference in the presence of these bodies in these types of adrenal tumors you describe. We have seen these bodies rather regularly in the mouse pheochromocytomas.

Dr. Wm. Ribelin: Dr. Snell was speaking about nodular hypertrophy of the adrenal cortex and she suggested that it might be a pre-malignant change. We see this hypertrophic change quite frequently in the adrenal cortex of our CFN rats and we very seldom see malignancies of the adrenal cortex. We have put together a picture that I would like to describe and then see if you agree with our reasoning: Initially the hypertrophic area focally undergoes fatty change. If you look at such areas closely you can find various amounts of lipid in the swollen hypertrophic cells. This is apparently hypertrophic rather than hyperplastic because if the cells are counted one will find that there are about the same number as would be expected normally. One sees this fatty change and then in areas the fat cells begin to break down (lipolysis) with fatty cysts then hemorrhage appearing to replace the disintegrating cortical epithelium.

This is thus a hemorrhage *in vacuo*. The hemorrhages enlarge by expansion, not dissection. They eventually completely replace the fatty cysts. One finds a large pool of free blood within the cortex. It is not lined by endothelium. One is faced with merely a large pool of stagnant blood.

Lastly, it is not infrequent that these pools of stagnant blood undergo thrombosis or even organization.

I am curious to know as to whether any of you have ideas other than this as to the possible sequence of these changes.

Dr. J. R. McCoy: I can vouch for these lesions in older rats. I often encounter such multiple massive hemorrhages. They may actually displace much of the cortex.

Dr. A. A. Nelson: My feeling is that the vascular changes here and also cortical hyperplasia are not related to adrenal cortical carcinoma.

Dr. H. S. N. Greene: In the rabbit the so-called localized hyperplasia of the adrenal cortex occurs in the spring. One can always tell the time of year. When one begins to find adenomas of the adrenal cortex you can be sure that spring is on the way They disappear later on.

Dr.Theodore W. Harris: There is one more comment I wish to make.

In aging rats three years old or older, we find quite a few animals wherein the sex organs are affected by senile changes. One encounters ovarian cystic hypoplasia in a perfectly normal guinea pig. We also see it in rats and mice and rabbits in older animals. In the male one encounters atrophy of the testes, vacuolization of individual tubules, and maybe prostatic metaplasia. These sort of things go on all the time. These are apparently endocrine in origin. One can relate them in the rat, for example, to a very large pituitary with accompanying degenerative changes in the adrenals.

Dr. Snell: I am quite willing to agree with Dr. Harris as to the testicular atrophy in the old rats. Atrophied tubules occur quite frequently in old rats as do also calcified blood vessels.

In ovaries of our female rats over two years old we frequently find nothing but corpora lutea, no functional tissue being present.

When we encounter atrophy of the testes or atrophy of the ovaries in old animals we find castration cells in the pituitary glands fairly often. I think it all goes together as senile change and there is not very much of a strain difference in that.

5

SPONTANEOUS RENAL LESIONS

FRANK BLOOM

RENAL TUBULAR FAT AND INTRAGLOMERULAR
PROTRUSIONS

THOSE WHO HAVE had experience with the cat will recognize Figure 1 as the kidney of that species. As seen in paraffin sections from which fat has been removed, there is pronounced vacuolization of the epithelium of the first portion of the proximal convoluted tubule. This lipid deposition is physiological, although it has been erroneously interpreted as degenerative by many investigators who were unfamiliar with this normal infiltration. In the cat the fatty infiltration is unrelated to dietary changes. The greatest amount of fat occurs in the pregnant cat, less in the adult male, still less in the young male and nonpregnant female, and least in the fetal cat. The fatty acids of which this is composed are more saturated and thus have a lower iodine value than those of the other viscera. They, therefore, differ from the renal lipids of other mammals in not being readily available for metabolic activity.

In the dog there is also a normal lipid infiltration, but instead of being limited to the first portion of the proximal convoluted tubule the fat occurs mainly in the terminal segment of the proximal convolution. As compared to the cat, much less fat is commonly present in the dog. The fat in the dog is much more labile than in the cat, its quantity varies with the nutritional state of the animal. There is the least in thin dogs and puppies and there is the greatest amount of older obese animals.

The distinct localization of lipid, as evidenced by vacuoles in paraffin sections, in the proximal convoluted tubule of the dog and cat offers positive identification of this portion of the nephron.

It would seem that the cat, because of the constant fatty in-filtration, would be an undesirable experimental animal to employ in studies in which degenerative lesions of the proximal convoluted tubule might occur.

Figure 1 also illustrates a spontaneously occurring normal change consisting of protrusion of the proximal convoluted tubular epithelium into Bowman's space of the glomerulus. This has been stated to occur in 50 per cent of the kidneys of cats and 72 per cent of the kidneys of dogs, although my observations indicate that it is considerably commoner in the cat. The protrusions consist of regular or irregular strands of masses of nuclear-containing cytoplasm without a basement membrane, and are morphological-ly identical with the epithelium of the proximal convoluted tubule. The epithelium of both the visceral and parietal layers of Bowman's capsule is intact and has no relation to the protrusions. Although it is believed that the protrusions apparently form by imagination or by telescoping and may be related to variations in intrarenal pressure, it is also considered that they are artefacts.

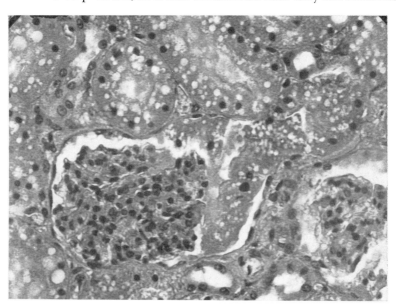

FIGURE 1. Vacuolated cytoplasm of proximal convoluted tubule and protrusion of epithelium of proximal convoluted tubule into Bowman's space. Cat kidney. x450.

One unfamiliar with these protrusions may incorrectly assume that they represent an abnormal condition or even alubminous material in Bowman's space.

INTRANUCLEAR CRYSTALS

In the dog but not in the cat, about 1 per cent of the nuclei of the renal proximal convoluted tubular epithelium and also hepatic cells normally contain crystals (Fig. 2). The crystals consist of hexagonal prisms and occupy a clear area or vacuole in the nucleus with the chromatin and nucleolus marginated toward the nuclear membrane. The average length is from seven to twelve microns and the width varies from two to seven microns. They stain pink with eosin, and are usually parallel to the tubular lumen.

CALCIUM INFARCTS

These are not really "infarcts" in the true meaning of the word, but represent the presence of calcific granules and clumps in the lumens and epithelium of collecting tubules, and less often in the adjacent interstitial tissue (Fig. 3). It is recognized grossly as fine, glistening, grayish white, linear streakings in the renal papilla.

The condition is clinically benign and occurs mainly in dogs over four years of age. It is seen in about 5 per cent of all dog autopsies and is commonly bilateral. There does not appear to be any relation to dystrophic or metastatic calcification, and neither are there any calcium disturbances in other organs and tissues.

GLOMERULAR LIPIDOSIS

This lesion is encountered in approximately 3 per cent of all dog autopsies. It is not seen in the cat. Microscopically, in paraffin sections from which fat has been removed, the lipidosis consists of conglomerations of foam cells in one or more lobules of the glomerular tuft (Fig. 4). In frozen sections stained with Sudan IV the lipids in the foam cells consist of orange-red, small, round, closely packed but discrete globules and also as droplets and masses. The foam cells have the typical appearance of xanthoma cells, and seem to arise from the endothelial cells of the capillaries. In some kidneys only an occasional glomerulus shows this change; in others as many as 70 per cent of the glomeruli are involved.

The cause is unknown, and clinical signs are absent. The kidney itself may otherwise be normal or else concomitant interstitial nephritis may be present.

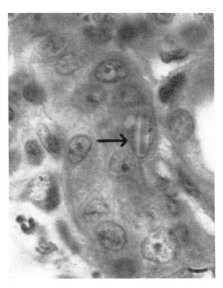

FIGURE 2. Intranuclear crystal *(arrow)* in epithelial cell of a proximal convolution. Dog kidney. x1084.

FELINE RENAL REGENERATION

A peculiar form of renal regenerative activity is occasionally seen in normal cats and in those with numerous other renal and nonrenal conditions. It is manifested by the presence of multinucleated giant-cell-like masses, mainly in the straight tubules and less often in the convoluted segments (Fig. 5). The nuclei number from eight to twenty, are usually pyknotic, and mitoses are absent.

ASCARID NODULES IN THE DOG

Of the different types of nematode larvae that may be found in the kidney, those of *Toxocara canis* are the most important.

Following encystment of the ascarid larvae, from few to many small tubercle-like nodules that are rarely larger than several millimeters in diameter are found on the surface and cross sec-

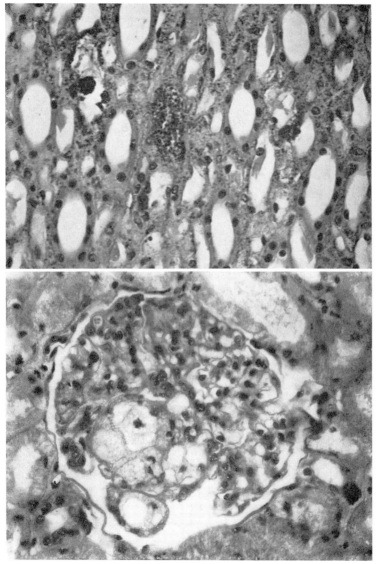

FIGURE 3. Calcium infarcts in kidney of dog. x450.
FIGURE 4. Glomerular lipidosis involving part of tuft in kidney of dog. x400.

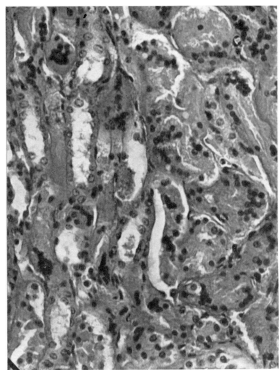

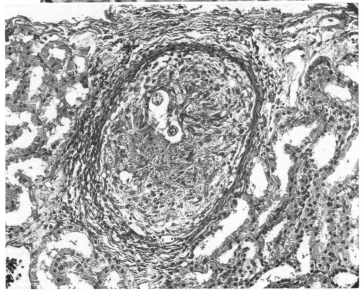

tion of the kidney. The parasitic nodules are largely located in the cortex and cortico-medullary zone. In the earlier stages they are gray-white to gray-yellow in color, opaque, and the centers may be soft and grumous. In later stages the nodules are firm, white, and glistening.

Microscopically, the ascarid nodules have a granulomatous appearance, and in early stages are composed of a centrally situated larva lying in a mass of epithelioid cells, lymphocytes, and occasional giant cells (Fig. 6). At the periphery is an early proliferation of fibrous connective tissue. In later stages the larva disappears and the central zone may undergo caseation necrosis and be surrounded by a richly cellular margin of granulation tissue, which is in turn bordered by lymphocytes (Fig. 7). Eventually, the nodules may persist as spherical masses of concentrically arranged layers of fibrous connective tissue with few cellular elements (Fig. 8).

The parasitic nodules are frequently found in the kidneys of dogs, especially in young animals. Even in the presence of numerous nodules, there is rarely if ever any disturbance in renal functional activity. I have never observed them in cat kidneys.

POLYCYSTIC KIDNEYS AND PERIRENAL HYGROMA

In my experience polycystic kidneys (congenital cystic kidneys) are not uncommon in cats. The lesion is usually bilateral, and the external surface of the kidney is either finely or coarsely lobulated by the projecting cysts (Fig. 9). The illustration of cut surface shows that the renal parenchyma is largely replaced by multiple cyst formation (Fig. 10). Microscopically, the cysts are present in both the cortex and medulla. They are lined by flattened or cuboidal epithelium and their walls consist of thin fibrous connective tissue. The adjacent renal tissue may be normal, atrophied, or exhibit chronic inflammatory changes, such as fibrosis and round cell infiltrations, together with destruction of tubules

---

FIGURE 5. Peculiar renal regenerative activity in form of multinucleated giant-cell-like masses in straight tubules of cat kidney. x400.

FIGURE 6. Early stage of ascarid nodule. Cross section of larvae in renal cortex of dog. x200.

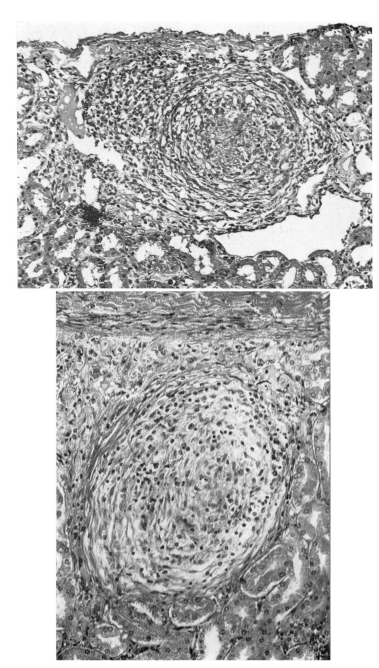

Figure 7. Later stage of ascarid nodule with disappearance of larvae. Renal cortex of dog. x200.
Figure 8. Terminal stage of ascarid nodule in renal cortex of dog. x260.

and fibrosis of glomeruli. Because of the facility with which the kidneys can be palpated in the living cat, the presence of the enlarged polycystic kidneys can often be suspected and diagnosed.

Figure 10 also illustrates the lesion of perirenal hygroma

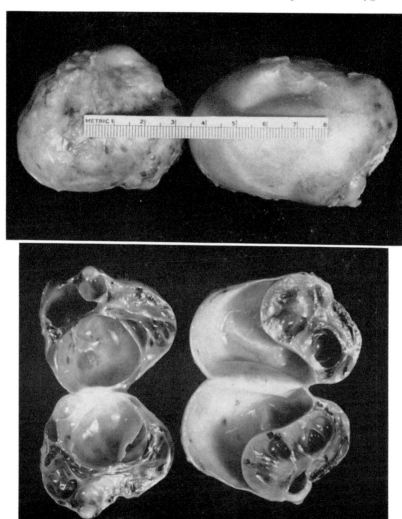

FIGURE 9. External appearance of congenital polycystic kidneys in aged male cat.

FIGURE 10. Cut surface of kidney shown in Figure 9. There are multiple renal cysts and perirenal hygroma. Approximately x¾.

(perirenal hydronephrosis, *renis hydrocele*) in which fluid accumulates in the kidney capsule causing decapsulation. The
capsular fluid has been variously considered as exudate from
inflammation of the renal capsule, as hemorrhage, as extravasation
of urine, or as lymph from blockage of lymph channels. The condition occurs mainly in swine and cats, although I once observed
this lesion in the left kidney of a five-year-old Capuchin monkey
that had ascites.

HYDRONEPHROSIS

Hydronephrosis, or dilatation or distention of the renal pelvis
with urine and associated pressure atrophy of the kidney parenchyma, may be unilateral or bilateral. It is frequently seen in the
dog and less commonly in the cat. The degree of distention varies
and depends on whether the condition is unilateral or bilateral.
In advanced cases the kidney becomes an enormous sac, several
times the size of the normal organ (Fig. 11). Microscopically, the
initial changes consist of progressive atrophy of tubules with
eventual fibrosis and hyalinization of glomeruli (Fig. 12).

PYONEPHROSIS

This refers to the presence of pus in the renal pelvis. It is
fundamentally the terminal stage of a chronic process, such as
hydronephrosis with infection or of a continuous purulent lesion
with destruction. The condition occasionally occurs in the dog
and cat, and is usually unilateral. The kidney may be of normal
or larger size, and a thick, creamy pus is seen on incising the renal
pelvis (Fig. 13). Depending upon the point of obstruction, the
accompanying ureter may become distended with pus (pyoureter)
(Fig. 14). Microscopically, there is suppurative pyelitis and purulent exudate in the lumen of the renal pelvis (Fig. 15). The renal
parenchyma is rarely normal, and lesions of pyelonephritis or
those of hydronephrosis with superimposed suppurative changes
are generally present.

FELINE TUBULAR CRYSTALLINE DEPOSITS

In the cat crystals of a specific type are frequently observed
in the tubular lumens, especially in the medullary collecting

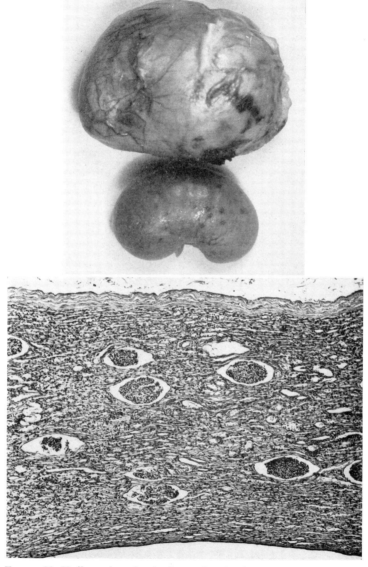

FIGURE 11. Unilateral canine hydronephrosis of advanced degree. x2/3.
FIGURE 12. Canine unilateral hydronephrosis. Entire thickness of kidney can be seen with capsule above and pelvis below. x85.

tubules. They are apparently acid soluble as they are not usually seen in kidneys fixed with acid-containing fixatives, such as Bouin's solution or Zenker's acetic acid fixative. The crystals are round, oval, or irregular, and the structure consists of fine, closely adjacent, radiating lines converging from the circumference to the center, like the spokes of a wheel (Fig. 16). With hematoxylin and eosin they are colorless to pale yellow; the central portion is often darker yellow and the peripheral border may be pale blue. Numerically, the crystals appear only in occasional tubules but they may be present in larger numbers.

They are found principally in obstructive lesions of the urinary tract, such as urine retention in the bladder resulting from

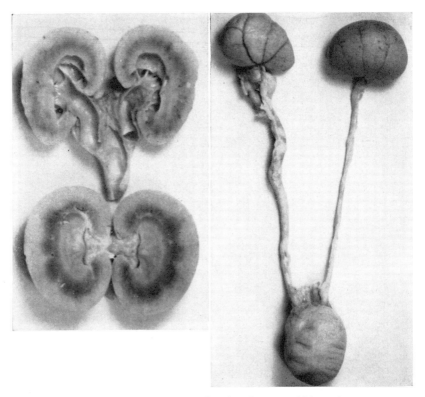

FIGURE 13. Feline unilateral pyonephrosis of upper kidney in contrast to lower normal organ. The purulent exudate that was present has been washed away. x¾.

FIGURE 14. Pyoureter and pyonephrosis of kidney (left) from a cat. x½.

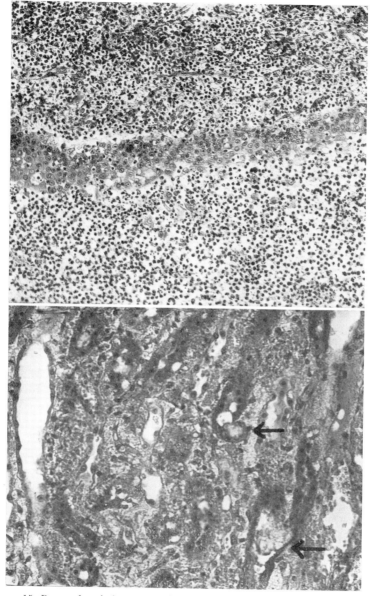

FIGURE 15. Pyonephrosis in a cat. There is suppuration in papilla above and purulent exudate in lumen of renal pelvis below. x200.

FIGURE 16. Crystals *(arrows)* in lumens of collecting tubules of kidney of cat with bladder calculi. x300.

urethritis and especially from "cystic gravel" in the urethra. The crystals may form by precipitation of urinary salts as a result of urinary obstruction, although they may possibly be micro-concretions and represent the early stages of gravel formation. The crystals are also occasionally observed in normal cats, possibly because of peculiarities in the renal excretion of phosphates in this species.

INTRANUCLEAR INCLUSIONS IN CONTAGIOUS CANINE HEPATITIS

The typical basophilic intranuclear inclusions, characteristically found in hepatic cells and in endothelial cells of other tissues and organs, also occur in the endothelial cells of the glomeruli in contagious canine hepatitis (Fig. 17). Usually from one to four are observed in each glomerulus, although in many glomeruli they are often absent. These inclusions are of relatively short duration, and their presence is positive evidence of the disease.

INCLUSIONS IN CANINE DISTEMPER

In canine distemper the typical eosinophilic cytoplasmic inclusions can be clearly observed in the epithelial cells of the renal pelvis (Fig. 18). In addition, basophilic intranuclear inclusions, that resemble those of contagious canine hepatitis, may coexist in the epithelial cells of the renal pelvis (Fig. 18), and also occur in renal tubular epithelium, acinar cells of the pancreas, and other epithelial cells, but not in the liver. My observations indicate that the coexisting basophilic intranuclear inclusions occur only in some cases of distemper accompanied by encephalitis.

In the same cases in which basophilic intranuclear inclusions are observed, there commonly occur focal granulomatous lesions in the interstitial tissue of the renal cortex (Fig. 19). The granulomas are composed mainly of cells of reticulo-endothelial type with variable numbers of lymphocytes. It is not uncommon to observe the basophilic intranuclear inclusions in tubular epithelial cells included within and adjacent to the granulomas (Fig. 20.)

The renal granulomas together with the coexisting basophilic intranuclear inclusions and typical distemper eosinophilic cyto-

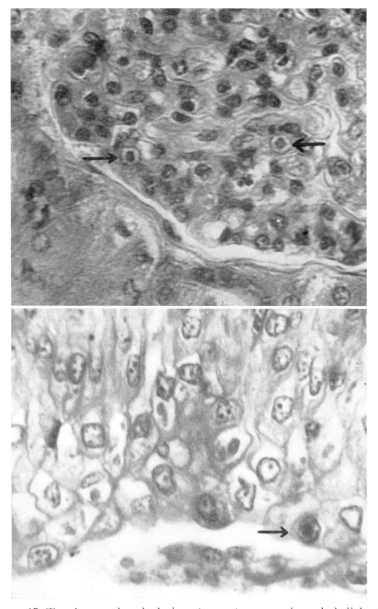

FIGURE 17. Two intranuclear inclusions *(arrows)* are seen in endothelial cells of glomerulus from a dog with contagious canine hepatitis. x880.

FIGURE 18. Eosinophilic cytoplasmic inclusions in epithelial cells of renal pelvis in canine distemper. A basophilic intranuclear inclusion *(arrow)* is seen in the right lower portion of the figure. x900.

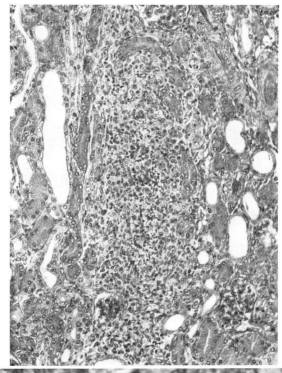

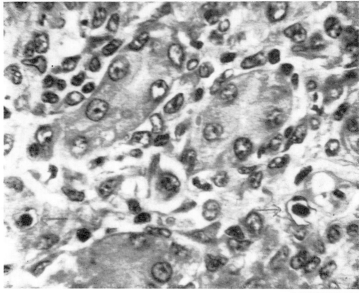

plasmic inclusions have apparently not been described in the available literature, and it would be of interest to hear from anyone who has seen similar lesions.

AMYLOID KIDNEY

The amyloid kidney (amyloid nephrosis) occasionally occurs in the dog but rarely in the cat. Most cases in the dog appear to be of primary type without any relation to long-standing chronic suppurative processes. Secondary types also occur and may be associated with amyloid in the liver, spleen, and other organs, although involvement of the kidneys alone is especially common in the dog.

The lesions in the dog are typical of amyloidosis in general but have extensive tubular atrophy. The replacement fibrosis ultimately produces the amyloid contracted kidney (Fig. 21).

PERINEPHRITIC INFLAMMATIONS IN THE DOG

Perinephritic inflammations often involve the renal capsule, the perinephritic tissue, and the pararenal tissue, and perinephritis combined with various types and degrees of renal suppuration is of special importance in the dog. In the combined lesion all varieties of gross appearances are presented depending on the degree of renal involvement. Usually there is considerable fibrosis-containing purulent foci with adhesions to the kidney and neighboring structures. Depending on the extent of involvement, the kidney contains fibrosis, scattered purulent foci, and frequently pyonephrosis (Fig. 22). The microscopic appearances vary, but in general are those of acute, subacute, and chronic suppuration of the renal parenchyma and pelvis. The lesions are similar to those seen in suppurative nephritis and pyelonephritis except that they are considerably more extensive. In the earlier stages there are diffuse massive infiltrations of polymorphonuclear leukocytes

FIGURE 19. Focal granuloma in renal cortex of dog with distemper accompanied by encephalitis. x200.

FIGURE 20. Higher magnification of preceding figure. There are two basophilic intranuclear inclusions *(arrow)* in lower part of photomicrograph at margin of granuloma. x900.

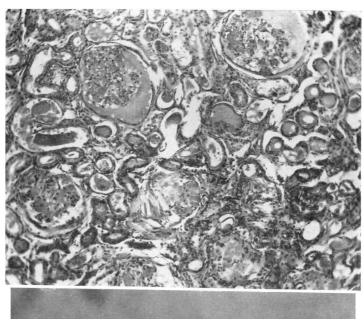

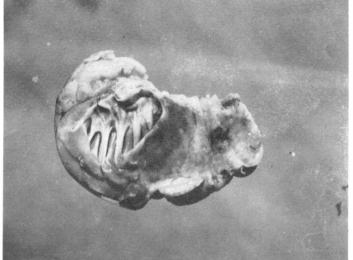

FIGURE 21. Amyloid contracted kidney of dog. x100.

FIGURE 22. Chronic perinephritis combined with pyonephrosis and chronic renal inflammation in a dog with chronic productive peritonitis. x¾.

FIGURE 23. Earlier stage of chronic perinephritis with renal suppuration. Chronic inflammatory perirenal tissue is evident above and diffuse infiltrations of polymorphonuclear leukocytes in cortex below. x60.

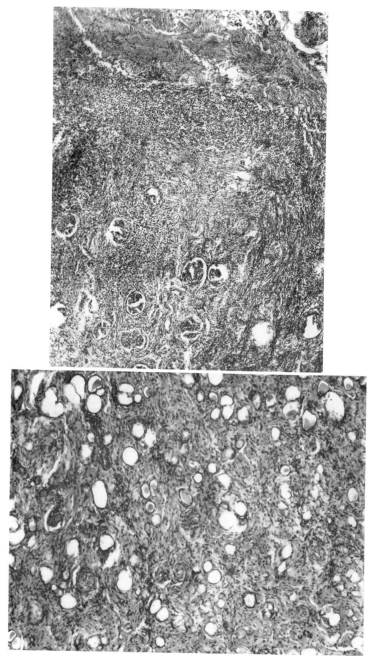

Figure 24. Terminal stage of combined chronic perinephritis and chronic renal inflammation. There is present diffuse fibrosis and atrophic tubules. x105.

throughout the cortex and medulla (Fig. 23). These often form small and large abscesses. Purulent changes commonly occur in the renal pelvis, and purulent exudate is found in the pelvic lumen in pyonephrosis. Later, there are mononuclear cell infiltrations and fibrous connective tissue proliferation. Terminally, the kidney is converted into a fibrous mass in which are atrophic tubules, scattered numbers of mononuclear cells, and destroyed glomeruli (Fig. 24).

The aforementioned lesions are renal and perirenal manifestations of direct extension of infection usually from chronic productive peritonitis. The latter condition is of frequent occurrence in the dog and in most instances is due to the use of silk or other nonabsorbable sutures in abdominal operations, especially spaying. Even with the strictest aseptic surgical technique, the use of nonabsorbable sutures will often incite a chronic progressive inflammation in the abdominal cavity of the dog. This inflammation is chronic from the onset and rarely exhibits the lesions of acute exudative inflammation. The frequent perirenal and renal involvement from spaying is explained by the close proximity of the chronic inflammatory process caused by the nonabsorbable ligatures on the ovarian artery.

Although the described lesions are generally well known to veterinarians, it seems that those working experimentally with dogs are unaware of the fact that a chronic productive inflammation may result from the use of nonabsorbable sutures in abdominal surgical procedures. The probable reason for this is that it takes a considerable length of time, from months to years, before an extensive development of the chronic process can occur. It is realized, of course, that not all dogs will develop the condition; however, the possibility of its occurrence ought to be kept in mind, especially in long-term experiments.

INTERSTITIAL NEPHRITIS

I think that the most important lesion that is seen in the kidney of the dog and cat as well as in laboratory and other domesticated animals, is interstitial nephritis. This is well known to veterinarians and veterinary pathologists, although the human pathologists, unfamiliar with the animal lesion, will often designate the chronic process as chronic pyelonephritis and sometimes as chronic glomerulonephritis.

My experience indicates that some degree of interstitial nephritis occurs in approximately 55 per cent of dogs of all ages in routine autopsies. The frequency increases with age, so that about 80 per cent of animals eight years old or over are affected. Investigators utilizing the dog in various experimental procedures in which the kidneys are examined may arrive at wrong conclusions if the high incidence of spontaneous interstitial nephritis is not recognized. The conditions in the cat are similar to those in the dog.

From a pathologist's point of view, interstitial nephritis is usually classified into acute, subacute, and chronic types, although it should be recognized that this division is artificial because all gradations between the three are seen. Nevertheless, for descriptive purposes such subdivisions are useful, even though it should be appreciated that sharp delineation between the different types is frequently impossible. From a comparative pathology point of view it is of interest to note that, although acute interstitial nephritis occurs in man, it practically never becomes chronic as it commonly does in animals.

Grossly, the kidneys have a variety of appearances depending on the type, severity, and duration of the interstitial nephritis. Both organs are usually equally affected, although one kidney may exhibit more advanced changes, especially in the cat. Acute types are characterized by the presence of scattered or confluent, sharply defined, round or oval, gray-white to gray-yellow, pinpoint to pinhead or even larger areas on the outer and cut surfaces of the organ (Fig. 25). Difficulties are encountered in recognizing the acute stage in the cat because of the normal yellowish color of the kidney. Healing of the acute lesions may occur with the development of few to many pinpoint to pinhead sized, pale gray scars on the outer and cut surface of the kidney. As the condition becomes chronic, the kidney becomes shrunken and contracted, fibrous, firm, and cuts with difficulty (Fig. 26). The organ is generally pale tan in the dog and gray-white to gray-tan in the cat. The surface is either regularly or irregularly nodular, and the nodules are often prominent in the cat (Fig. 27). Recognition of chronic interstitial nephritis is frequently possible in the living animal, especially in cats and thin dogs, simply by abdominal palpation of the kidneys.

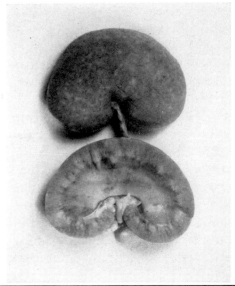

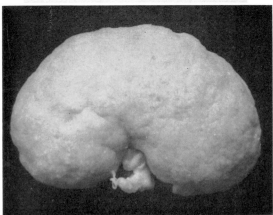

FIGURE 25. Outer and cut surfaces of dog kidney with acute diffuse interstitial nephritis. x¾.

FIGURE 26. Chronic interstitial nephritis in dog. x1¼.

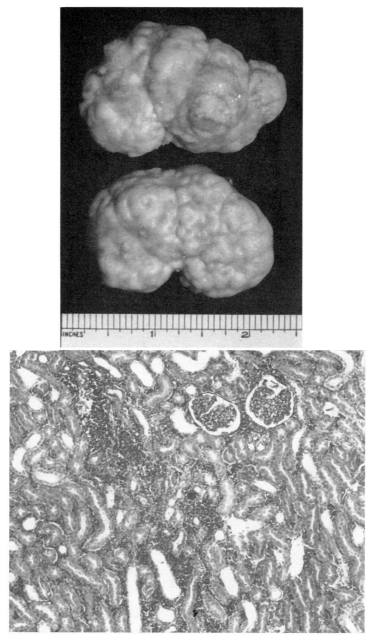

FIGURE 27. Marked nodular formations in feline chronic interstitial nephritis.
FIGURE 28. Acute focal interstitial nephritis accompanying bronchopneumonia
of dog. x90.

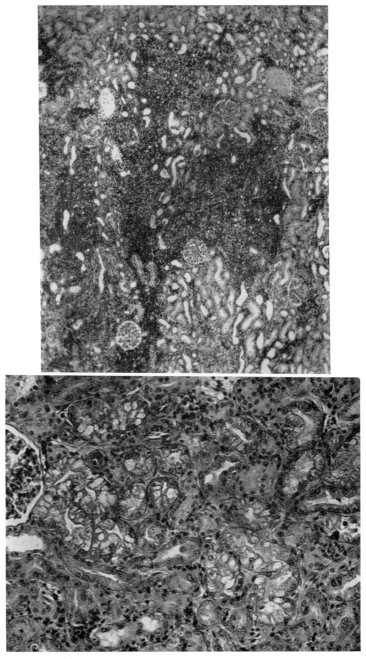

FIGURE 29. Acute diffuse interstitial nephritis in canine leptospirosis. x60.
FIGURE 30. Vacuolar degeneration of proximal convoluted tubular epithelium
in kidney of dog with icteric form of leptospirosis. x240.

Microscopically, the picture is variable and consists of inflammatory changes of infiltration and proliferation. The infiltrations consist of lymphocytic cells in the interstitial tissue. These may be perivascular, periglomerular, and intertubular in distribution. The number of infiltrative cells depends on the acuteness and extent of the nephritis. Acute focal types are characterized by small to large numbers of lymphocytic cells present mainly in the cortex and outer medullary zone (Fig. 28). In the acute diffuse type the infiltrations are particularly dense, heavy, and widely distributed, and there are often greater concentrations of inflammatory cells at focal points with the diffuse involvement (Fig. 29). The tubular epithelium may be normal or have slight to advanced regressive changes. Often present in leptospiral interstitial nephritis is a characteristic vacuolar degeneration of the proximal convoluted epithelium (Fig. 30).

The aforementioned changes can terminate in several ways: (1) They may disappear completely by resolution and absorption. (2) They may heal with the production of connective tissue. (3) They may continually progress until more of the renal structure is involved.

Although exact data are not available concerning the number of kidneys in which healing occurs with complete disappearance of the inflammatory cells, nevertheless this must be relatively rare as judged by the high incidence of scars seen in routine microscopic examination of dog and cat kidneys. However, the incidence is probably now greater with the advent of antibiotic therapy. The scars arise in the following manner:

Fibroblasts appear in the areas of cellular infiltration, with subsequent fibrous connective tissue proliferation. With increased fibrosis there is a corresponding reduction in the number of lymphocytic cells. A variety of tubular and glomerular changes such as atrophy, distortion, fibrosis, and disappearance (Fig. 31) occur in the scarred areas. In these cases the kidney has the appearance of having gone through an attack of acute interstitial nephritis that has healed with the formation of a variable number of scars.

In some cases fresh cellular infiltrations appear and the process of infiltration and scarring appears to be continuous (Fig.

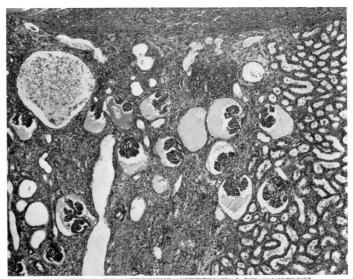

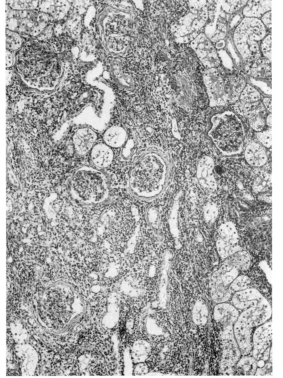

32). This is the subacute type and the tubular, glomerular, and fibrotic changes are considerably more advanced than in the acute form.

Eventually, the subacute type may result in chronic interstitial nephritis in which case the quantitative structural changes vary considerably. Connective tissue proliferation is extensive in all instances and either the cortex, medulla, or the cortico-medullary zone is more involved (Fig. 33). Scattered throughout the fibrosis are collections of lymphocytic cells with no definite distribution. The glomerular changes of distortion, fibrosis, and hyalinization are extensive, although in numerous kidneys many glomeruli are little affected. Associated with the fibrosis are marked tubular changes; many are atrophied from connective tissue compression and have disappeared, others have an irregular cystic dilatation with atrophic flattened epithelium, the lumens of which tubules often contain albuminous material or hyaline casts (Fig. 34). Fairly constant in the inner medullary zone, especially in dogs and very rarely in cats, is the presence of dilated hyperplastic collecting tubules which have a gland-like appearance (Fig. 35). The cell boundaries of such tubules are indistinct and the nuclei are arranged in irregular rows. The lumens of the latter tubules, as well as those of the cystically dilated collecting tubules with atrophic epithelium, may contain eosinophilic hyaline casts. Calcium deposits in the fibrotic periglomerular tissue, in the glomeruli, around atrophied tubules, in necrotic epithelium, and in the tubular lumens, are extremely common in uremia of the dog but not of the cat (Fig. 34).

FIGURE 31. Scar formation in cortex of dog kidney in healed acute focal interstitial nephritis. x55.

FIGURE 32. Subacute interstitial nephritis in cat. Scarring, with atrophic tubules and periglomerular fibrosis, and recent interstitial cellular infiltrations are all present. x85.

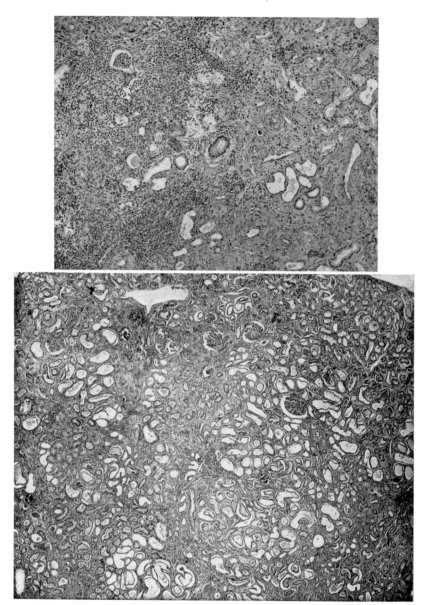

FIGURE 33. Canine chronic interstitial nephritis. There is marked interstitial fibrosis and fairly diffuse cellular interstitial infiltrations. x85.

FIGURE 34. Canine uremic chronic interstitial nephritis. There are present diffuse interstitial fibrosis and numerous irregularly dilated tubules with flattened atrophic epithelium. The dark areas represent calcification. x32.

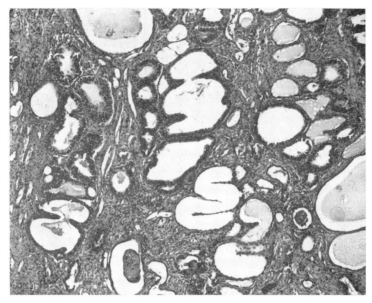

FIGURE 35. Canine chronic interstitial nephritis with dilated medullary collecting tubules, some with atrophic and others with hyperplastic epithelium. x70.

DISCUSSION

Dr. Clinton V. Z. Hawn: You asked for confirmation of your observation of the renal granulomatous lesions of canine distemper. We have seen this on many occasions, particularly in the dogs immunized which are then subjected to immunization, transplantation or other studies, and it is exactly as you have described.

Question: Please discuss renal lesions of the rat.

Dr. Bloom: My experience with the small laboratory animals has been relatively limited. I have never seen such an advanced chronic nephritis as I showed here in the dog. I have seen focal infiltrations in the interstitial tissue of lymphocytic type cells. I don't think I would like to dignify that by calling it a real interstitial nephritis. The fact that there are some few, relatively few, interstitial collections does not necessarily indicate nephritis in the true sense of the word. I think you have to think that that is very similar to lymphocytic cellular infiltrations that are occasionally seen in other organs.

Dr. Geoffrey T. Mann: Regarding the slide you showed of the cat kidney with the oxalic acid crystals—it looks for all the world like oxalic acid that one sees in ethylene glycol poisoning. The crystals of oxalic acid are bluish around the border and brownish toward the middle. They are also acid-soluble.

Dr. Bloom: I am sorry, I don't know enough about it. I can't answer that.

Chairman: Is there anyone in the audience who would like to comment on Dr. Mann's question?

Dr. T. C. Jones: Oxalic acid crystals do occur in ethylene glycol poisoning and this is a fairly common thing in cats.

Chairman: Is this the lesion that Dr. Bloom was talking about?

Dr. Bloom: The animals I described show no lesions whatsoever, just the presence of these crystals. Sometimes they are very numerous. Many tubules will contain them.

I think Dr. Mann's comment merits investigation.

Question: In this characterization of oxalic acid crystalluria does clinical uremia develop?

Dr. Bloom: It can be either compensated, in which the animals have polyuria with low urinary specific gravity, or it can be uremic, in which there is an NPN elevation. In these nonuremic cases, the NPN is normal.

Question: Is there hypertension?

Dr. Bloom: There is some difference of opinion on that. Some people think so and other people do not. We haven't done any blood pressure studies in these cases, but the literature indicates that hypertension does occur in some instances.

Dr. Theodore W. Harris: If I might make a comment on the interstitial nephritis, I think there are many of us that see interstitial nephritis in rats, whether they are young or old. This has been reported in literature and it is very common in our laboratory.

I don't think a few initial lymphocytes make this thing nephritis, but on the other hand, as one follows these animals, with age they progress and finally they develop a completely fibrous area with glomeruli included.

This is not an uncommon thing. If this is caused by leptospirosis maybe we are missing the boat, but I have never been able to isolate them in our laboratory.

Dr. Benjamin Berg: May I add something regarding these rat lesions.

The primary lesion is in the tubule, and it is a degenerative lesion. With progression, as more and more tubules become involved, there is an interstitial nephritis and there is blockage of the tubular system with the formation of relatively large cysts. Ultimately the cortex may be honeycombed with cysts and little functional tissue remains. There is glomerular atrophy and the picture finally is that of chronic glomerular nephritis. The condition increases with age and is associated with anemia, hypertension, and cardiac changes.

Dr. Tage Moller: You mentioned polycystic kidneys and perirenal hygroma in the kidney of a cat. I would like to emphasize that it also occurs in swine. In swine the pathogenesis is particularly well understood in that the disease occurs in a whole litter as an acute phase of the disease, and those litters of pigs are extremely uremic. There is fluid in the renal capsule, composed of blood and urine with a urine content which is five to six times the blood content, so we treat that as a blend of urine, blood, and serous exudation. Most of the pigs die in the acute phase of the disease but those who survive develop this cyst, the intracapsular cyst, as you showed in the cat. We think that an acute *nephrosis* which these pigs also show is part of the pathogenesis of those cysts.

The reason why such little pigs get this acute nephrosis we don't know.

6

LESIONS OF THE CARDIOVASCULAR SYSTEM*

DAVID LEHR**

INTRODUCTION

Among the most important disease entities encountered in human beings, afflictions of the cardiovascular system have maintained their pre-eminent position as the "number one killer" of man. It is not surprising, therefore, that research efforts in this area have been of the greatest intensity for many decades and have assumed gigantic proportions to date. It stands to reason that it would be of the utmost importance if spontaneous lesions could be discovered in mammals used in the laboratory which resemble alterations found in human cardiovascular disease. Spontaneous alterations in the cardiovascular system of laboratory animals have, therefore, been studied extensively and in a most thorough-going manner. It is understandable, moreover, that for the same reasons, many research projects on an increasingly vast scale, aim at the reproduction in the experimental animal of conditions resembling well-known cardiovascular disease entities in man. Major efforts in this area are directed in particular towards the entity encompassed by the somewhat diffuse term "arteriosclerosis."

Unfortunately, there is much confusion and disagreement in the nomenclature of both spontaneous and experimental lesions described by various authors. The names or the designations utilized, often reflect a great deal of wishful thinking rather than exacting standards of terminology. Thus, for instance, some investigators speak of spontaneous atheroma in the rabbit simply be-

*This work has been supported in part by grant No. HE-00890-13 from the National Heart Institute, National Institutes of Health, United States Public Health Service.

**Dr. Lehr was unable to present the paper because of illness. The paper was read by Dr. Bernard Wagner.

cause intimal plaques in the aorta constitute one aspect of the injury; others speak of atheroma in the rat because fatty infiltration is encountered as part of the degenerative lesion, although in both instances the main injury is found in the arterial media. Still others, finally, describe isolated foci of necrosis or scars in the myocardium as fresh and old infarcts, without presenting any evidence for vascular occlusion or even substantial injury to the coronary arterial system.

Exact knowledge of the incidence, morphology, and as far as possible also of the pathogenesis of spontaneous cardiovascular disease in the experimental animal would be vital for two reasons in particular: On the one hand, it may aid, as pointed out earlier, in the understanding of human cardiovascular disease if similar appearance and etiology could be demonstrated, and, on the other hand, such knowledge is vital for the purpose of distinguishing spontaneous lesions from those induced by the experimenter. I shall have occasion to demonstrate in the course of this presentation that inadequate information may lead to serious misinterpretations and erroneous claims.

My personal long-time experience with small laboratory animals is limited to the albino rat, although I have at times carried out studies of considerable proportions with other species of the rodent family, mice and rabbits in particular. Yet even in the albino rat, despite my more than twenty-five years of intensive preoccupation with experimental cardiovascular disease of this species, my interest in spontaneous lesions remained peripheral because it concerned itself primarily with efforts to avoid situations, conditions or age ranges which might result in a high incidence of spontaneous lesions and thus serve to becloud my experimental endeavors. I gradually learned that one has little to worry on this score if one uses young and healthy rats and, in particular, if one stays away from aging female breeder rats.

This paper deals with the spontaneous lesions which occur with relative frequency in the rodent family and which, because of their nature or their significance, may make differentiation from experimentally induced lesions particularly important. For the sake of clarity in presentation I have chosen to divide the alterations into *inflammatory* and *degenerative* types. They are enumerated in tabular form (Tables I and II). The discussion will follow the sequence indicated in the tables.

Table I contains a listing of important *inflammatory* lesions encountered in small laboratory animals together with a selection

TABLE I
SPONTANEOUS CARDIOVASCULAR DISEASE IN SMALL LABORATORY ANIMALS

Inflammatory Lesions

Type of Lesion	*Reporting Author*
HEART	
myocarditis	Miller, 1924; Löwenthal, 1931; Vaubel, 1932; Seifried,* 1937; Pearce, 1939; Veith, 1941; Hermanek & Slapak, 1956; Jaffé & Gavallér, 1958; Wilgram & Ingle, 1959
endocarditis	Pearce, 1939; Hermanek & Slapak, 1956; Jaffé & Gavallér, 1958
pericarditis	Pearce, 1939; Jaffé & Gavallér, 1958
BLOOD VESSELS	
periarteritis nodosa	Wilens & Sproul,* 1938; Berg & Harmison,* 1955; Simms & Berg,* 1957; Jaffé & Gavallér, 1958

*Authors reporting kidney damage.

TABLE II
SPONTANEOUS CARDIOVASCULAR DISEASE IN SMALL LABORATORY ANIMALS

Degenerative Lesions

Type of Lesion	*Reporting Author*
HEART	
focal and disseminated myocardial necrosis	Löwenthal,* 1927; Löwenthal, 1931; Hummel & Barnes,* 1938; Wilens & Sproul,* 1938; Farris *et al.*, 1946; Berg & Harmison,* 1955; Simms & Berg,* 1957; Jaffé & Gavallér, 1958; Wilgram & Ingle, 1959
BLOOD VESSELS	
arteriosclerosis and related alterations	Hedinger & Loeb,# 1907; Miles,* 1907; Ophüls, 1907; Bennecke, 1908; Lucien & Parisot, 1908; Pearce, 1908; Weinberg, 1908; Levin & Larkin, 1909-10; Hornowski,# 1914; Hesse, 1924; Seegal, 1927; Wolkoff, 1927; Nuzum *et al.*,* 1930; Löwenthal, 1931; Vaubel, 1932; Anitschkow, 1933; Blumer *et al.*, 1933; Fox, 1933; Duff, 1935; Hueper, 1935; Kesten, 1935; Seifried,* 1937; Hummel & Barnes,* 1938; Wilens & Sproul,* 1938; Hueper, 1939; Dill & Isenhour, 1942; Wissler *et al.*, 1952; Lopes de Faria, 1955; Berg & Harmison,* 1955; Malinow, 1956; Jaffé & Gavallér, 1958; Gillman and Hathorn, 1959; Humphreys, 1959; Wilgram & Ingle, 1959; Wexler *et al.*, 1960; Harvey, 1961; Renaud,* 1962; Studer & Reber, 1963; Wexler & Epstein, 1963; Wexler & Fine, 1963

*Authors reporting kidney damage.
#Authors reporting zero incidence.

of authors reporting on such alterations. It should be emphasized that three of four authors giving detailed descriptions of periarteritis nodosa, report the concomitant occurrence of marked kidney damage (indicated by asterisk). Table II depicts, in similar fashion, *degenerative* lesions in the heart and blood vessels, together with a rather substantial group of investigators, whose work was studied in the original, to arrive, if possible, at generalizations useful in a review of this kind. Authors specifically reporting that no spontaneous lesions were seen in their series are marked with the symbol #. Attention is again directed to the large group of authors reporting kidney damage. It should be stressed, moreover, that failure to mention such injury does not necessarily exclude its occurrence. Many authors, in fact, deliberately limit their discussion to the main injury. One would, therefore, not be far amiss in assuming that renal injury is part of the pathologic-anatomical picture. This theme will be developed further in the course of this paper.

First we will consider briefly the lesions that were listed in the two tables.

A. INFLAMMATORY LESIONS

1. Heart

a. Myocarditis

Myocarditis is the most frequently encountered inflammatory injury of the heart, usually recognizable only under the microscope. It consists commonly of irregularly distributed foci of interstitial infiltrates. Occasionally there may be more diffuse distribution of mostly mononuclear inflammatory cells resulting in a picture of hypercellularity. In accordance with Miller (45), who offered a detailed description of spontaneous myocarditis in twenty of thirty-four apparently healthy adult rabbits, foci, which were never visible to the naked eye, were found to be distributed in order of frequency, as follows: papillary muscles, septum, left ventricle wall, right ventricle wall, auricles. Most frequently, such foci were situated in the interstitial connective tissue framework, occasionally close to a medium sized blood vessel. No lesion was ever found in the valves or at the bases of valves. Some occurred immediately beneath the epicardium and endocardium, but the majority were within the myocardium itself.

Microscopically (Fig. 1) the lesions appeared as collections of cells more or less densely packed, lying between the muscle fibers. In size they ranged from small groups of six to ten cells up to areas the size of a high power field. They were usually elliptical with their long axes parallel to the muscle fibers. Some were diffuse, appearing as cords of cells.

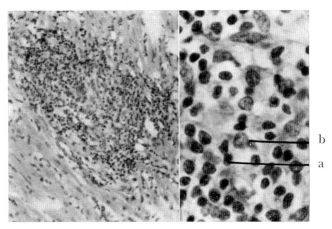

FIGURE 1. Interstitial myocarditis. Focal infiltrates, (a) Lymphocyte-like cell, (b) cell with large nucleus, apparently histiocytic element. Hematoxylin-eosin, right: x540, left: x120. (Taken from Hermanek and Slapak (17) with permission of the publisher.)

For convenience in description, Miller divides the lesions arbitrarily into two groups according to the predominating cell type. Those in the first group were most frequently encountered. They consisted almost entirely of cells with irregularly round nuclei and very little or no visible cytoplasm. The other type of lesion was made up principally of cells with large, pale, elliptical, vesicular nuclei and more or less cytoplasm, always non-granular.

While these two types of lesions were found, others were encountered that consisted of mixtures of lymphocytes and endothelial leucocytes in varying proportions. Other cells were also occasionally found—mature connective tissue cells, polymorphonuclear eosinophils, polymorphonuclear neutrophils, plasma cells, and mast cells.

When muscle fibers ran through a lesion they often showed loss of striation, but no other degenerative change.

Many of the lesions have been carefully searched for micro-organisms, but no bacteria or protozoa have been seen, nor have any cell inclusion bodies been found.

Though only healthy animals were used in this study, the author states that the myocardial lesions may be the result of mild infection. These rabbits did not suffer from snuffles, cocci-diosis, or hydatid disease, but the lesions occurred during the years when these diseases were more prevalent among their stock rabbits.

The findings of Vaubel (61) are somewhat at variance with Miller's observations. Vaubel did not encounter any major altera-tions in the myocardium of his control rabbits. Yet he confirmed the occurrence of small lymphocytic infiltrates, consisting of five to ten lymphoid cells often situated in perivascular areas but also between muscle fibers or near the epi- or endocardium. He empha-sizes that the surrounding of these cell masses is always entirely free of any reaction and that he never found signs of muscular in-jury. He, therefore, questions the significance of these small groups of lymphoid cells as a pathologic process. According to this author, they are certainly not the expression of a severe myocarditis, since in his experience such infiltrates can be found in a very large per-centage of clinically and anatomically healthy rabbits. On the other hand, Saphir (55), working with the Belgian hare found so much spontaneous myocarditis in control animals that he was forced to abandon his experiments.

Although the description of myocarditis is based upon observa-tions in rabbits, lesions of a similar kind have been found in guinea pigs (10, 46), rats (14, 69) and mice (10, 47, 59). As to incidence and etiology there is a wide divergence of opinion.

Jaffé and Gavallér (24) believe that spontaneous myocarditis may be a consequence of intercurrent infections or inadequate nutrition encountered in colonies which are maintained under poor hygienic conditions.

A possible virus etiology was considered by Pearce (50). Since

Virus III causes at times a spontaneous infection in rabbit colonies, this author inoculated Virus III intravenously, intratesticularly or intranasally into seventy-five young male rabbits and observed the development of myocarditis in a small percentage of the animals. If inoculation was preceded by cardiac puncture or by intravenous administration of large doses of acacia solution the incidence of myocarditis approached 100 per cent and the severity and extent of the lesions were greatly increased. Moreover, the lesions occasionally included non-vegetative endocarditis and fibrinous pericarditis.

An allergic origin of myocarditis has been postulated by Jaffé and Gavallér. They believe that such injury can be produced in the rat by repeated avitaminotic or hypovitaminotic diet. Similarly, Moore and co-workers (47) considered minimal alterations in the myocardium of untreated mice as the result of spontaneous sensitization through natural contact with protein. Slye (59) found only four instances of myocarditis among several thousand mice examined. Gillman, Gilbert and Spence (14), on the other hand, reported an incidence of 70 per cent chronic myocarditis and nephrosclerosis among 356 rats who had died spontaneously. In the face of these divergent results summarized in part by Jaffé and Gavallér, these authors state that they have examined a great number of healthy animals of various species in connection with their experiments on myocarditis without ever finding spontaneous myocardial alterations.

b. Endocarditis

Spontaneous endocarditis was not reported in the earlier literature. Löwenthal (38) remarks in 1931 that nothing is known about this disease entity in small laboratory animals and Seifried (57) also makes no mention of it. More recently, however, such alterations were seen to occur either separately or in combination with myocarditis in rabbits (17), guinea pigs (10), and rats (52, 69).

Hermanek and Slapak (17) in particular, present a detailed macroscopic and histological description of serous endocarditis in the rabbit (Fig. 2) based on thirteen observed cases. In five animals both the mitral and aortic valves were involved; in the remaining eight, the mitral valves alone were affected. In twelve cases the disease was combined with interstitial myocarditis as described by Miller. The authors emphasize that the combination is not obligatory and that either alteration can occur independently of the other. They believe that endocarditis may have been frequently overlooked because it can usually be recognized only by microscopic examination. Hermanek and Slapak further express the view that in all experiments where production of endocarditis is attempted in the rabbit, one also has to have an adequate number of untreated control animals from the same strain, who have been maintained under identical conditions. In this connection they refer to the work of numerous authors who either did not use such control animals or who do not make any mention of them. It is their conclusion that the frequency of endocarditis produced by experimental means must be compared with the frequency of spontaneous endocarditis occurring in control animals and that the significance of the difference in incidence can only be determined statistically. Quoting from the extensive literature, they give numerous illustrative examples of unacceptable statements such as:

> . . . fibrinoid swelling and cell proliferation in several of *ten* experimental animals and none of *two* controls;
> . . . acute rheumatic-like valvular lesions in twenty out of 102 experimental animals and none of *eight* controls;
> . . . valvular lesions in nine of *seventeen* experimental animals and none of *seven* controls.

c. Pericarditis

Pericarditis has apparently not been described as an independent spontaneous lesion. In the rare instances in which it was seen, it was considered a direct extension of pathological alterations of the lungs or of the pleura (69).

2. Blood vessels

Periarteritis

Periarteritis has been reported to occur in many species. In the rat, according to Wilens and Sproul, it is one of the most common

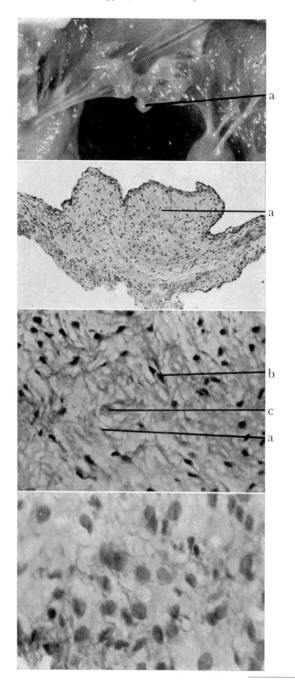

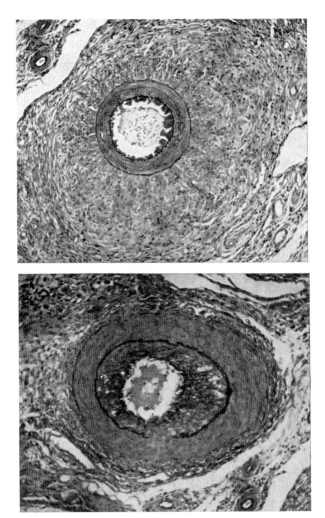

FIGURE 3. Periarteritis nodosa in a rat. *Top:* Elastica interna and externa preserved. Intimal proliferation. Enormous proliferation of the adventitia. *Bottom:* Elastica externa almost completely destroyed. Ruptures in the elastica interna. Very marked proliferation of the intima. (Taken from Jaffé and Gavallér (24) with permission of the publisher.)

FIGURE 2. (1) Mitral valve. Small transparent wart at the closing rim (a). (2) Mitral valve. Circumscribed wart-like serous endocarditis. (a) Wart-like swelling. Hematoxylin-eosin x50. (3) Serous endocarditis of the mitral valve. Loosening of the tissue with formation of vacuoles between single fibres (a), chromatin-rich nuclei (b), pale swollen nuclei (c). Hematoxylin-eosin x225. (4) Rim zone of the serous focus of swelling from (3). Proliferation of connective tissue elements. Hematoxylin-eosin x360. (Taken from Hermanek and Slapak (17) with permission of the publisher.).

forms of systemic vascular disease, though limited to old animals. These authors report the following relationship between incidence and age:

Age of Rat in Days	Incidence in %
<500	0
500-700	3
700-900	13.1
>900	15.7

Moreover there was a striking preponderance in female rats. The complete absence of periarteritis in rats less than 500 days old may explain why its occurrence as a spontaneous lesion was not discovered in this species until 1938.

Wilens and Sproul present a detailed description of the gross and microscopic appearance of spontaneous periarteritis. They state that the changes are readily recognized grossly when the mesenteric vessels are extensively involved or when small aneurysmal outpouchings occurred elsewhere. Involved arteries appear greatly enlarged, ropey, thick, and tortuous. As a rule both large and medium sized branches of the arterial tree are involved. Arterioles are almost never affected.

Under the microscope the most characteristic early alteration consists of infiltration of the adventitia with inflammatory cells completely engulfing the circumference of smaller arteries (Fig. 3) or forming eccentrically placed crescentic masses about larger arteries. A nodular or beaded appearance of affected vessels is created by multiple but discrete formations of such granulomas along the course of a single vessel. The infiltrates consist of a mixture of lymphocytes, plasma cells, monocytes, polymorphonuclear neutrophils and a few eosinophils. The inflammatory changes may invade the media and lead to muscle necrosis, disruption of elastic lamellae and subintimal deposition of fibrin. Finally there may be complete destruction of the normal architecture with irregular thickening of the wall, narrowing of the lumen or the formation of aneurysmal widening. Some of these narrowed areas may become thrombosed. Healing is characterized by dense scar tissue which may assume a hyaline appearance and become calcified.

All stages of the disease are sometimes found in the same animal and even in a single artery. In fact even healed areas are not immune from repeated flare-ups so that fresh lesions can be seen superimposed on older organizing ones. It is of great interest that animals so afflicted manifest usually widespread tubular and glomerular changes described by Wilens and Sproul as indistinguishable in many respects from glomerulonephritis. As will be developed later the renal injury may be in part responsible for the later phases of the pathologic-anatomical alterations, which strongly resemble changes occurring in degenerative arterial disease as a consequence of renal dysfunction.

Löwenthal (38) actually described periarteritis nodosa-type lesions in the mouse among the degenerative arterial lesions. Long before Wilens and Sproul, he emphasized that a single artery of a mouse may show severest alterations of various kinds simultaneously. These alterations are composed of various degrees of fatty infiltration and fibrosis of the intima, muscle necrosis of the media, rupture of elastica, massive cellular infiltration, especially of the adventitia, scars, aneurysm with thrombus formation and calcification. Here, he says, one is forced to think of a certain similarity with periarteritis nodosa. Löwenthal concludes, that with morphological methods alone, it is not possible to decide how much of the injury is based upon arteritis caused by infection and how much is due to wear and tear and nutritional damage. Unfortunately, the description of findings in individual mice, provided by Löwenthal, fails to give information on the renal status of these animals.

B. DEGENERATIVE LESIONS

1. Heart

Focal and Disseminated Myocardial Necrosis and Calcification

More than three decades ago the prevailing view, as expressed by Löwenthal (38), ascribed no significance to circulatory disturbances or anatomical alterations of the coronary arteries in the development of spontaneous degenerative myocardial alterations in experimental animals. No explanation is offered by Löwenthal for his personal observation in a one and one-quarter year-old gray mouse with advanced aortitis, of extensive disseminated calcification of heart muscle fibers without any evidence of reaction in the surrounding tissues or preceding inflammatory alteration (39). He expressed the belief to have observed the same picture repeatedly afterwards. Contracted kidneys are mentioned as a concomitant finding in one such animal.

In contrast to this earlier concept, Jaffé and Gavallér (24) recently devoted considerable attention to changes in the myocardium caused by diminished blood flow in the coronary vessels, particularly of the rat. They apparently believe this to be the mechanism for the development of "sclerosis" in the rat heart, described by Dumas (8) as occurring in the left ventricle, the septum, and particularly in the apex.

Microscopically, one finds replacement of muscle fibers by connective tissue. Affected areas have a tendency to expand and to lead to the formation of large scars. Similar scars were seen in 7 per cent of 336 grey Norwegian rats and 1 per cent of 807 white rats, investigated specifically for senile alterations by Farris and co-workers (9). The scars exhibited cartilaginous metaplasia and calcification. Again Jaffé and Gavallér emphasize that these scars are most probably a consequence of vascular occlusion. Similarly, Wilens and Sproul express the view that coronary sclerosis is the cause of fibrous foci found in 60 per cent of their aged rats and emphasize that the frequency and intensity of coronary sclerosis ran parallel with the extent of myocardial fibrosis. But neither these authors nor Jaffé and Gavallér, who show a histological picture of a small focus of myocardial necrosis which they suspect to be an infarct (Fig. 4), present any direct evidence for the exist-

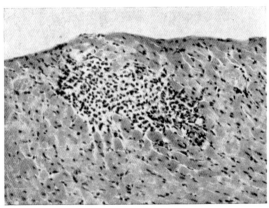

Figure 4. Small infarct, delineated by connective tissue, in the left ventricle of a rat. (Taken from Jaffé and Gavallér (24) with permission of the publisher.)

ence of circulatory embarrassment or for any connection between vascular damage and myocardial degeneration. In fact, in contradiction to their own concept, just explained, Jaffé and Gavallér illustrate a similar focus in the atrium which could not have been produced by circulatory disturbance and which they ascribe to inflammatory causes. The authors emphasize that myocardial lesions caused by coronary occlusion or narrowing, have thus far only been observed in the rat. In their view this is due primarily to the fact that sufficiently aged animals of other species have as yet not been examined and if this is done similar mechanisms will be found to exist in other species as well.

On the basis of our studies on experimental cardiovascular necrosis, we believe that one need not postulate a circulatory etiology for ventricular lesions, and an inflammatory origin for atrial foci, but that both alterations can be explained on the basis of one and the same mechanism, namely renal injury, which in fact may also encompass degenerative injury in the *arterial* system. The concept will be detailed following discussion of the last and most important aspect of my assignment, namely spontaneous lesions in the arterial system.

2. Blood Vessels

Arteriosclerosis and Related Alterations

If one surveys the literature carefully paying attention to the description of lesions rather than to the name given by the particular investigator, it will be found that spontaneous degenerative alterations of the arterial tree in mammals employed in the laboratory are almost always of the type characterized by degeneration, necrosis and calcification of the *media* and secondary involvement of the intima.

In my earliest experimental approaches to the enigma of arteriosclerosis, which date back to 1939, I was soon attracted to the school of thought which considered *primary* damage to the arterial wall a prerequisite for the development of the various well-known manifestations of vascular disease. In accordance with this concept, primary local injury—by whatever mechanism produced—precedes not only such degenerative processes as hyalinization, fibrosis and calcification, but also atheroma formation.

Now, after more than two decades of intensive personal pre-occupation with the problem of experimental cardiovascular disease, during which we have seen the "cholesterol-saturated fat" theory of atherosclerosis reach new peaks of popularity only to recede again in more recent years, I have become increasingly convinced, on the basis of the work of others and of my own studies, that primary injury of the arterial wall is indeed the focal point for initiation of all lesions encompassed by the term—*arteriosclerosis.*

Whether one agrees with this point of view or whether one adheres to the opposite notion—secondary damage to the vascular wall as a consequence of cholesterol deposition or calcium salt imbibition—there is little disagreement among workers in this field that we are at present still in an advanced state of ignorance. This state, in fact, accounts for the cyclic waxing and waning of various theories, and the existence of "camps" whose adherents are ready to sally forth into battle at the mere mention of the word "arteriosclerosis," "atherosclerosis," or simply "cholesterol" in an effort to drown their adversaries in a flood of words or printers' ink.

Yet, even in the worst heat of dispute most workers in this field readily admit that the current status of our knowledge about the *mechanism* of arteriosclerosis is inadequate, that advance, despite the vast research efforts, has been painfully slow, and finally that a true breakthrough is yet to come.

In view of the signal importance of spontaneous arteriosclerotic lesions in experimental animals, I have chosen to give a separate accounting of alterations in the rabbit and rat as the two species most frequently employed among small mammals in research on arteriosclerosis.

Rabbits: It is of course vital to distinguish spontaneous arterial lesions from those produced experimentally. This may become difficult when there are great variations in incidence of spontaneous disease and when the experimental lesion cannot be readily distinguished from the spontaneous one. Arteriosclerosis of the rabbit may serve as a classical example of such difficulty which led to considerable controversy in the literature (35, 40, 44, 51). Early in this century the rabbit was employed preferentially for the study of arteriosclerosis. Spontaneous lesions in this species are found only in the aorta, especially in the arch.

The areas of the vessel wall affected are whitish and hard, the intimal surface is either elevated (plaques) or retracted, often showing aneurysmic saccular dilatation. Hence the vessel wall may be either thickened or thinned. Under the microscope the process

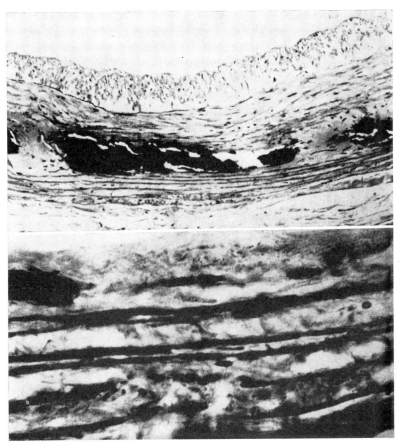

FIGURE 5. *Top:* Control animal. Thoracic aorta. Collagenous metaplasia in the media with hyalinization (light gray) and extensive calcification (black). Hematoxylin-eosin x130. *Bottom:* Same animal as top. Thoracic aorta. Media sclerosis in higher magnification. Newly-formed collagenous tissue fibers in the partly enlarged interlamellar spaces. In part, fragmentation of elastic lamellae. Elastica-van Gieson x850. (Taken from Lopes de Faria (37) with permission of the publisher.)

is seen to start with necrosis of muscle fibers and is followed by stretching, rupture and disintegration of elastic lamellae and finally hyalinization or calcification (Figs. 5 and 6). Subintimal layers of the media are sometimes more affected than outer layers. In such cases there may be considerable reactive proliferation of the intima. Occasionally there may be cartilaginous or bony metaplasia in affected areas of the media. The injury is apparently indistinguishable from that which can be produced by injection of epinephrine and a number of other drugs. This led some authors to suspect that what was described as experimental lesions, actually represented a higher incidence of spontaneous arteriosclerosis.

In view of the general importance of the problem exemplified by this controversy, I have compiled data on the incidence of spontaneous arteriosclerosis as reported by nineteen different laboratories (Table III). In some instances, lesions recognizable only under the microscope were counted separately, as is apparent in the tabulation. Incidence figures are based on the sum total of lesions. It should be pointed out that lack of uniformity in reporting made it impossible to obtain sufficiently broad information on

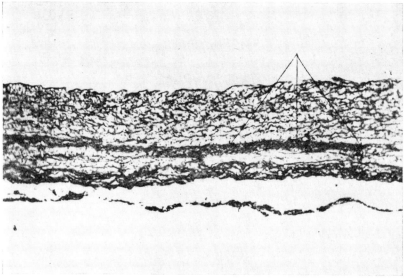

FIGURE 6. Control animal. Abdominal aorta. Spontaneous sclerosis of the media. Connective tissue strip in the outer media (arrows). No thickening of the intima. Elastica-van Gieson x130. (Taken from Lopes de Faria (37) with permission of the publisher.)

many important parameters such as age, sex, laboratory conditions, health of the colony, uniformity of strain, etc.

It can be seen that the reported incidence of spontaneous arteriosclerosis in the rabbit varies from zero to as much as 59 per cent, and that these figures, as well as those lying between these two extremes, are based on substantial groups of animals examined. It would seem, on the other hand, that more thorough examination using the microscope may lead to the recognition of alterations which may otherwise remain undiscovered, since by far the highest incidences are described by three among four authors reporting separate figures for microscopic lesions. As far as we could determine, age cannot account for these substantial differences. It must be assumed, therefore, that such factors as nutrition, general hygienic conditions, and health within the colony and perhaps genetic factors may play a vital role in the development of these spontaneous lesions. Proof for the production of *experimental* lesions in such instances should be predicated upon the employment of sufficiently large control groups of the same strain maintained under identical conditions.

TABLE III

INCIDENCE OF SPONTANEOUS ARTERIOSCLEROSIS IN RABBITS
REPORTED BY VARIOUS INVESTIGATORS

No. of Animals in Group	No. of Animals with Arteriosclerosis		Total Incidence %	Reporting Author
	Macro	Micro		
100	0		0	Hedinger & Loeb
280	0		0	Loeb*
400	12		3	Bennecke
200	10		5	Lucien & Parisot
51	3		6	Pearce
18	1		6	Thevenot**
562	37		7	Weinberg
25	2		8	Giovani-Quadri**
190	17		9	Nuzum
30	3		10	Kalamkarov**
210	—		15	Hill***
16	4		25	Harvey *et al.*
30		8	27	Seegal
9	3		33	Johnstone
49	17		35	Miles
240	31	78	45	Levin & Larkin
125	51	17	54	Kesten
29		17	59	Lopes de Faria

*As cited by Bennecke.
**As cited by Lucien and Parisot.
***As cited by Levin and Larkin.

Rats: Spontaneous macroscopic alterations of the arterial tree in rats are closely similar to those in rabbits and thus consist in the main of degenerative processes in the media as the primary injury. This conclusion was reached after a comprehensive review of the pertinent literature and after critical examination of all reports including those that speak of atheroma or atherosclerosis in the rat. Some of those latter reports, dealing with sporadic *microscopic* alterations, have appeared without qualification in important review articles and thus help to perpetuate the notion of the prevalence of spontaneous atheroma in the rat. It seems justified, therefore, to take issue with this concept which I believe to be based on rather weak foundations. I should like to illustrate this with two frequently quoted sources of reference. Malinow and assoc. (43) examined thirty rats of the William strain, aged fifteen to twenty-four months, selected at random from their stock colony. In seventeen of their rats, these South American workers found what they believed to be atherosclerotic lesions, consisting of and I quote:

> "a) endothelial and/or subendothelial infiltration sometimes extending into the media of a Sudanophilic, Liebermann positive, material (atheromatosis) b) proliferation of endothelial and/or subendothelial? cells forming tiny protruding plaques (early atherosclerosis) ."

Only a few microscopic lesions were found per animal in *fifty* of more than *10,000* arterial sections examined by the authors. Moreover, Malinow and assoc. emphasize that one-third of their rats had some *"macroscopic"* infections such as cervical abscess, subcutaneous abscess, different degrees of pulmonary infections and infected carcinoma of the liver, and that most of their animals had extensive inflammatory changes. They do not exclude the relationship between infection and the minimal arterial injury observed, but rest on the statement that no clear connection between these two conditions has been demonstrated. The uniqueness of their findings is interpreted by Malinow and assoc. as due either to: (1) a uniqueness of their rat strain to develop these spontaneous lesions, or (2) considered more likely by the authors, to the great scarcity of such lesions, which can be detected only when a large number of sections are examined.

Using a similar experimental approach, namely serial sections of the heart, Humphreys (23) describes what she calls atheromatous plaques in the coronary arteries of rats of her colony, 300 to 900 days of age. To explain the uniqueness of her findings, this author uses arguments identical to those offered by the South American workers, namely: (1) unique susceptibility of her rat colony, or, more likely (2) microscopic size and scarcity of the lesion which can be found only after a diligent and meticulous search. Interestingly enough, she also reports that the animals in her colony suffered from a number of infections. Most significantly, Humphreys states that with the use of a high fat diet she was unable to induce any increase in the incidence or extent of lesions over those found in animals on the stock diet. Since many groups of investigators have produced experimental atheroma in the rat by the use of a high fat diet in combination with other procedures, it seems strange that the addition of fat to the diet should have no influence whatsoever on lesions purported to be spontaneous atherosclerosis. It would seem wise, therefore, to withhold acceptance of the term spontaneous atherosclerosis on the basis of the exceptional findings of sporadic microscopic foci described by Malinow and assoc. and by Humphreys.

I have quoted these papers in some detail because they illuminate the difficulty of arriving at uniform and acceptable terminology when we have no common baseline or standards by which to judge the importance and correct designation of spontaneous lesions reported by various authors. The quoted reports and the misunderstanding that they may introduce into the literature, raise a number of important questions.

(1) Is it really justified to expect that one should search ten thousand arterial sections in order to rule out the presence of atherosclerosis in a small group of rats? Why then stop here? Why not go further and demand that the entire arterial tree be searched with the electron microscope?

(2) Is it acceptable to use infected animals suffering from a variety of abnormalities as untreated stock animals of random selection for the establishment of spontaneous lesions?

(3) Finally, can the few "spots" of microscopic alterations in such animals with an otherwise normal arterial tree be considered atherosclerosis?

In my opinion, all three questions should be answered in the negative. I, therefore, would be inclined to assign the term *microscopic* atheroma-*like* lesions to the findings reported by the South American workers and by Humphreys.

There are actually only two types of well-documented macroscopic, degenerative arterial lesions that are found with reasonable frequency, namely, those seen in senile animals and those encountered especially in aging female breeder rats.

1. Degenerative Arterial Changes of the Senile Rat: There is good agreement in the descriptions of Wolkoff (74) and Wilens and Sproul (69). The latter authors in particular examined almost 500 rats, 80 per cent of which were over 600 days old. The most common pathologic alterations consisted of moderate calcification of the media in various areas of the arterial tree, more prevalent in the male than in the female animal. In the aorta, the coronaries and pulmonary arteries, there was, in addition, thickening of the wall with preservation of the architecture, while the intima remained entirely normal. Wilens and Sproul make a point of emphasizing the absence of lipid-containing atheromas. They note, on the other hand, that the kidneys of senile rats are seldom entirely normal and that they found, in fact, a high incidence of pelvic calculi leading to hydronephrotic atrophy as a consequence of healed pyelonephritis. In many animals the kidneys exhibited widespread tubular and glomerular changes indistinguishable in a number of respects from true glomerulonephritis.

2. Lesions in Aging Female Breeder Rats: This injury involves primarily the aorta and its larger branches which to the naked eye appear rigid, often containing thick white areas interspersed between aneurysmic saccular dilatations. The sequential arrangement of patchy white calcified rings often results in the well-known "goose trachea" or "bamboostick" appearance of affected arteries. The excellent and detailed account of this lesion presented by Wilgram and Ingle (72) will be used as a basis for description. It is fully in accord with our earlier account of arterial injury following various procedures that cause interference with renal excretory function (29, 30) and those of many other authors describing vascular changes in rats with various types of renal injury (12, 27, 36, 70, 71).

Microscopic analysis reveals that intimal changes are rarely encountered. When present they are caused by a slight increase in endothelial cells, superimposed on a small increase in connective tissue ground substance. The most striking changes are seen in the media. They involve splitting, wrinkling and fragmentation of the elastic membranes, disintegration of the muscular layers and replacement of them by necrosis and calcified debris. The final picture is similar to the well-known human disease entity described by Mönckeberg as medial sclerosis.

In instances of coronary artery involvement, the walls of the vessels appear thickened and slightly edematous. Frequently, the muscular layer is hyperplastic and the intima shows irregular foldings, with small nodules protruding into the lumen. The protrusions consist of a slightly increased number of endothelial cells "sitting" on nodules which are the result of an increase of subendothelial connective tissue ground substance. Occasionally the media shows signs of calcification and condensation. The injury to the renal arteries is of similar appearance.

Visible changes are observed also in the mesenteric vessels. The arteries have slight to marked kinking and spiraling with varying degrees of swelling and hardening. In their severest form the changes appear as grape-like clusters of dark nodules. According to Wilgram and Ingle, these nodules closely resemble periarteritis nodosa. Histologically, the alterations seen in these vessels are similar to those described for the coronary and renal arteries, except that the protrusions into the lumen are more pronounced, while medial hypertrophy is less conspicuous. The kidneys of all such animals exhibit advanced degrees of injury which resemble those described as "obstructive nephropathy."

In discussing the pathogenesis of the vascular lesions, Wilgram and Ingle state their belief that the diseased kidney and electrolyte disturbances ensuing from renal malfunction may play an important role in the development of these vascular changes. In support of their concept they cite a variety of experimental procedures which, though decidedly different, lead to various forms of kidney damage and have in common a reduction of the number of functioning nephrons. All these procedures, among which are quoted some of those developed in our laboratories (31, 32), lead to Mönckeberg type medial sclerosis of the arterial tree in the rat. Wilgram and Ingle conclude that frequent pregnancies in female breeder rats may lead to obstructive nephropathy and thus result in the emergence of mediosclerosis of the arterial tree.

Initial lack of recognition of this mechanism by Wexler and Miller led to the erroneous claim that corticothrophin in almost therapeutic amounts may induce severe arteriosclerosis in the rat and aggravate pre-existing lesions (67). Attempts to reproduce this work in our laboratory (28), as well as by Wilgram and Ingle in Chicago (72) and Mäkinen and Näätänen in Finland (42) were unsuccessful. It is quite evident that the arteriosclerotic alterations are neither produced nor influenced by corticotrophin in the recommended dosage. These lesions in aging female breeder rats were solely dependent on the severity of pre-existing, and aggravated by induced additional, renal injury. This unfortunate misinterpretation, which continues to haunt the medical literature, is cited as an example of the importance one must ascribe to a careful knowledge of the incidence, appearance and extent of spontaneous alterations before one undertakes the interpretation of experimental data.

COMMENTS

It may now perhaps have become clear why I have continuously emphasized the presence of renal injury in spontaneous cardiovascular disease of laboratory animals. In more than two decades of experimental work which concerned itself with cardiovascular injury produced by impairment of renal function, my associates and I have been able to reproduce most of the degenerative spontaneous lesions seen in small mammals (Figs. 7, 8 and 9).

I am therefore in full accord with Wilgram and Ingle's view concerning pathogenesis of spontaneous arterial mediosclerosis in aging female breeder rats except that I wish to go one step further in implicating excess function of the parathyroid gland in the wake of renal dysfunction as the probable ultimate common denominator. Our concept is based on the demonstration that prior removal of the parathyroid glands fully protects animals with severe renal injury against the development of Mönckeberg type

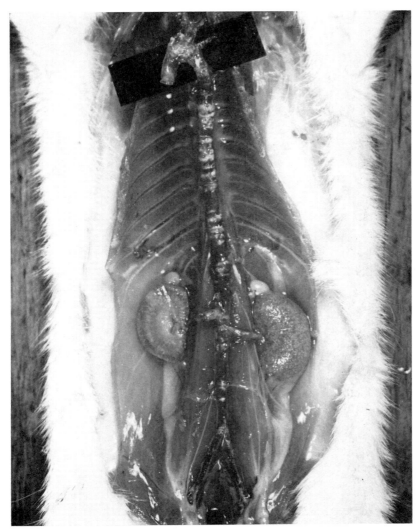

FIGURE 7. Medionecrosis and "bamboo-stick" calcification of the stem and large branches of the arterial tree in the albino rat. Note the rigidity of the aortic arch and the broken-off stump of the celiac artery which points towards the cross section of the right kidney. Also visible are the enlarged adrenals and kidneys. The rough granular surface apparent in the left kidney is due to severe obstructive nephropathy and calcification. (Taken from Lehr (30) with permission of the publisher.)

mediosclerosis and incidentally also disseminated myocardial necrosis, and that the ability to develop such injury can be restored in parathyroidectomized rats by the administration of parathyroid extract (33). It is our belief that focal myocardial necrosis and focal "necrotizing myocarditis" sometimes suspected or described as infarct without evidence of vascular occlusion, may be based on the same mechanism of production.

It should be stressed that many authors reporting spontaneous cardiovascular injury, describe the simultaneous occurrence of severe renal damage although they may not suspect any connection between the two. If one takes a bird's eye view of reports on spontaneous cardiovascular lesions in various species of animals by investigators working independently often separated by decades in time and polar distances in space, one may discern an uncanny similarity in the description of the pathologic-anatomical picture though coupled with an amazing variety of theories on pathogenesis. Such theories run the gamut from nutritional disturbances and deficiencies of all kinds, to infections, hormonal imbalances, hemodynamic phenomena to, finally, the "wear and tear" of aging.

$\longrightarrow$

FIGURE 8. Mönckeberg-type mediosclerosis of the arterial tree as a consequence of obstructive nephropathy (renal sulfonamide block). Macroscopic appearance: A to F. Microscopic picture: G to I. A. Aortic arch and large branches. Bamboo-stick lesion of the aorta extending into innominate, carotid and subclavian arteries. B. Calcified aneurysm of aortic arch and upper part of descending aorta. Note normal thin-walled aorta below crossing of V. azygos. (Protection apparently due to mechanical pressure of vein.) C. Abdominal aorta. Multiple aneurysmic dilatations of thinned out wall. D. Dilation and bamboo-stick calcification of arch and descending aorta. Also visible are enlarged adrenal glands and contracted kidneys. E. Open view of the aorta of Figure D. F. Same as Figure E, close-up. Note irregular, bulging sub-intimal nodules. There is superficial resemblance to human atheromatosis. G. Aorta and a large branch, showing necrosis and calcification of media. H. Wall of aorta. Subintimal necrosis of muscle fibers in the media with swelling and breakdown of elastic membranes, and proliferation of endothelial cells over the lesion. I. Longitudinal section of coronary artery. Wall is markedly thinned out, necrotic and irregularly calcified. (Taken from Lehr *et al.*, *Proc. Soc. Exp. Biol. Med.*, *85*:615-624, 1954, with permission of the publisher.)

The concept of "wear and tear" has probably been more abused than any other. It is well-known, e.g., that advanced coronary sclerosis has been found frequently in so-called healthy young men, whereas octogenarians may be entirely free of this condition. In many instances, it is not the inevitable consequence of aging but the frequency of exposure which accounts for increased incidence of lesions with advancing age. If, e.g., one were

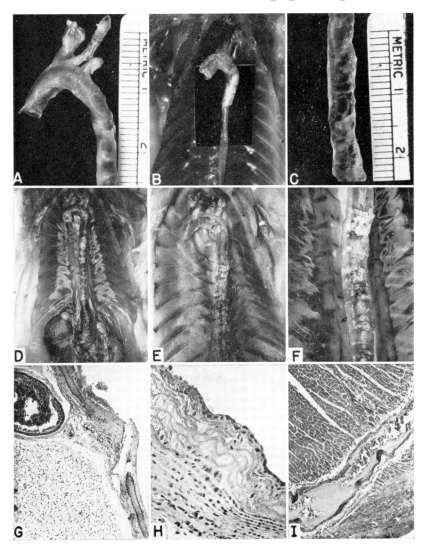

to determine the incidence of car injuries suffered by various age groups, the curve will rise with age, among other reasons, because of cumulative exposure to such situations during a lifetime. By the same token young animals are not always protected by a special resistance of their tissues or other protective mechanism. The low incidence of lesions in young animals may be due to a low exposure ratio. If such exposure is provided artificially, characteristic injury may be induced. This is not to deny that there is a true age dependency often unexplained. Sometimes one can find both situations combined. For example, it was noticed in my laboratory, that weanling rats are remarkably resistant to poisoning with parathyroid hormone. Yet with sufficiently large dosage, extremely severe cardiovascular lesions of the adult type can be induced in the weanling rat (34).

It is clear that many of the divergent causes implicated by various workers as responsible for similar or identical spontaneous cardiovascular lesions may lead to severe impairment of renal excretory function, thus establishing one important common pathway in the etiology of spontaneous lesions.

It should be remembered that spontaneous lesions in contrast to experimental, carefully timed, injury, usually represent a mixture of various stages and phases of a chronic condition so that one can find necrosis, calcification and scars often in one and the

---

$\longrightarrow$

FIGURE 9. Histological appearance of lesions in the kidneys, the myocardium, and the muscularis of stomach following renal sulfonamide block. J. Ascending pyelonephritis in renal medulla. Note interstitial infiltration with inflammatory cells and tubular casts composed of polymorphonuclear leucocytes. K. Renal cortex in obstructive nephropathy. Note interstitial infiltration with inflammatory cells, dilated tubules filled with pus cells, necrosis and calcification of tubular epithelium and foci of tubular regeneration. L. Focal and interstitial myocarditis. Note focal collection of predominantly mononuclear cells in area of muscular disintegration, and diffuse infiltration with mononuclear cells. M. Focus of myocardial necrosis. Note darkly stained necrotic fibers in left lower corner of photograph. There is little inflammatory reaction. N. Myocardium, showing necrosis and calcification of individual muscle fibers. O. Stomach wall, showing necrosis and calcification of muscularis. (Taken from Lehr *et al., Proc. Soc. Exp. Biol. Med., 85*:615-624, 1954, with permission of the publisher.)

same area of injury. To compound the picture further, inflammatory lesions such as panarteritis may so damage the kidneys that mediosclerosis occurs secondarily in vessels already afflicted with inflammatory injury.

The recognition of renal injury as a definite and important factor in the pathogenesis of certain spontaneous degenerative alterations, should not detract from the need of searching for other possible mechanisms in the development of spontaneous lesions. It is my hope, therefore, that efforts will continue toward the ex-

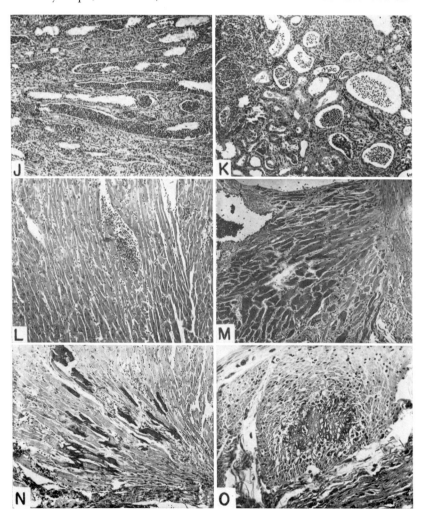

ploration of the pathogenesis of spontaneous cardiovascular disease, particularly with the aid of experimental injury. Success in
this area may serve a double purpose: It may contribute to the
recognition of the pathogenesis of certain human conditions and
thus perhaps assist in the discovery of new preventive or therapeutic measures, and it may result in the raising of healthier experimental animals.

REFERENCES CITED

1. ANITSCHKOW, N.: Experimental arteriosclerosis in animals. In,
   Arteriosclerosis: A Survey of the Problem (Cowdry, E.V., Ed.).
   New York, Macmillan, 1933.

2. BRAGDON, J. H.: Spontaneous atherosclerosis in the rabbit. *Circulation, 5:*641, 1952.

3. BENNECKE, A.: Studien über Gefässerkrankungen durch Gifte.
   *Virchow Arch. Path. Anat., 191:*208, 1908.

4. BERG, B. N., and HARMISON, C. R.: Blood pressure and heart size
   in aging rats. *J. Geront., 10:*416, 1955.

5. BLUMER, C., GORDONOFF, T., and REZNIKOFF, L.: Cholesterinstoff-
   wechsel und Chlorophyll. *Naunyn Schmiedeberg Arch. Exp.
   Path., 173:*42, 1933.

6. DILL, L. V., and ISENHOUR, C. E.: Occurrence of atheroma in the
   aorta in rabbits with renal hypertension. *Arch. Path., 33:*655,
   1942.

7. DUFF, G. L.: Experimental cholesterol arteriosclerosis and its relationship to human arteriosclerosis. *Arch. Path., 20:*81, 259,
   1935.

8. DUMAS, quoted by Jaffé and Gavallér. See ref. 24.

9. FARRIS, E. J., YEAKEL, E. H., and SEITNER, M. A.: Ossifying cartilage
   and thrombi in the hearts of rats. *Amer. J. Path., 22:*613, 1946,

10. FISCHER, quoted by Jaffé and Gavallér. See ref. 24.

11. FOX, H.: Arteriosclerosis in lower mammals and birds: Its relation
    to the disease in man. In, *Arteriosclerosis: A Survey of the Prob-
    lem* (Cowdry, E. V., Ed.). New York, Macmillan, 1933.

12. GILLMAN, J., and GILBERT, C.: Calcium, phosphorus and vitamin
    D as factors regulating the integrity of the cardiovascular sys-
    tem. *Exp. Med. Surg., 14:*136, 1956.

13. GILLMAN, T., and HATHORN, M.: Sex incidence of vascular lesions
    in aging rats in relation to previous pregnancies. *Nature*
    (Lond.) , *183:*1139, 1959.

14. GILLMAN, GILBERT, and SPENCE, quoted by Jaffé and Gavallér. See ref. 24.

15. HARVEY, T. S., SMITH, D. H., and PIKUZINSKI, A. E.: Aortic lesions in rabbits treated with bacterial endotoxins. *Circulation, 24:* 1095, 1961.

16. HEDINGER, E., and LOEB, O.: Über Aortenceränderungen bei Kaninchen nach subkutaner Jodkaliverabreichung. *Naunyn Schmiedeberg Arch. Exp. Path., 56:*314, 1907.

17. HERMANEK, P., and SLAPAK, L.: Über spontane seröse Endokarditis des Kaninchens. *Schweiz. Z. Allg. Path., 19:*318, 1956.

18. HESSE, M.: Vergleichend-histologische Untersuchungen über die Mediaverkalkung der Arterien. *Virchow Arch. Path. Anat., 249:*437, 1924.

19. HORNOWSKI, J.: Untersuchungen über Atherosklerosis. *Virchow Arch. Path. Anat., 215:*280, 1914.

20. HUEPER, W. C.: Cartilaginous foci in the hearts of white rats and mice. *Arch. Path., 27:*466, 1939.

21. HUEPER, W. C.: Spontaneous arteriosclerosis in rats. *Arch. Path., 20:*708, 1935.

22. HUMMEL, K. P., and BARNES, L. L.: Calcification of the aorta, heart and kidneys of the albino rat. *Amer. J. Path., 14:*121, 1938.

23. HUMPHREYS, E. M.: The occurrence of atheromatous lesions in the coronary arteries of rats. *Quart. J. Exp. Physiol., 42:*96, 1957.

24. JAFFÉ, R., and V. GAVALLÉR, B.: Kreislauforgane. In, *Pathologie der Laboratoriumstiere* (Cohrs *et al,* Eds.). Berlin, Springer, 1958.

25. JOHNSTONE, O. P., added note to article by Miles. See ref. 44.

26. KESTEN, H. D.: Early incidence of spontaneous medial degeneration (arteriosclerosis) in the aorta of the rabbit. *Arch. Path., 20:*1, 1935.

27. KOLETSKY, S.: Necrotizing vascular disease in the rat. *Arch. Path., 59:*312, 1955.

28. KRUKOWSKI, M., LEHR, D., and RICARD, O.: The role of corticotrophin (ACTH) in experimental arteriosclerosis. *Fed. Proc., 18:*412, 1959.

29. LEHR, D.: Studies on the prevention and treatment of experimental renal obstruction from sulfadiazine. *Bull. N. Y. Acad. Med., 20:* 424, 1944.

30. LEHR, D., and CHURG, J.: Eine Methode zur Erzeugung disseminierter Nekrosen und Verkalkungen im kardiovaskulären System von Albinoratten. *Wien. Klin. Wschr., 64:*639, 1952.

31. LEHR, D., and CHURG, J.: Human and experimental arteriosclerosis. *J. Mount Sinai Hosp. N. Y., 19*:106, 1952.

32. LEHR, D., and MARTIN, C.: Pathogenesis of experimental arteriosclerosis in the rat. *Proc. Soc. Exp. Biol. Med., 93*:596, 1956.

33. LEHR, D.: Causative relationships of parathyroid hormone to renogenic and reniprival cardiovascular disease. *Ann. N. Y. Acad. Sci., 72*:901, 1959.

34. LEHR, D., and KRUKOWSKI, M.: Unpublished observations.

35. LEVIN, I., and LARKIN, J. H.: The early stages of spontaneous arterial lesions in the rabbit. *Proc. Soc. Exp. Biol. Med., 7*:109, 1909-1910.

36. LOOMIS, D.: Hypertension and necrotizing arteritis in the rat following renal infarction. *Arch. Path., 41*:231, 1946.

37. LOPES DE FARIA, J.: Medionekrose der grossen und mittelgrossen Arterien nach orthostatischem Kollaps des Kaninchens. *Beitr. Path. Anat., 115*:373, 1955.

38. LÖWENTHAL, K.: Kreislauforgane. In, *Anatomie und Pathologie der Spontanerkankungen der Kleinen Laboratoriumstiere* (Jaffé, R., Ed.). Berlin, Springer, 1931.

39. LÖWENTHAL, K.: Nekrotisierende Aortitis mit Aortenruptur bei einer Maus. *Virchow Arch. Path. Anat., 265*:424, 1927.

40. LUCIEN, M., and PARISOT, J.: L'athérome spontané chez le lapin, sa fréquence et ses caracteres généraux. *C.R. Soc. Biol. Par., 64:* 917, 1908.

41. LUCIEN, M., and PARISOT, J.: Les lésions de l'athérome experimental et spontané chez le lapin. *C.R. Soc. Biol. Par., 64*:919, 1908.

42. MÄKINEN and NÄÄTÄNEN, quoted by Studer and Reber. See ref. 60.

43. MALINOW, M. R., HOJMAN, D., and PELLEGRINO, A. A.: Spontaneous atherosclerosis in the rat. *Arch. Path., 61*:11, 1956.

44. MILES, A. B.: Spontaneous arterial degeneration in rabbits. *J.A.-M.A., 49*:1173, 1907.

45. MILLER, C. P., JR.: Spontaneous interstitial myocarditis in rabbits. *J. Exp. Med., 40*:543, 1924.

46. MILLER, C. P., JR.: Attempts to transmit rheumatic fever to rabbits and guinea pigs. *J. Exp. Med., 40*:525, 1924.

47. MOORE et al, quoted by Jaffé and Gavallér. See ref. 24.

48. NUZUM, F. R., ELLIOT, A. H., EVANS, R. O., and PRIEST, B. U.: The occurrence and nature of spontaneous arteriosclerosis and nephritis in the rabbit. *Arch. Path., 10*:697, 1930.

49. OPHÜLS, W.: Spontaneous arteriosclerosis of the aorta (atheroma) in a rabbit. *J.A.M.A., 48*:326, 1907.

50. PEARCE, J. M.: Cardiac lesions in rabbits produced by a filterable virus (Virus III). *Arch. Path., 28:*827, 1939.

51. PEARCE, R. M.: Occurrence of spontaneous arterial degeneration in the rabbit. *J.A.M.A., 51:*1056, 1908.

52. RATCLIFFE, H. L.: Spontaneous diseases of laboratory rats. In, *The Rat in Laboratory Investigation* (Griffith, J. Q., Jr. and Farris, E. J., Eds.). Philadelphia, Lippincott, 1942.

53. RATHER, L. J.: Experimental aortic disease in albino rats following renal operations. *Proc. Soc. Exp. Biol. Med., 85:*285, 1954.

54. RENAUD, S.: Calcification in the renal-cardiovascular system of female breeder rats. *Brit. J. Exp. Path., 43:*387, 1962.

55. SAPHIR, quoted by Jaffé and Gavallér. See ref. 24.

56. SEEGAL, B. C.: Spontaneous bone and marrow formation in the aorta of a rabbit. *Arch. Path., 3:*73, 1927.

57. SEIFRIED, O.: *Die Krankheiten des Kaninchens.* Berlin, Springer, 1937.

58. SIMMS, H. S., and BERG, B. N.: Longevity and the onset of lesions in male rats. *J. Geront., 12:*244, 1957.

59. SLYE, as quoted by Jaffé and Gavallér. See ref. 24.

60. STUDER, A., and REBER, K.: Der Tierversuch in der Arteriosklerose-forschung. *Ergebn. Allg. Path., 43:*1, 1963.

61. VAUBEL, E.: Die Eiweissüberenfindlichkeit (Gewebshyperergie) des Bindegewebes (II Teil). *Beitr. Path. Anat., 89:*374, 1932.

62. VEITH, G.: Experimentelle Untersuchungen zur Wirkung von Adrenalin auf den Herzmuskel. *Arch. Kreislaufforsch., 6:*335, 1941.

63. WEINBERG, M.: Athérome spontané chez le lapin. *C.R. Soc. Biol., Par., 65:*561, 1908.

64. WEXLER, B. C., and EPSTEIN, M. J.: Blood coagulation in arterio-sclerotic rats. *Nature* (Lond.), *197:*159, 1963.

65. WEXLER, B. C., BROWN, T. E., and MILLER, B. F.: Atherosclerosis in rats induced by repeated breedings, ACTH and unilateral nephrectomy—Acid mucopolysaccharides, fibroplasia, elastosis and other changes in early lesions. *Circulat. Res., 8:*278, 1960.

66. WEXLER, B. C., and MILLER, B. F.: Coronary arteriosclerosis and thrombosis in the rat. *Proc. Soc. Exp. Biol. Med., 100:*573, 1959.

67. WEXLER, B. C., and MILLER, B. F.: Severe arteriosclerosis and other diseases in the rat produced by corticotrophin. *Science, 127:*590, 1958.

68. WEXLER, B. C., and TRUE, C. W.: Carotid and cerebral arterio-sclerosis in the rat. *Circulat. Res., 12:*659, 1963.

69. WILENS, S. L., and SPROUL, E. E.: Spontaneous cardiovascular disease in the rat. *Amer. J. Path., 14:*177, 1938.
70. WILGRAM, G. F., and BLUMENSTEIN, J.: Aetiology of cardiovascular disease in choline deficiency. *Fed. Proc., 15:*384, 1956.
71. WILGRAM, G. F.: Vascular disease associated with choline deficiency in rats. *Amer. J. Clin. Nutr., 6:*274, 1958.
72. WILGRAM, G. F., and INGLE, D. J.: Renal-cardiovascular pathologic changes in aging female breeder rats. *Arch. Path., 68:*690, 1959.
73. WISSLER, R. W., EILBERT, M. L., SCHROEDER, M. A., and COHEN, L.: Arterial atheromatous lesions in rat. *Fed. Proc., 11:*434, ·1952.
74. WOLKOFF, K.: Über die Altersveränderungen der Arterien bei Tieren. *Virchow Arch. Path. Anat., 252:*208, 1924.

DISCUSSION

Question: What kind of technique was used to produce renal damage in these rats, Goldman's or Goldblatt's?

Dr. Wagner: No, Dr. Lehr's method has been the use of a sulfonamide renal block, consisting of a single injection of sodium acetyl sulfathiazole intraperitoneally—a technique that he has published some time ago (*Wien. Klin. Wschr., 64:*639-642, 1952). Rats so treated develop severe renal damage in a very precise period of time.

Question: How long does it take to develop coronary disease after the renal damage has been accomplished.

Dr. Wagner: One can begin with the early changes in these animals within twenty-four hours and they become progressively more severe, and at the end of three to five days after this acute renal block, the damage in the cardiovascular system is well defined.

Chairman: Does that answer your question?

Dr. Eades: Yes. I might comment that we had three male Wistar rats approximately nine months old that had renal injury by the technique of rolling cellophane on one kidney and then removing the other kidney. In about two weeks they developed high blood pressure of 160 or 170 and in a few months we began to see depositions in the hypertrophic medias of the coronary arteries. We feed our rats hamburger. This produces the disease more rapidly than pure chow.

Dr. Benjamin N. Berg: I have been tremendously impressed by the fact that aging comes into the picture in many, many conditions. It seems to me as though if the isolated observations were collected and really systematized we would get a great deal more out of them.

An additional point is that I think the speaker very clearly showed the importance of the environmental conditions of the laboratory animals. There should be standardized temperature, composition of the diet, etc.; all of which is of tremendous relationship to these lesions.

Chairman: It has occurred to me frequently that summaries are often made from a large number of animals but their age and conditions could vary enormously, interfering with any percentages which are tabulated. Dr. Wagner, do you have any comments on this?

Dr. Wagner: I think that from the standpoint of the cardiovascular system in laboratory animals, all too often the species selected is the one of convenience and not necessarily the one that we would ideally like to work with.

For a long time now the rabbit has been selected as the animal in which we would like to produce rheumatic heart disease. Unfortunately the rabbit doesn't develop streptococcal infection spontaneously, it has a very, very low incidence of any valvular disease and also does not eat the same diet that man eats. All of this, in trying to relate a lesion experimentally in rabbits seems a little bit far-fetched, so we find more and more investigators in cardiovascular disease moving to the primates and also moving to swine, especially these new small pigs. It could be that when we talk about standardization of laboratory animals and experiments in spontaneous lesions that we should expand our vistas as to the kinds of animals used.

I was impressed recently in seeing widespread use of lizards and toads and animals of this kind in an experimental dermatopathology set-up at St. Thomas's Medical School in London. They feel this is an excellent way to study some basic problems of pigmentation and of tumor formation. Perhaps we will expand beyond the accepted rat, the mouse and the rabbit. We have found in working with the mink, that this has given us exciting information as regards the so-called virus-transmitted polyarteritis, with important relationships to human connective tissue diseases.

Dr. K. M. Das: If I may be permitted, I want to give a few findings from a cardiovascular pathology study conducted at the Animal Medical Center. This covered 297 consecutive necropsies in dogs, which came to the necropsy room in the course of the regular flow from the clinics and hospital. These were not selected dogs.

Of 297 dogs we found 134 (about 45 per cent) with cardiovascular lesions. Of this 134 cardiovascular lesions we saw mitral disease in 101 (or 34 per cent) dogs. Only 29 had tricuspid lesions - that is about 10 per cent.

One finding of some significance is that we often see arteriosclerosis in the posterior part of the abdominal aorta in dogs above seven years of age. This is not to be taken as identical with atheromatosis, the type of lesions one often sees in the human. This definitely is arteriosclerosis, but the lipid fraction is less dominant and it is more of an intimal hyperplasia. Cholesterol appears a little later.

This same type of arteriosclerosis is also found in the intima of the main trunk and branches of the pulmonary artery in most dogs with congestive heart failure. This would indicate that perhaps there was pulmonary hypertension.

The total number showing arteriosclerosis of the aorta was sixty-nine out of 297, which is about 23 per cent. Also thirty-nine cases (or 13 per cent) had arteriosclerosis of the pulmonary artery.

We have not yet seen any evidence of rheumatic heart disease. To my knowledge there is no record of such disease in the published literature of this country. This rheumatic heart disease can be differentiated by simple criteria such as the absence of Aschoff bodies. Most of the mitral lesions seen here consist of gross deformity of valves up to nodularity and fibrosis, and microscopically one sees proliferation of fibrous and loose connective tissue cells. As a result of deformity there is insufficiency and regurgitation, the morphological indicator of which is seen as a "jet" lesion in the left atrial endocardium.

I might also mention that in a survey of the cholesterol level of dogs versus cats we saw a significant difference between the cholesterol level of the dog and the cat. The dog cholesterol was high, with a mean of 218 milligrams per cent and the cat 118 milligrams per cent (p=less than 0.001). Simultaneously, when we compare the incidence of cardiovascular lesions in the dog and the cat population, there is a marked difference. The cat has a low incidence of cardiovascular lesions when compared with the dog. We could not say this categorically because our study has been limited to about 150 cats and 297 dogs. How this lesion incidence relates to different cholesterol levels, we don't know.

I feel that we should have a meeting permitting more discussion on the cardiovascular problem in dogs and cats. They provide us, perhaps, with the best laboratory animals for the study of heart disease because of the following facts:

First, they share the same environment as the humans. Second, they eat almost the same kind of food as humans. No other animal with which we experiment so often seems to have these two common denominators which would seem necessary for the study of cardiovascular disease.

Question: I would like to ask: In cats occasionally one finds hypertrophy of the media in the pulmonary arterioles. You may not see any other lesions and I don't know of any good explanation for its occurrence. Would anyone care to comment?

Dr. K. M. Das: Hypertrophy of the media of the pulmonary arterioles in the cat has been reported from various laboratories in this country and abroad. In some places they have reported that about 36 per cent of cats had this type of vascular lesion. The cause of this condition is not known.

In our experience we also find the same type of lesion although of a lesser incidence and especially it occurs in the middle lobes of both lungs. I have doubts that the cat lung worm (*Aelurostrongylus*), as suggested by one of the speakers is the final answer to this question.

7

HEPATITIS AND OTHER SPONTANEOUS LIVER LESIONS OF SMALL EXPERIMENTAL ANIMALS*

BORIS H. RUEBNER, J. RUSSELL LINDSEY, AND EDWARD C. MELBY, JR.

INTRODUCTION

H EPATIC INVOLVEMENT of some degree is seen in many systemic diseases. We have decided to concentrate on those lesions which affect the liver predominantly or which present a relatively specific histologic appearance. The topics selected have not been treated exhaustively but it is hoped that the bibliography will help with a fuller study of specific subjects. Tumors are alluded to only briefly.

NUCLEAR HYPERPLASIA AND INCLUSIONS

The hepatic cells of aged animals may have extremely bizarre nuclei which are attributable to the aging process alone and not to malignancy as might be suspected. Striking examples have been described for aged mice (Andrew *et al.*) and men (Carr *et al.*), and include: (1) extreme variation in cell size; (2) giant, irregularly shaped hyperchromatic nuclei (Fig. 1); (3) multiple nucleoli (up to fifteen) within giant nuclei; (4) large, round or oval, poorly staining hyaline nuclear inclusion bodies not related to glycogen vacuolation (Fig. 2), and (5) binucleate cells. It

$\longrightarrow$

FIGURE 1. Elderly mouse. A large bizarre nucleus is in the center. Above it is a hyaline intracytoplasmic inclusion body. Hematoxylin and eosin. X600.
FIGURE 2. Same animal as Figure 1. In the center is a hyaline type B intranuclear inclusion. H. and E. x600.

*This work was supported by a Career Research Development Award to B. H. Ruebner and by Grants E 3598 and FR-00130 from the Public Health Service and by contract DA 49-193, MD2310, Department of the Army, Office of the Surgeon General.

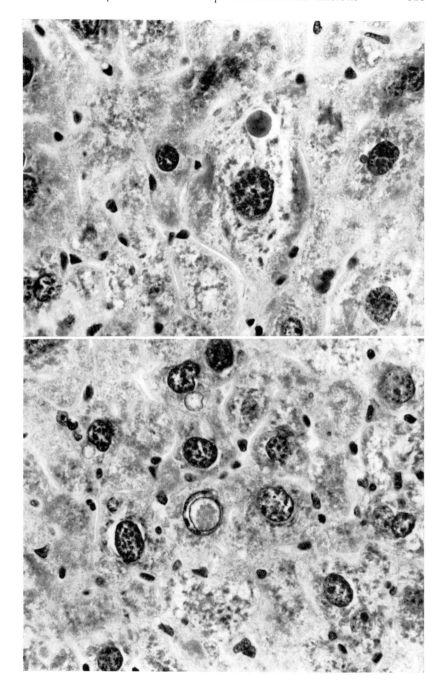

seems likely that these nuclear lesions are associated with the increased polyploidy which has been demonstrated in old rats (Post *et al.*).

The intranuclear inclusions associated with ageing deserve special comment as they have been attributed to viral infection (Findlay). Cowdrey pointed out that this type of inclusion does not affect the entire nucleus. The nucleoplasm may not be noticeably altered and the basophilic chromatin does not become marginated. He classified them as "Type B" inclusions and differentiated them from "type A" inclusions which are typical of certain viral infections such as herpes and canine hepatitis. Type B inclusions occur not only in elderly animals but may be seen after many different types of liver injury (Andervont and Dunn, 1947; Leduc and Wilson; Wessel). They are Feulgen negative (Wessel) and have been shown by electron microscopy to consist of damaged cytoplasmic organelles which have herniated into the nucleus (Leduc and Wilson; Wessel). It seems unlikely that type B inclusions are directly related to a latent viral infection.

The ingestion of lead or bismuth may result in the formation of inclusions resembling the type A variety produced by viruses. However, unlike viral inclusions, they are acid fast, P.A.S. positive, and Feulgen negative. The renal tubules are more susceptible to development of these inclusions than the liver (Blackman, Wachstein).

INCLUSIONS AND OTHER CHANGES IN THE CYTOPLASM

"Waxy" globules (Fig. 1) resembling red blood cells have been described in the parenchymal cytoplasm of elderly mice (Campbell) and in mouse hepatomas (Andervont and Dunn, 1952). We have found these bodies to be weakly P.A.S. positive.

Watery vacuoles (Aterman) and hyaline droplets (Anderson *et al.*; Schlicht; Doniach and Weinbren) have been observed in experimental animals subjected to a great variety of procedures. There is disagreement whether watery and hyaline droplets are similar in nature (Aterman, Doniach and Weinbern). Cells containing such droplets appear healthy by light microscopy. Hyaline droplets (Fig. 3) are generally strongly P.A.S. positive even after diastase digestion (Anderson *et al.*; Schlicht). It has been sug-

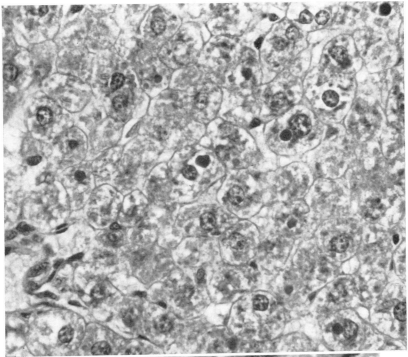

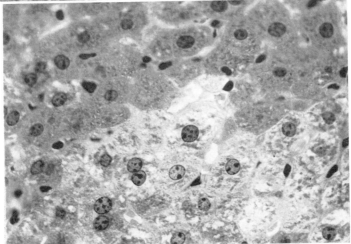

FIGURE 3. "Normal" rat. Cytoplasmic hyaline droplets are present in many parenchymal cells. P.A.S. (digested) x600.

FIGURE 4. Swiss mouse twenty-four hours after experimental inoculation with MHV₃ hepatitis. No focal necroses are seen but the distinction between "light" and "dark" liver cells is clear. Methacrylate embedded section, 1μ thick H. and E. x600.

gested that these droplets represent enlarged lysosomes which may contain plasma proteins (Anderson *et al.*). We have seen a striking number of such globules in an apparently normal Spague Dawley rat.

Hydropic degeneration (Fig. 4) consists of marked cellular enlargement probably due to dilatation of the endoplasmic reticulum (Bassi, Jézéquel *et al.*). "Light" liver cells (Steiner and Baglio) appear to represent the same lesion which may be caused by various hepatotoxic agents including viral hepatitis and is unrelated to glycogen content. If the damage is not too severe it appears to be reversible.

BACTERIAL DISEASES AFFECTING THE LIVER

SALMONELLOSIS: This is one of the diseases most likely to be encountered as a serious problem in any laboratory animal. A wide variety of Salmonella species have been reported but *S. typhimurium* and *S. enteritidis* are by far the most common offenders (Edwards and Bruner; Edwards *et al.*; Habermann and Williams). The disease is generally considered as varying from acute to chronic but Innes *et al.* have reported two fulminant outbreaks in hamsters with a mortality of almost 100 per cent. The pathogenesis of the liver lesions is apparently similar in all species although the most complete information available concerns mice (Bakken and Vogelsancy; Böhme *et al.*). Early in the course of the disease one may see a few aggregates of histiocytes with swelling of the Kupffer cells or patchy parenchymal necrosis without an inflammatory reaction. Later the necrotic foci become abscesses which may then progress to nodules of histiocytes. If recovery occurs, there is essentially complete restoration of the normal liver histology even though the organ remains infected for a prolonged period of time. Affected mice occasionally have thrombi in branches of the portal vein, rarely resulting in infarction (Böhme *et al.*).

PSEUDOTUBERCULOSIS: This is a disease occurring chiefly in guinea pigs, occasionally in rats, and rarely in mice, rabbits and several other species (Wilson and Miles). The etiologic agent is *Pasteurella pseudotuberculosis.* In guinea pigs the gross lesions are greyish-white nodules 2-3 mm. in diameter occurring in the liver, spleen, and lungs. The mesenteric lymph nodes are enlarged and caseous. The fully developed microscopic lesions consist of foci of coagulation necrosis surrounded by a variable inflammatory reaction including histiocytes. True Langhans giant cells are most unusual. Colonies of bacilli may be conspicuous even in sections stained by hematoxylin and eosin. A similar disease, also referred to as pseudotuberculosis, is caused by *Corynebacterium kutscheri* (formerly *Bacillus pseudotuberculosis murium*) for which mice apparently serve as the natural host (Breed *et al.*). Rats are found infected much less frequently. This disease has been reported in mice given excessive doses of cortisone (Antopol) or exposed to total body radiation (Shechmeister and Adler) as well as in rats treated with cortisone (Le Maistre and Tompsett).

TULAREMIA: Although tularemia is not usually considered to be a spontaneous disease of laboratory animals, it deserves attention here because of the remarkable hazard it may present to laboratory workers (Francis). Transmission of the causative agent, *Pasteurella tularensis*, is by a variety of routes including direct contact with the unbroken skin and a large number of bloodsucking arthropods. Burroughs *et al.* have listed forty-eight mammals and birds in which natural infection is known to occur. The natural disease has been most frequently encountered in wild rabbits and ground squirrels for which the lesions are well described by Smith and Jones. The gross lesions include numerous pin-point to large whitish foci scattered through the liver, spleen, and lymph nodes. Microscopically the early liver lesions show a purulent or caseous center and a surrounding zone of lymphocytes with a few neutrophils and macrophages. We have seen one case in which the lesions had progressed to well developed granulomas with large numbers of giant cells. Because of the difficulty in demonstrating the organisms in tissue sections, cultural identification is valuable in establishing the diagnosis.

BACILLUS PILIFORMIS *Hepatitis (Tyzzer's Disease):* This is generally a fotal disease of mice, occurring particularly in the Japanese dancing strain (Saunders, 1958; Cohrs *et al.*). It may develop in such animals if they are employed for experimental investigations or subjected to adverse environmental conditions. The disease affects only the liver where it produces bluish grey to yellowish nodules. Histologically these consist of large necrotic foci tending to be periportal. The surrounding parenchymal cells contain characteristic long slender spore-forming gram negative bacilli with tapered ends. The organisms are made particularly conspicuous by Azure Eosin staining (Fig. 5). So far they have not been grown on artificial media. Dr. James Craigie of the Imperial Cancer Research Fund, London, England, has recently isolated a non-spore forming variant of this organism which multiplies in embryonated eggs. He believes that extracellular survival depends on spore formation.

Many other bacteria may produce diffuse inflammation, focal hepatic necrosis, or actual abscesses. Among these are *Streptococcus, Alkaligenes, Klebsiella, Listeria,* and organisms of the *Proteus* group. The latter are particularly likely to become troublesome in animals treated with antibiotics. Actinomycotic hepatitis has been described in rabbits which were wrongly thought to have coccidiosis (Cohrs *et al.*).

VIRAL HEPATITIS

The Mouse Hepatitis Viruses, *(MHV):* This family of viruses includes several different agents for which the literature has been recently reviewed by Gledhill. They are latent in most strains of laboratory mice. Such infections have become activated in the course of experiments with leukemia agents (Gledhill) and during attempts to adapt the virus of human hepatitis to mice (Cohrs *et al.*). MHV viruses may also become manifest in mice superinfected with *Eperythrozoon coccoides,* a common protozoan blood parasite. Murine hepatitis may therefore complicate a wide variety of experimental procedures. The disease is most severe in suckling animals and mortality decreases with increasing age. If

---

$\longrightarrow$

FIGURE 5. Tyzzer's disease. Intra- and extracellular bacillary organisms are seen at the margin of a necrotic focus. Azure Eosin. x1000.

FIGURE 6. Swiss mouse twenty-four hours after intraperitoneal inoculation with MHV_3 hepatitis. A focus of necrosis in the center contains several small round cells and an acidophilic body. H. and E. x600.

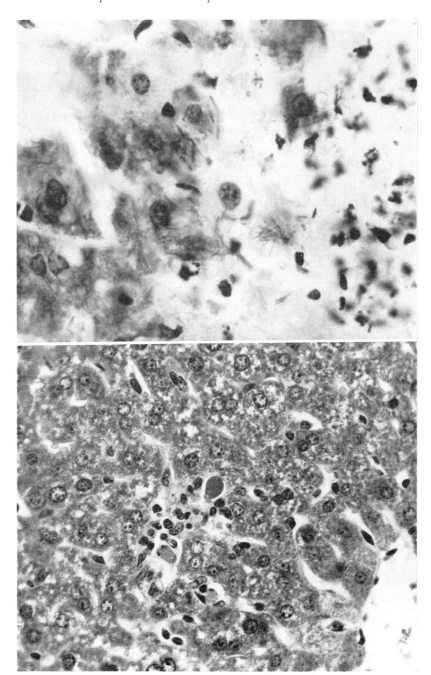

fatal, the infection usually kills within a week of inoculation. Histologically a focal necrosis is produced. The earliest lesions appears to be centered around a sinusoid and seems to involve chiefly Kupffer cells (Ruebner and Miyai). Acidophilic bodies are frequently seen in these early lesions (Fig. 6). They occur not only in viral hepatitis but also in many other types of liver injury and may perhaps develop from Kupffer cells as well as parenchymal cells. The lesions quickly increase in size (Figs. 7 and 8) and soon become confluent (Ruebner and Bramhall). Characteristic viral inclusions have never been detected and cholestasis has never been observed. If the mice survive, the foci of necrosis become filled with mesenchymal cells and the liver quickly regenerates to appear virtually normal.

ECTROMELIA (MOUSE POX) : This virus is related to rabbit pox and vaccinia (Jansen). It may produce epidemics or may be present in a latent form which can become activated by the inoculation of biologic products (Gledhill). Hepatic focal necrosis without any particular lobular distribution is the dominant histologic lesion in fulminant ectromelia (Saunders) but the characteristic acidophilic cytoplasmic inclusions described by Marchal do not seem to occur in the liver (Habermann *et al.*).

PARASITIC DISEASES INVOLVING THE LIVER

CYSTICERCOSIS: The adults of *Taenia pisiformis* and *T. taeniaformis* are tapeworms commonly found in dogs and cats. Rodents serve as intermediate hosts and are infected by ingesting the ova in contaminated food. The larval stages or cysticerci occur in the liver and peritoneal cavity. The cysticercus of *T. pisiformis* measures up to about ten mm. in diameter and occurs most frequently in the rabbit. The larval stage of T. taeniaformis, also known as *Cysticercus fasciolaris*, is encountered most often in rats

---→

FIGURE 7. Swiss mouse forty-eight hours after infection with MHV_3. The focus of necrosis is larger than at twenty-four hours and contains some polymorphs as well as other cells. H. and E. x600.

FIGURE 8. Swiss mouse seventy-two hours after inoculation with MHV_3. Confluent hepatic necrosis. H. and E. x600.

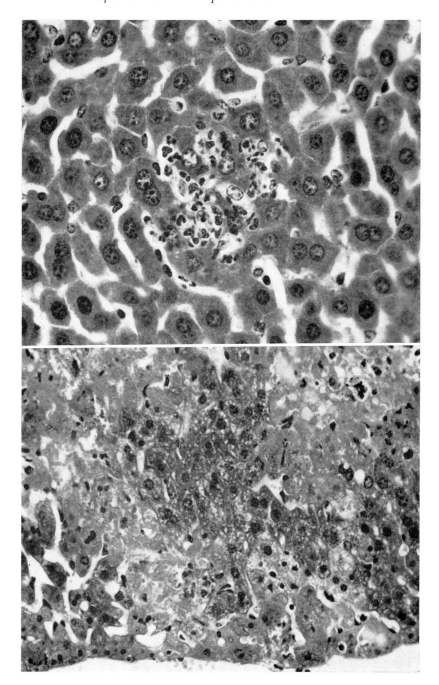

and mice (Fig. 9). After several months the larvae may die and be replaced by foreign body granulomas. The fibrous tissue reaction in such lesions may be severe and sarcomas capable of metastasis can develop as the result of *Cysticercus fasciolaris* infection (Cohrs *et al.*).

CAPILLARIA HEPATICA: The liver of an infected animal contains both the adult roundworms and their ova. Wild rodents, especially sewer rats frequently harbor this parasite and a few cases have actually been described in man (Calle). Animals apparently obtain the infection by ingesting food contaminated with the infected liver from another animal. Small subcapsular whitish nodules develop which histologically show eggs measuring approximately 60 x 35 μ. The eggs are ovoid with terminal opercula and are surrounded by a connective tissue reaction (Fig. 10) which in severe cases may progress to cirrhosis (Cohrs *et al.*, Calle).

HEPATIC COCCIDIOSIS: *Eimeria stiedae* is an extremely common protozoan infection and potential hazard of major significance in the rabbit. Briefly, the life cycle involves ingestion of sporulated oocysts, migration of the released sporozoites to the liver by the portal circulation, multiplication in the epithelium of the bile ducts, and passage of oocysts in the bile and intestinal contents. Microscopic examination usually reveals the presence of developmental stages in the epithelium of bile ducts and oocysts free in the lumens. The most striking lesion is hyperplasia of the ductular epithelium (Fig. 11). This, combined with varying degrees of surrounding fibrosis, may be severe enough to produce obstruction. Recovery with healing is possible so that only a residual lesion resembling biliary cirrhosis may be observed (Smetana). In the opinion of most observers the disease is sufficiently prevalent, even in apparently healthy stock, to render the rabbit unsuitable for the experimental production of cirrhosis.

$\longrightarrow$

FIGURE 9. Mouse. Liver with cysticercus. The scolex is seen at the right. H. and E. x12

FIGURE 10. Rat. Fibrous nodule containing eggs of *Capillaria hepatica*. H. and E. x200.

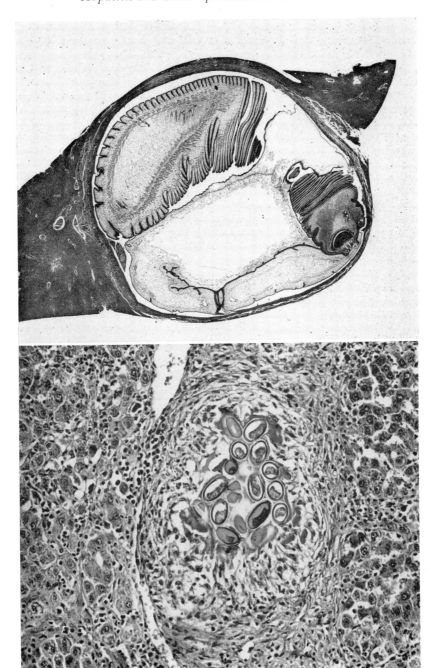

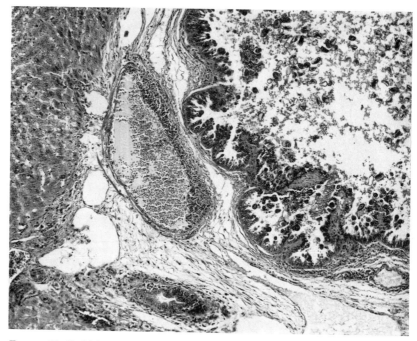

FIGURE 11. Rabbit. Dilated bile duct with papillary hyperplasia showing developmental forms of *E. stiedae* in the epithelium and oocysts in the lumen. H. and E. x100.

ASCITES HEPATITIS: This disease was apparently first recognized in 1955 by Jordan and Mirick during attempts to infect mice with the virus of human hepatitis. It was later seen by Morris *et al.* during efforts to infect mice with viruses of human origin and by Nelson in mice used in the study of carcinogens. The natural disease has been detected only in mice of the Swiss W strain. The etiologic agent, probably a microsporidian, is easily demonstrated in monocytes of ascitic fluid by Giemsa stained smears or wet mounts. Experimental infection is readily accomplished by inoculation of normal mice with ascitic fluid or splenic homogenates. Ascites appears two to three weeks after experimental infection and continues to increase through about the fifth week after which it gradually subsides. Apart from ascites the most salient gross feature is hepatosplenomegaly. Microscopically the liver shows dilated sinusoids, focal mononuclear infiltrates associated with small groups of necrotic cells, and lymphocytic infiltration of the portal areas. Nelson found the mortality in a series of 500 experimentally infected mice to be 8 per cent and showed that the organism may persist in the tissues of recovered animals for at least a year.

BARTONELLOSIS: *Hemobartonella muris* produces hemolytic anemia in mice and rats. Anemia may become evident only after splenectomy. The organisms appear as rods about 1 micron long in the red blood cells and are best seen after Giemsa staining. The liver may show centrilobular necrosis, hemosiderosis, and erythrophagocytosis by Kupffer cells (Griesemer).

NEOPLASTIC DISEASE: Spontaneous hepatoma is seen, particularly in elderly mice of certain strains such as C3H and CBA. It resembles its human and experimental counterparts histologically but it is generally more differentiated and is rarely associated with cirrhosis. In the rat most spontaneous hepatic tumors reported have been sarcomas secondary to *Cysticercus fasciolaris* infection. Benign, frequently cystic hamartomas of the bile ducts may be found in various laboratory animals.

DISEASES OF UNCERTAIN ETIOLOGY

PREGNANCY TOXEMIA occurs in guinea pigs (Paterson, Sauer) and rabbits (Cohrs *et al;* Greene) and is thought to be due to malnutrition (Paterson, Sauer), possibly combined with a disturbance of endocrine balance (Greene, Sauer). Animals in advanced pregnancy are most frequently affected. Toxemic animals may become lethargic and die within twenty-four hours but the severity of the disease is variable. Obese animals appear to be particularly liable to this disease. Focal necrosis tending to be peripheral or midzonal is characteristic but severe fatty change may also be present. In a few cases the lesions are actually hemorrhagic and thrombosis may be seen. Generally there is little or no inflammatory reaction. The occasional finding of old healing lesions in these animals suggests that the disease may be present for an extended period of time in a subclinical form (Greene).

SOFT TISSUE CALCIFICATION: Spectacular calcifications may be seen in guinea pigs. The lesions can affect the liver (Fig. 12), kidney, lungs, stomach, intestine, skeletal muscle and aorta, and have been attributed to dietary imbalance (Paterson).

AUTOIMMUNE HEMOLYTIC ANEMIA develops spontaneously in the NZB strain of mice (Mackay and Burnet). These animals develop focal hepatic necroses which tend to be located in the subcapsular zone. In addition there is widespread hemosiderin deposition, particularly in Kupffer cells. Identical lesions have been observed by Davidsohn *et al.* in experimentally induced hemolytic anemia and were considered to be infarcts.

AMYLOIDOSIS affecting the liver, among other organs, is common in certain strains of mice (Dunn) and hamsters. The

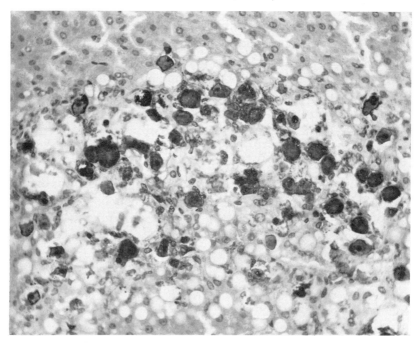

FIGURE 12. Guinea pig. A focus of calcification in a liver with mild fatty change. H. and E. x300.

———————————————→

FIGURE 13. Mouse. Amyloid deposition surrounding portal area. H. and E. x150.
FIGURE 14. Guinea pig. Focus of necrosis in gall bladder. H. and E. x75.

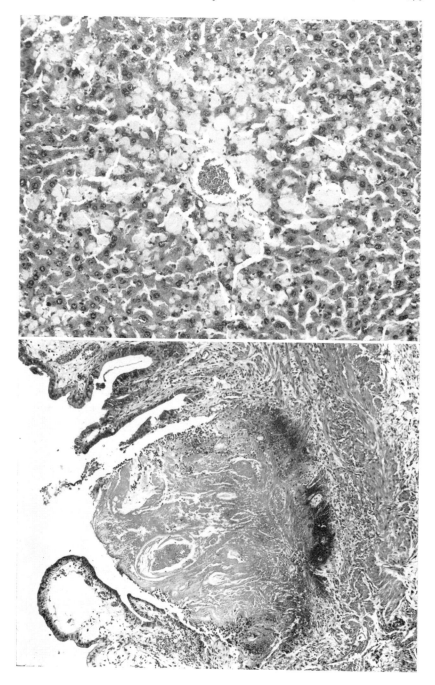

material is deposited preferentially in the periportal (Fig. 13) or midzonal areas (Popper and Schaffner). The incidence of amyloidosis in a particular strain tends to increase with age (Wagner and Bedell).

TORSION OF THE CAUDATE PROCESS may occur in rabbits and is generally fatal (Cohrs *et al.*). It can produce a subcapsular hepatic rupture several centimeters long and a hemorrhagic exudate in the peritoneal cavity. Grossly the lesion may mimick a hemorrhagic tumor but histologically it is an infarct.

CHOLECYSTITIS: We have seen this in a guinea pig with proven disseminated salmonellosis. We have also examined sections from a few guinea pigs showing a focal necrosis of the gallbladder epithelium with a surrounding zone of acute inflammation (Fig. 14). These animals did not have any other significant hepatic lesions. Although there is no proof to support such a contention, it seems possible that this lesion also might have been caused by salmonellosis or perhaps some other bacterial hepatitis.

ACKNOWLEDGMENTS

The authors are most grateful for the loan of materials and helpful suggestions given by Dr. R. J. Habermann, Dr. F. Bielschowsky, Dr. Doris N. Collins, Dr. I. Davidsohn, Dr. Thelma B. Dunn, Major F. M. Garner, Dr. W. J. Hadlow, Dr. C. P. Handforth, Dr. G. S. Mirick, Dr. Janet S. Niven and Dr. M. Wachstein.

REFERENCES

ANDERSON, PAUL J., COHEN, S., and BARKA, T.: Hepatic injury. A histochemical study of intracytoplasmic globules occurring in liver injury. *Arch. Path., 71*:89, 1961.

ANDERVONT, H. B.: Studies on the occurrence of spontaneous hepatomas in mice of strains C₃H and CBA. *J. Nat. Cancer Inst., 11:* 581, 1950.

ANDERVONT, H. B., and DUNN, T. B.: Effect of castration and sex hormones on the induction of tumors in mice with o-amino azotoluene. *J. Nat. Cancer Inst., 7:*455, 1947.

ANDERVONT, H. B., and DUNN, T. B.: Transplantation of spontaneous and induced hepatomas in mice. *J. Nat. Cancer Inst., 13:*455, 1952.

ANDREW, W., BROWN, H. M., and JOHNSON, J. B.: Senile changes in the liver of the mouse and man with special reference to the similarity of the nuclear alterations. *Amer. J. Anat., 72*:199, 1943.

ANTOPOL, W.: Anatomic changes produced in mice treated with excessive doses of cortisone. *Proc. Soc. Exp. Biol. Med., 73*:262, 1950.

ATERMAN, K.: Observations on the nature of watery vacuolation. The response of the liver cell to the intravenous injection of hypertonic saline, Evans Blue, Dextran and Heparin. *Lab. Invest., 7*:577, 1958.

BAKKEN, K., and VOGELSANCY, T. M.: Pathogenesis of Salmonella typhimurium infections in mice. *Acta. Path. Microbiol. Scand., 27*: 41, 1950.

BASSI, M.: Electron microscopy of rat liver after carbontetrachloride poisoning. *Exp. Cell Res., 20*:313, 1960.

BLACKMAN, S. S., JR.: Intranuclear inclusion bodies in the kidney and liver caused by lead poisoning. *Bull. Johns Hopkins Hosp., 58*: 384, 1936.

BÖHME, D. H., SCHNEIDER, H. A., and LEE, J. M.: Some physiological parameters of natural resistance to infection in murine salmonellosis. *J. Exp. Med., 110*:9, 1959.

BREED, R. S., MURRAY, E. G. D., and SMITH, N. R. (and 94 contributors) : *Bergey's Manual of Determinative Bacteriology.* Baltimore, Williams & Wilkins, 1957.

BURROUGHS, A. L., HOLDENRIED, R., LONGANECKER, D. S., and MEYER, K. F.: A field study of latent tularemia in rodents with a list of all known naturally infected vertebrates. *J. Infect. Dis., 76*:115, 1945.

CALLE, SIMON: Parasitism by Capillaria hepatica. *Pediatrics, 27*:648, 1961.

CAMPBELL, J. A.: An inclusion body in the liver cells of the mouse. *J. Path. Bact., 48*:223, 1939.

CARR, R. D., SMITH, M. J., and KEIL, P. G.: The liver in the ageing process. *Arch. Path., 70*:1, 1960.

COWDRY, E. V.: The problem of intranuclear inclusions in virus diseases.. *Arch. Path., 18*:527, 1934.

DAVIDSOHN, I., TAKAHASHI, T., and LEE, C. L.: Liver infarction in mice following injection of antierythrocyte serum. *Fed. Proc., 22*: 545, 1963.

DONIACH, I., and WEINBREN, K.: The development of inclusion bodies in the cells of the rat's liver after partial hepatectomy. *Brit. J. Exp. Path., 33*:499, 1952.

DUNN, T. B.: The importance of differences in morphology in inbred strains. *J. Nat. Cancer Inst., 15*:573, 1954.

EDWARDS, P. R., and BRUNER, D. W.: The occurrence and distribution of salmonella types in the United States. *J. Infect. Dis., 42:*58, 1943.

EDWARDS, P. R., BRUNER, D. W., and MORAN, A. B.: Further studies on the occurrence and distribution of salmonella types in the United States. *J. Infect. Dis., 83:*220, 1948.

FINDLAY, G. M.: Intranuclear bodies in the liver cells of mice. Brit. J. *Exp. Path., 13:*223, 1932.

FRANCIS, EDWARD: Tularemia. *J.A.M.A., 84:*1243, 1925.

GLEDHILL, A. W.: In, *The Problems of Laboratory Animal Disease.* Ed. by R. J. C. Harris. London and New York, Acad. Press, 1962.

GREENE, H. S. N.: Clinical manifestations and pathology of toxemia of pregnancy in the rabbit. *J. Exp. Med., 65:*809, 1937.

GREENE, H. S. N.: Etiological considerations with especial reference to hereditary factors. *J. Exp. Med., 67:*369, 1938.

GRIESEMER, R. A.: Bartonellosis. *J. Nat. Cancer Inst., 20:*949, 1958.

HABERMANN, R. T., and WILLIAMS, F. P.: The identification and control of helminths in laboratory animals. *J. Nat. Cancer Inst., 20:* 979, 1958.

HABERMANN, R. T., and WILLIAMS, F. P.: Salmonellosis in laboratory animals. *J. Nat. Cancer Inst., 20:*933, 1958.

HABERMANN, R. T., WILLIAMS, F. P., and FITE, G. L.: Inclusion bodies associated with viral diseases of man and other animals. *J. Amer. Vet. Med. Ass., 137:*161, 1960.

INNES, J. R. M., WILSON, C., and ROSS, M. A.: Epizootic Salmonella enteritidis infection causing septic pulmonary phlebothrombosis in hamsters. *J. Infect. Dis., 98:*133, 1956.

JANSEN, J.: In, *The Problems of Laboratory Animal Disease,* Ed. by R. J. C. Harris. London and New York, Acad. Press, 1962.

JÉZÉQUEL, A. M., ALBOT, G., and NEZELOF, C.: The clarified cells in parenchymatous hepatitis. Comparative study by optical and electron microscopy, *Int. Congress of Gastroenterology.* Amsterdam, London, and New York, Excerpta Medica Foundation, 1961.

JORDAN, J., and MIRICK, G. S. with the technical assistance of M. G. HUCK: An infectious hepatitis of undetermined origin in mice. I. Description of the disease. *J. Exp. Med., 102:*601, 1955.

LEDUC, E., and WILSON, J. W.: An electron microscopic study of intranuclear inclusions in mouse liver and hepatoma. *J. Biophys. Biochem. Cytol., 6:*427, 1959.

LE MAISTRE, C., and TOMPSETT, R.: The emergence of pseudotuberculosis in rats given cortisone. *J. Exp. Med., 95:*393, 1952.

MACKAY, I. R., and BURNET, F. M.: *Autoimmune Diseases, Pathogenesis, Chemistry and Therapy.* Springfield, Thomas, 1963.

MARCHAL, J.: Infectious ectromelia. A hitherto undescribed virus disease of mice. *J. Path. Bact., 33:713,* 1930.

MORRIS, J. A., McCOWN, J. M., and BLOUNT, P. E.: Ascites and hepatosplenomegaly in mice associated with protozoan-like cytoplasmic structures. *J. Infect. Dis., 98:306,* 1956.

NELSON, J. B.: An intracellular parasite resembling a microsporidian associated with ascites in Swiss mice. *Proc. Soc. Exp. Biol. Med., 109:714,* 1962.

PATERSON, J. S.: In, *The Problems of Laboratory Animal Disease.* Ed. by R. J. C. Harris. London and New York, Acad. Press, 1962.

COHRS, P., JAFFE, R., and MEESSEN, H.: *Pathologie der Laboratoriumstiere,* Vols. I and II. Berlin, Göttingen and Heidelberg, Springer, 1958.

POPPER, H., PARONETTO, F., and BARKA, T.: P.A.S. positive structures of nonglycogenic character in normal and abnormal liver. *Arch. Path., 70:300,* 1960.

POPPER, H., and SCHAFFNER, F.: *Liver: Structure and Function.* New York, Toronto and London, McGraw-Hill, 1957.

POST, J., KLEIN, A., and HOFFMAN, J.: Responses of the liver to injury. Effects of age upon the healing pattern after carbon tetrachloride poisoning. *Arch. Path., 70:314,* 1960.

RUEBNER, B., and BRAMHALL, J. L.: The pathology of experimental virus hepatitis in mice. *Arch. Path., 69:190,* 1960.

RUEBNER, B. H., and MIYAI, K.: The Kupffer cell reaction in murine and human viral hepatitis with particular reference to the origin of acidophilic bodies. *Amer. J. Path., 40:425,* 1962.

SAUNDERS, L. Z.: Tyzzer's disease. *J. Nat. Cancer Inst., 20:893,* 1958.

SAUNDERS, L. Z.: Mouse pox (Infectious Extromelia). *J. Nat. Cancer Inst., 20:875,* 1958.

SAUER, F.: Fasting ketosis in the pregnant guinea pig. *Ann. N. Y. Acad. Sci., 104:787,* 1963.

SCHLICHT, I.: Experimentelle Untersuchungen über die hyalintropfige Eiweisspeicherung der Leber. *Virchow Arch. Path. Anat., 336:342,* 1963.

SHECHMEISTER, I. L., and ADLER, F. L.: Activation of pseudotuberculosis in mice exposed to sublethal total body radiation. *J. Infect. Dis., 92:228,* 1953.

SMETANA, H.: Coccidiosis of the liver in rabbits. III. Experimental study of the histogenesis of coccidiosis of the liver. *Arch. Path., 15:* 516, 1933.

SMITH, H. A., and JONES, T. C.: *Veterinary Pathology.* Philadelphia, Lea, 1961.

STEINER, J. W., and BAGLIO, C. M.: Electron microscopy of the cytoplasm of parenchymal liver cells in α-Naphthyl-isothiocyanate-induced cirrhosis. *Lab. Invest., 12:*765, 1963.

WACHSTEIN, M.: Studies on inclusion bodies. I. Acid fastness of nuclear inclusion bodies that are induced by ingestion of lead and bismuth. *Amer. J. Clin. Path., 19:*608, 1949.

WAGNER, B. M., and BEDELL, L.: Comparative histochemical reactivity of amyloid. *Fed. Proc., 22:*191, 1963.

WESSEL, W.: Elektronenmikroscopische Untersuchungen von intranuclearen Einschlusskörpern. *Virchow Arch. Path. Anat., 331:*314, 1958.

WILSON, G. S., and MILES, A. A.: Topley and Wilson's *Principles of Bacteriology and Immunity.,* Vols. I and II. Baltimore, Williams & Wilkins, 1955.

DISCUSSION

Dr. Jack E. Gray: With respect to the lesions shown in the guinea pig (Fig. 14), you might be interested in some observations we made in guinea pigs. Three were put on an experiment for the development of a new antibiotic. After several injections over a period of a week or two, nearly every guinea pig that was injected with the antibiotic died. This particular antibiotic was one which was effective against gram positive organisms and we eventually came to believe that the guinea pig is a species which is very dependent upon its gram positive flora. An effect on mortality can be demonstrated with other gram positive-effective antibiotics.

The reason I bring this up is that there were a few disseminated focal lesions in the various organs, but the most consistent lesions were pustules in the wall of the gall bladder. These were very prominent subserosal, and had more inflammatory character than the ones you showed. From such lesions a *Pseudomonas* organism was isolated.

This phenomenon of *Pseudomonas* infection is pretty well established in the literature and it is positively established that it produces fatalities in artificially infected guinea pigs because after two weeks one usually loses the whole group, but the control animals are not affected.

Question: The intracytoplasmic inclusion body you showed in the first slide (Fig. 1), could it consist of ceroid?

Dr. Ruebner: I don't think so. It does not fluoresce and is not fat positive in paraffin sections. Therefore it does not have the histochemical reactions of ceroid. Ceroid is also more common in reticuloendothelial cells.

Question: Do you have any understanding of the structure of a mouse liver to explain why they do not develop cirrhosis?

Dr. Ruebner: I have no explanation at all except that it seems to me they regenerate very well. I think it must be a property of the species because it is quite difficult to produce cirrhosis, at least with one injury, and it has been very difficult to produce cirrhosis with even two or three injuries. I think if one injured the liver every week with something like carbon tetrachloride one might be able to produce cirrhosis. My opinion would be that the mouse liver regenerates so well that it is very difficult to make it regenerate abnormally.

Question: I would like to have a term for the unequal nuclear size for aged rats livers. The term I have used has been anisonucleosis.

Dr. Ruebner: I am not sure that term expresses the situation. It seems to me an increase in size rather than variation. It is variation as well, but the increased size impresses me more.

Dr. S. Sternberg: Dr. Ruebner, a number of years ago we had the opportunity of studying a mouse hepatitis virus that Dr. Friend isolated from a leukemic mouse. You mentioned that there are a variety of hepatitis viruses apparently in mice. The interesting thing about this one was that there were also extra-hepatic lesions and in this case in the lymph nodes and other lymphoid tissues we found a conglomeration of lymphocytes in the form of giant cells that had a very strong resemblance to the giant cells that one sees in the prodromal stage of measles. This was the only instance that I know of where such a phenomenon has occurred in an animal.

Dr. Ruebner: The virus which we have studied was isolated at the National Institute for Medical Research in London where it was named M.H.V.$_3$. They isolated another less pathogenic virus which they called M.H.V.$_1$ (Gledhill). They were also struck by giant cell formation, but in their animals it occurred in serosal cells. I have looked for this and have been really disappointed at the infrequency of giant cells in our mice. We have seen extra-hepatic lesions in M.H.V.$_3$ infections. The most impressive of these has been necrosis of lymphoid tissues.

I think there is no doubt that these viruses are closely related. They are apparently antigenically similar, but this is difficult to study because they are not very antigenic. In spite of their close relationship there are differences between these viruses and among these may be the degree of lymphoid involvement and giant cell formation. I think also the liver lesions are not exactly the same. Dr. Walter Jones has been using the Nelson strain, and he considers that the liver lesions are not quite identical with those produced by M.H.V.$_3$.

Question: I would like to ask Dr. Ruebner about the liver lesions that you describe in the mouse, the light hepatic cells and the dark cells. Have you noticed any change in the structure of each individual lobule that you note this in? Obviously this is a spotty sort of thing in the mouse, so that when you look at it in the scanning lens you see what appears to be swirling lobules as against radiating sinusoids. Have you noticed this? This is fairly common in an aging rat and I was wondering whether you had seen this sort of thing in the mouse.

Dr. Ruebner: I haven't noticed a lobular change. In paraffin sections this lesion is not as conspicuous as in material embedded in plastics such as methacrylate or araldite (Fig. 4). In such tissue this change may be quite extensive. Dr. Wilson has suggested that it might be related to sectioning because sometimes almost one half of a lobule is involved. I doubt this because very often individual liver cells are affected to varying extent. It has been said that dark and light liver cells differ in their glycogen content but this is probably not true (Steiner and Baglio).

8

SPONTANEOUS AND INDUCED TUMORS IN THE GUINEA PIG*

HERMAN T. BLUMENTHAL AND JAMES B. ROGERS

INTRODUCTION

Despite the frequent use of the guinea pig as an experimental animal, this species has been utilized relatively infrequently in cancer studies. Prevalent opinion holds that the guinea pig only rarely develops spontaneous tumors, and is also resistant to the experimental induction of neoplasms. This opinion has even given rise to a search for some component of guinea pig serum which might confer a resistance to the development of neoplasms, and indeed there have been several reports (1,5-8) showing that serum of this species contains a factor which inhibits the growth of lymphomas in mice.

By contrast, in a previous report (11) we showed that while the overall incidence of spontaneous tumors in the guinea pig was only 2.4 per cent, the incidence in animals surviving to three years or more was as high as 14.4 per cent. In a second study (2) it was observed that over 50 per cent of two strains of guinea pigs, differing in their susceptibility to the development of spontaneous tumors, developed sarcomas following the injection of methylcholanthrene into the abdominal wall.

In the present report we have reviewed the spectrum of spontaneous tumors which have been reported to date, and have added two more which have occurred since our previous report (11). This brings the number of reported spontaneous tumors to 140. We are also presenting the spectrum of tumors of the guinea pig which occurs following the injection of methylcholanthrene.

*These studies were supported by Research Grant #C-1500, from the National Cancer Institute of the National Institutes of Health, Department of Health, Education and Welfare.

SPONTANEOUS TUMORS IN GUINEA PIGS

The R7 inbred strain of guinea pigs is susceptible to a toxemia of pregnancy, but no spontaneous tumors have been discovered in the examination of approximately 2500 guinea pigs of this strain, although it should be pointed out that the number of females, in particular, surviving to over three years of age is relatively small. On the other hand, the R9 inbred strain does not develop a toxemia of pregnancy, and all of the spontaneous tumors discovered to date have occurred in this strain, always in animals surviving to three years or longer. Approximately 4200 animals of this strain have been examined to date.

The various spontaneous tumors in guinea pigs are shown in Table I. Of the 140 represented, ninety (64 per cent) contained epithelial and forty-four (31 per cent) mesenchymal derivatives; an additional ten (7 per cent) were cases of leukemia. Included in these are four cases which were mixed in that they contained both epithelial and mesenchymal derivitives. On the basis of frequency of organ or structure of origin, there were sixty-five lung tumors, seventeen of soft mesenchymal and skeletal tissues, thirteen of the reticulo-endothelial system, twelve of mammary gland, nine each of the gastro-intestinal tract (including liver and gall bladder) and of the uterus, three of the endocrine glands, three of the ovary, two each of heart and kidney, and single cases involving a variety of other organs or structures.

This tabulation does not include twenty-three cases of an ovarian "tumor" described by Loeb (10) and others (3,4,9). This "tumor" consists of embryonal structures, apparently of parthenogenetic origin, and should not be considered as a true neoplasm, since, as Loeb has pointed out, they have limited duration of life, being destroyed at an early date and replaced by connective tissue. The three cases of ovarian tetratoma listed in Table I were not this type of lesion.

Most of the tumors reported were small and discovered incidentally at autopsy. However, occasionally large tumors were encountered. Three of these, as examples, are shown in Figures 1-3. Figure 1 is of a benign adenomyoma of the uterus, and Figures 2 and 3 the two additional cases found since our first report on spontaneous tumors. The latter two were both lipofibrosarcomas involving the mesentery.

TABLE I

THE DISTRIBUTION OF SPONTANEOUS TUMORS*

Organ	Tumor	Number of Cases	
Bronchus	Papillary adenoma	64	
	Adenocarcinoma	1	(65)
Subcutaneous and Mesentery	Fibrolipoma	2	
	Neurilemmoma	2	
	Fibrosarcoma	7	
	Fibro-liposarcoma	3	
	Neurogenic sarcoma	1	(15)
Reticulo-endothelial	Lymphosarcoma (spleen)	1	
	Lymphosarcoma (lymph nodes)	2	
	Leukemia	10	(13)
Mammary gland	Adenoma and papillary cystadenoma	3	
	Adenocarcinoma (3 in males)	8	
	Lipo-fibrosarcoma	1	(12)
Uterus	Fibro- and leiomyoma	4	
	Adenomyoma	1	
	Fibro- and leiomyosarcoma	3	
	Mesenchymal mixed tumor	1	(9)
Gastro-intestinal	Fibromyoma and lipoma (stomach)	5	
	Liposarcoma (intestine)	1	
	Adenoma (liver)	1	
	Cavernous hemangioma (liver)	1	
	Papilloma (gall bladder)	1	(9)
Ovary	Teratoma	3	(3)
Endocrine	Adenoma (adrenal)	1	
	Adenoma (thyroid)	1	
	Carcinoma (adrenal)	1	(3)
Bone	Osteo- and chondrosarcoma	2	(2)
Heart	Fibro- and round cell sarcoma	2	(2)
Kidney	Osteo- and round cell sarcoma	2	(2)
Skin	Epithelioma adenoides cysticum	1	
Eye	Dermoid of cornea	1	
Brain	Teratoma of pons	1	
Testis	Embryonal carcinoma	1	
Undesignated site	Carcinoma	1	
TOTAL		140	

*References to reports of these tumors can be found in Rogers and Blumenthal, *Cancer Resarch,* 20:191, 1960.

The histological characteristics of spontaneous tumors in our study can be divided into groups. The papillary adenomas of the lung (Fig. 4) consist of numerous papillary structures with a core of loose connective tissue covered by a single layer of cuboidal cells. The papilloma of the gall bladder presents a similar appearance on the surface, but tubular structures occur deeper in the

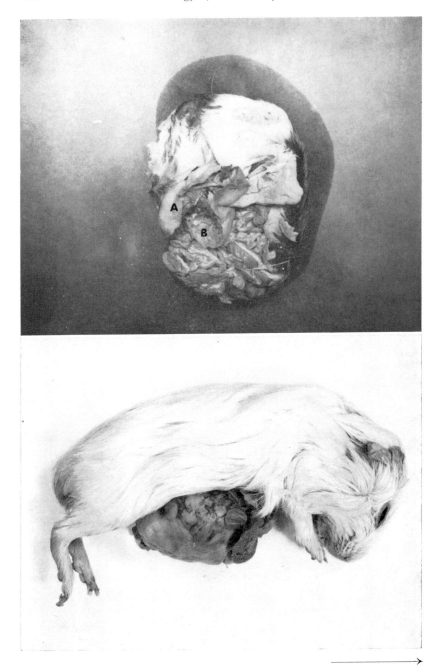

———→

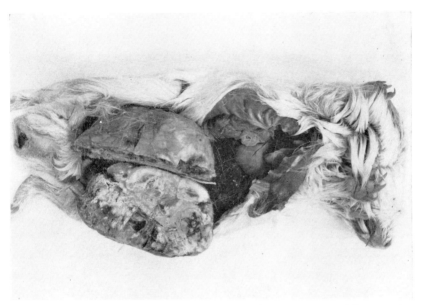

FIGURE 3. Gross specimen of fibroliposarcoma of the mesentery. The anterior wall has been opened, and protruding through it is a large ovoid mass which has been bisected. There are whitish yellow areas of tumor with interspersed dark areas of hemorrhage which can be seen on the cut surface.

tumor (Fig. 5). The only spontaneous malignant tumor with epithelial derivatives was an embryonal carcinoma of the testis (Figs. 6 and 7) which contains small tubular structures, occasional papillary formations, and a stroma of small cells compactly arranged.

The mesenchymal tumors, whether in definitive organs or in the various soft connective tissue structures of the body usually appear as discrete tumors, either gray or yellow, depending on the

FIGURE 1. Gross specimen of fibrosarcoma of the uterus. The nodule has been bisected and arranged so that one-half shows the intact serosal surface (A) and the other half the cut surface of yellow-gray tumor with small dark foci of hemorrhage (B).

FIGURE 2. Gross specimen of fibroliposarcoma of the mesentery. The anterior abdominal wall has been opened, and protruding through the incision is a yellow gray mass with projections between coils of intestine producing a matted yellow lobulated mass of the gut.

proportion of fat present. The leiomyomatous tumors have typical bundles of elongated strap-like cells (Fig. 8). The fibrous tumors, when benign, have areas of fibrocollagenous tissue replacing cellular structures, while if malignant, they are quite cellular, with hyperchromatic, often pleomorphic nuclei (Fig. 9). Their compactness varies, depending upon the quantity of interstitial fluid. Figure 10 shows a myxosarcoma of the uterus with a particularly loose arrangement of neoplastic cells, and a considerable area occupied by interstitial fluid. Mixed tumors are occasionally en-

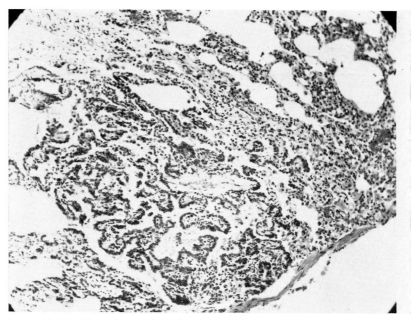

FIGURE 4. Papillary bronchial adenoma. Hematoxylin-eosin stain; mag. approx. X100. The tumor is composed of numerous papillary fronds covered by cuboidal epithelium. Along the margins are pulmonary alveoli.

⟶

FIGURE 5. Papilloma of the gall bladder. Hematoxylin-eosin stain; mag. approx. X100. The tumor occupies the left half of the figure showing a papillary glandular arrangement of epithelial structures, protruding deep into the wall.

FIGURE 6. Embryonal carcinoma of the testis. Hematoxylin-eosin stain; mag. approx. X100. There are numerous glands separated by compactly arranged small cells with scanty cytoplasm.

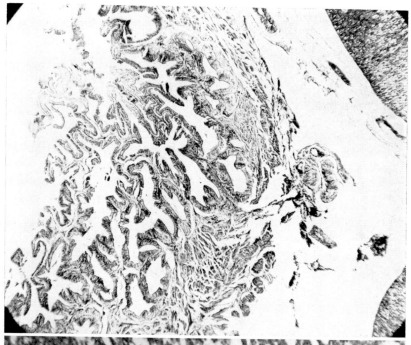

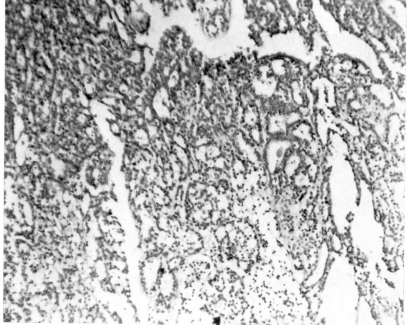

countered, especially in the uterus, containing both epithelial and mesenchymal elements. (Fig. 11).

INDUCED TUMORS IN GUINEA PIGS

Of 735 animals injected with methylcholanthrene, 421 (57 per cent) developed tumors. Certain general aspects of the induction of such tumors in guinea pigs are noteworthy. Both strains and both sexes were about equally susceptible to the development of tumors following the subcutaneous or intramuscular injection of methylcholanthrene. Tumors could be produced within a relatively wide range of dosage, varying from one to ten mg. per injection, usually two to three injections spaced at fifteen-day intervals. In general, however, the tumors appeared to grow more rapidly in animals receiving larger doses, and with this more rapid growth there was, generally, a shortening of the survival time. Age, in some instances, appeared to constitute an appreciable factor, since there was a trend toward a diminishing frequency of tumor formation with advancing age.

All of the tumors were of mesenchymal orgin; no induced carcinomas were found. Most of the small tumors lay within the musculature of the abdominal wall (Fig. 12), although, in some instances they occupied both the subcutaneous connective tissue and muscle. Tumors consisting of only a single tissue component were rare, whereas tumors containing two or more mesenchymal components were common. The frequency of occurrence of various histological components are shown in Table II, and examples of these various histological types are illustrated in Figures 13-23.

Areas having whorl formation and palisading of nuclei and cells were considered neurogenic in origin (Fig. 13). Foci showing lamellar formation were considered of smooth muscle origin (Fig.

---------------→

FIGURE 7. Same tumor as in preceding figure. Hematoxylin-eosin stain; mag. Approx. X100. Papillary structures are seen consisting of central fibrous cores covered by hyperchromatic cuboidal epithelium.

FIGURE 8. Leiomyosarcoma of the uterus. Hematoxylin-eosin stain; mag. approx. X100. There are bundles of smooth muscle coursing in several directions. Muscle fibers are compactly arranged, with little stromal connective tissue.

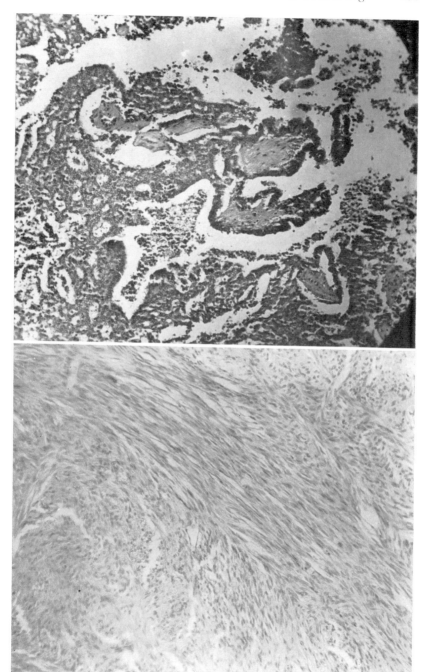

TABLE II
FREQUENCY OF VARIOUS HISTOLOGICAL COMPONENTS IN INDUCED TUMORS

Histological Component	Number	Per Cent
Neurogenic	7	2
Leiomyomatous	145	34
Fibroblastic	78	18
Spindle cell	60	14
Reticulum cell	271	64
Giant cell	213	50
Lipoblastic	178	42
Mesenchymal	117	28
Chondroblastic	25	6
Osteogenic	44	10
Hemangioblastic	7	2
Total animals with tumor	421	

14). Sites containing elongated fusiform fibroblastic cells were considered fibrosarcoma (Fig. 15) ; these were often admixed with small ovoid spindle cells (Fig. 16). In other areas of tumors, plump compactly arranged cells predominated, and these were considered as foci of spindle-cell sarcoma. Compactly arranged ovoid cells almost resembling lymphoma were designated as reticulum cell sarcoma (Fig. 17) and reticulum fibers could be demonstrated in such areas by the use of Wilder's silver bath impregnation technique. When multinucleated tumor giant cells were prominent in certain fields they were classified as areas of giant cell sarcoma (Fig. 18), and when neoplastic cells containing large vacuoles were seen they were considered liposarcomatous in character (Fig. 19). The latter also gave positive staining with oil red 0 in selected cases. Some tumors contained foci of loosely arranged stellate cells in a basophilic matrix; these were considered to be undifferentiated primitive mesenchymal cells and were classified as mesenchymal sarcomas (Fig. 20). Still other areas contained neoplastic cartilage cells (Fig. 21), and in some places neoplastic

———————————————————————→

FIGURE 9. Fibrosarcoma of the uterus. Hematoxylin-eosin stain; mag. approx. X250. There are compactly arranged spindle cells with hyperchromatic nuclei varying somewhat in size and shape.

FIGURE 10. Myxosarcoma of the uterus. Hematoxylin-eosin stain; mag. approx. X100. The tumor is composed of loosely arranged stellate cells with a few remaining strands of muscle along the margins.

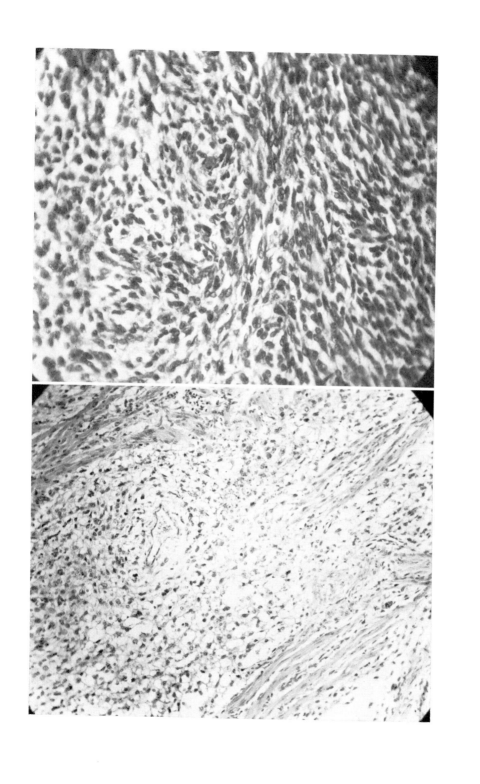

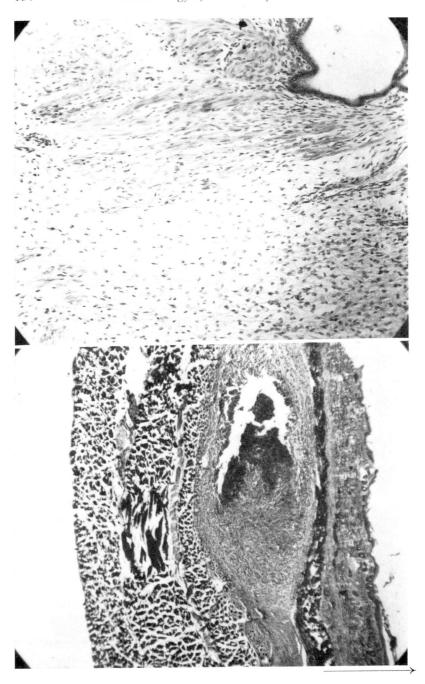

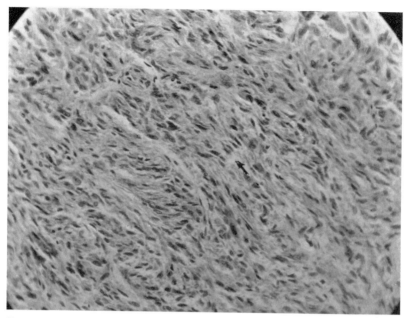

FIGURE 13. Section of an induced tumor with an area appearing to be neurogenic in origin. Hematoxylin-eosin stain; mag. approx. X250. Cells are arranged in whorl-like mass, and there is palisading of nuclei.

osteoid tissue (Fig. 22) was encountered. Some tumors contained prominent vascular components in which the endothelial cells had neoplastic characteristics. Such sites were considered hemangiosarcoma (Fig. 23).

About one-fifth of the guinea pigs which developed tumors at the site of injection of methylcholanthrene had evidence of metastases. The distribution by organ frequency is shown in Table III, with the order of frequency being lung, liver, spleen, adrenal,

FIGURE 11. Mesenchymal mixed tumor of the uterus. Hematoxylin-eosin stain; mag. approx. X100. The connective tissue element of the tumor is similar to that in the preceding figure. A cystic gland is seen along the upper right margin.

FIGURE 12. Small subcutaneous tumor produced by methylcholanthrene injection. Hematoxylin-eosin stain; mag. approx. X40. A discrete ovoid tumor is seen separating dermis from underlying abdominal musculature. Epidermis is along right margin.

heart and kidney. In addition one guinea pig showed peritoneal seeding of tumor, and another metastasis to the tunica of the right testis.

TABLE III
FREQUENCY AND DISTRIBUTION OF METASTASES

Organ	Number	Per Cent
Lung	62	82
Liver	9	12
Spleen	7	9
Adrenal	7	9
Heart	5	7
Kidney	5	7
Miscellaneous	2	3
Total Cases	76	18

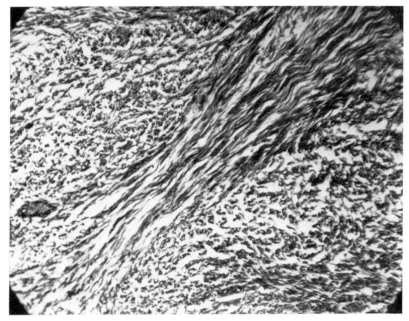

FIGURE 14. Induced leiomyosarcoma. Hematoxylin-eosin stain; mag. approx. X250. Section again shows muscle bundles coursing in various directions.

FIGURE 15. Induced fibrosarcoma. Hematoxylin-eosin stain; mag. approx. X250. Section shows elongated, closely packed cells.

FIGURE 16. Mixed fibrosarcoma. Hematoxylin-eosin stain; mag. approx. X100. Section shows a mixture of elongated fusiform and small round cells.

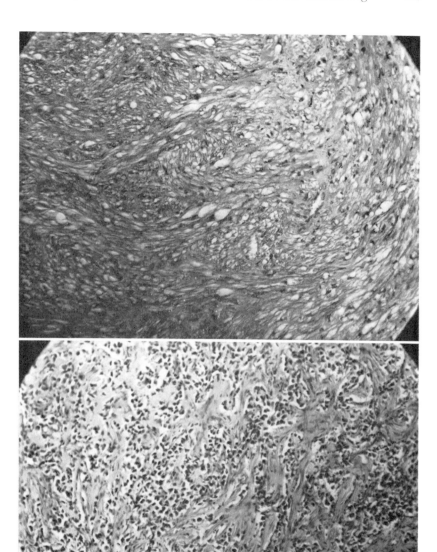

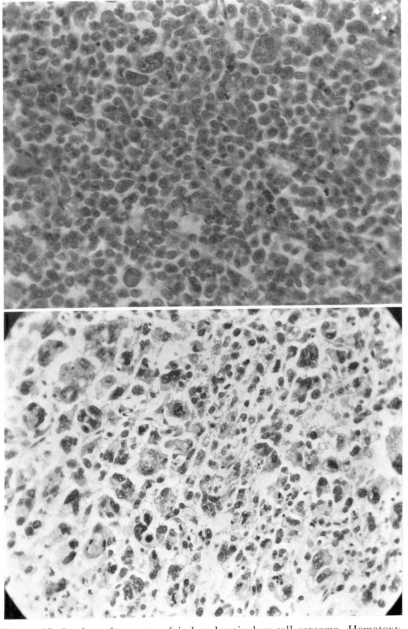

Figure 17. Section of an area of induced reticulum-cell sarcoma. Hematoxylin-eosin stain; mag. approx. X450. Section shows round and ovoid cells resembling atypical lymphocytes. Reticulum fibers could be demonstrated with the silver impregnation technique.

Figure 18. Section of an area of induced giant-cell sarcoma. Hematoxylineosin stain; mag. approx. X500. Note abundance of bizarre giant cells.

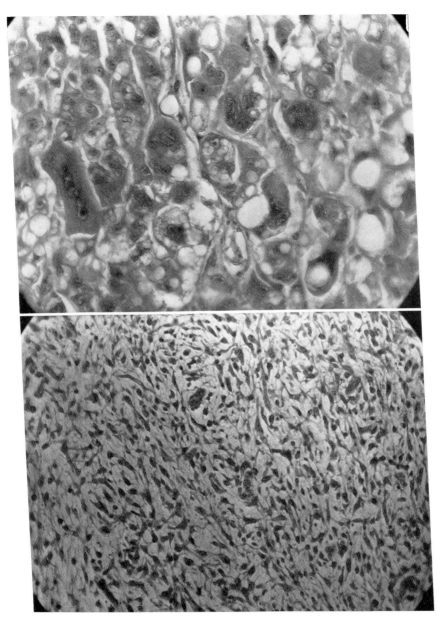

FIGURE 19. Section of an area of induced liposarcoma. Hematoxylin-eosin stain; mag. approx. X500. Note large fat vacuoles in markedly enlarged bizarre tumor cells.

FIGURE 20. Section of an area of induced mesenchymal sarcoma. Hematoxylin-eosin stain; mag. approx. X450. The area is composed of loosely arranged stellate cells resembling embryonal mesenchyme. Intercellular spaces contain a basophilic mucoid material.

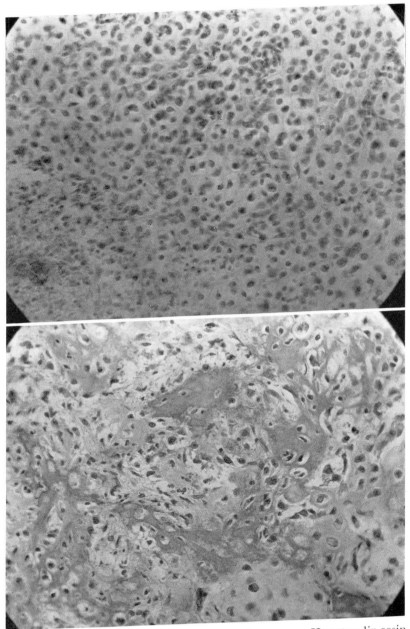

FIGURE 21. Section of an area of induced chondrosarcoma. Hematoxylin-eosin stain; mag. approx. X450. The whole field is occupied by atypical chondroblasts.

FIGURE 22. Section of an area of induced osteogenic sarcoma. Hematoxylin-eosin; mag. approx. X450. Note acellular osteoid surrounded by osteoblastic cells.

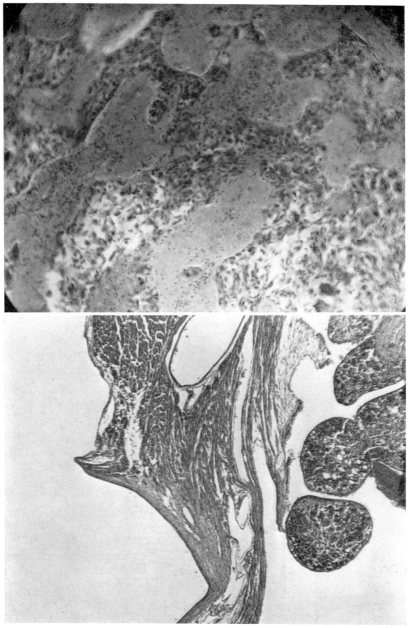

FIGURE 23. Section of an area of induced hemangiosarcoma. Hematoxylin-eosin; mag. approx. X450. Note large spaces filled with blood surrounded by compactly arranged fusiform cells.

FIGURE 24. Section of atrium of heart with tumor emboli in the atrial cavity. Hematoxylin-eosin stain; mag. approx. X45. Round nodules along the right margin are tumor emboli.

Metastases evidently occurred primarily via the blood stream. Tumor cells were found within the atrial cavities of the heart and in pulmonary arteries (Figs. 24 and 25), as well as in the parenchyma of various organs, some of which are illustrated in Figures 26-28. While tumor of the atrial cavities was actually observed in only five cases with metastasis, these represent instances of grossly obvious tumor; it is likely that there were additional instances of this phenomenon judging from the frequency of tumor in pulmonary arteries (sixty-two cases).

DISCUSSION AND CONCLUSION

These observations indicate that the guinea pig is a useful animal for cancer research. It develops spontaneous tumors and is readily susceptible to the induction of experimental neoplasms. A complete bibliography of references to reports dealing with this subject and covering the period from 1908 to 1962 are included in our previous report (11). The fact that spontaneous tumors do not develop in guinea pigs under the age of three years indicates that an aging factor is involved in the genesis of such neoplasms. A particular advantage in the use of the guinea pig for the induction of experimental tumors is the frequency of development of metastases. This phenomenon is often absent in induced tumors in other species, and is a particularly important consideration in the testing of possible therapeutic agents.

REFERENCES

1. AINIS, H., KURTZ, H. M., KRAMER, P. I., WEINER, H. E., RYAN, R. M., and JAMESON, R.: In vivo and in vitro studies of the action of guinea pig serum against the ascites form of the Murphy-Sturm lymphosarcoma. *Cancer Res., 18:*1309-1313, 1958.
2. BLUMENTHAL, H. T., and ROGERS, J. B.: Studies of guinea pig tum-

————————————————————————————————→

FIGURE 25. Section of lung with tumor embolus. Hematoxylin-eosin stain; mag. approx. X100. In the center is a large pulmonary artery filled with tumor embolus.

FIGURE 26. Section of lung with subpleural metastasis. Hematoxylin-eosin stain; mag. approx. X45. The metastases lies in a cup-like depression along the right margin.

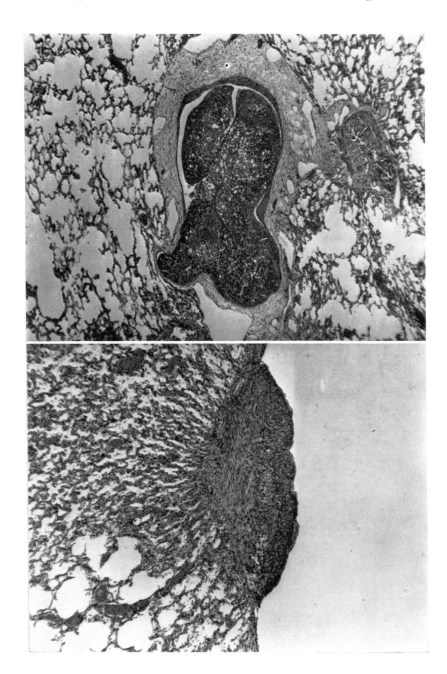

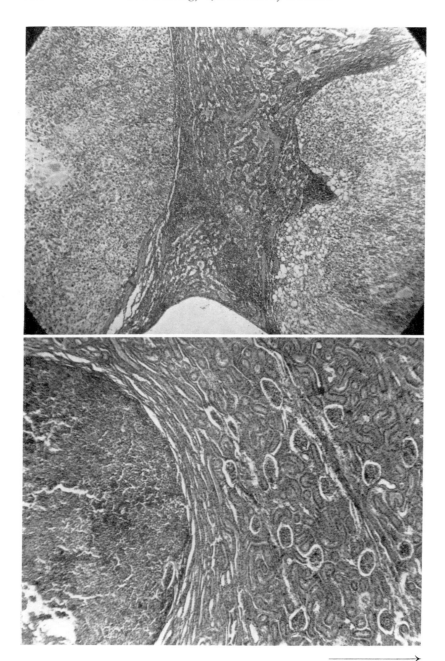

ors. II. The induction of malignant tumors in guinea pigs by methylcholanthrene. *Cancer Res., 22:*1155-1162, 1962.

3. BRANCA, A.: L'ovocyte atrésique et son involution. *Arch. Biol.,* 324-440, 1925-26.

4. COURRIER, R., and OBERLING, C.: Parthénogénèse spontanée dans l'ovaire du cobaye. *Bull. Soc. Anatomique* (Paris), *93:*724-730, 1923.

5. HERBUT, P. A.: Studies on the properdin system in transplantable cancer. *Trans. Coll. Physicians Phila., 26:*129-133, 1939.

6. HERBUT, P. A., KRAEMER, W. H., MCKEON, P. A., and TAYLOR, R. C.: The effect of serums from tumor susceptible and non-susceptible guinea pigs on lymphosarcoma 6C₃HED in C₃H mice. *Amer. J. Path., 38:*387-391, 1961.

7. HERBUT, P. A., KRAEMER, W. H., and PILLEMER, I.: The effects of components of guinea pig serum on lymphosarcoma 6C₃HED in C₃H mice. *Blood, 13:*733-739, 1938.

8. KIDD, J. G.: Regression of transplanted lymphomas in vivo by means of normal guinea pig serum. I. Course of transplanted cancer of various kinds in mice and rats given guinea pig serum, horse serum or rabbit serum. II. Studies on the nature of the active serum constituent; histological mechanism of the regression; tests for effects of guinea pig serum on lymphoma cells in vitro. Discussion. *J. Exp. Med., 98:*565-606, 1953.

9. LELIÈVRE, P. A., and CORSY, F.: Le parthénogénèse dans l'ovaire des mammifères et le problème de l'origine des embryones. *Bull. Ass. Franc. Cancer, 16:*711-743, 1927.

10. LOEB, L.: The parthenogenetic development of eggs in the ovary of the guinea pig. *Arch. Path., 31:*702-705, 1932.

11. ROGERS, J. B., and BLUMENTHAL, H. T.: Studies of guinea pig tumors. I. Report of fourteen spontaneous guinea pig tumors, with a review of the literature. *Cancer Res., 20:*191-197, 1960.

FIGURE 27. Section showing metastases to the spleen. Hematoxylin-eosin stain; mag. approx. X45. The band of tissue in the center is composed of splenic sinusoids. Large tumor nodules are seen on both sides of the splenic tissue.

FIGURE 28. Section showing metastasis to the kidney. Hematoxylin-eosin stain; mag. approx. X45. A sharply circumscribed tumor nodule is present along the left margin.

DISCUSSION

Question: I noticed in your section on induced tumors and metastasis you didn't have brain or lymph node listed. Did you find many in these areas?

Also, did you examine the brain in searching for spontaneous tumors?

Dr. Blumenthal: We didn't find any tumors in brain though they were specifically looked for.

I must say, however, that there wasn't any systematic exploration of lymph nodes, so we didn't report anything concerning lymph node metastases.

Dr. Harry S. N. Greene: I have three questions I would like to ask:

First, do the spontaneous guinea pig tumors metastasize?

Secondly, are they transplantable to normal guinea pigs?

And, third, what was the vehicle used for the methylcholanthrene in the tumor induction experiments? I tried everlastingly to produce tumors in guinea pigs using methylcholanthrene but was never successful and then when I read the literature and found that generally sesame oil was used I tried sesame oil alone and was successful in producing the same sarcomas in guinea pigs with sesame oil alone without methylcholanthrene. This is rather important because sesame oil is used considerably in human therapeutics, particularly as a vehicle for penicillin. I have now seen three cases in adult women who received penicillin in sesame oil who subsequently developed the same liposarcomas as one finds in guinea pigs.

Dr. Blumenthal: To answer the third question first, we did use sesame oil as a vehicle. There was a group of some fifty guinea pigs injected with sesame oil alone and we did not get any tumors from them. Now, this, of course, is no proof that one can't get tumors from sesame oil alone.

Dr. Greene: It takes a year or two.

Dr. Blumenthal: I see, and it may very well be that with the methylcholanthrene the tumors develop sooner and we simply didn't observe them long enough. This is quite possible.

What were the other two questions?

Dr. Greene: Are these spontaneous tumors or not?

Dr. Blumenthal: These are spontaneous tumors.

Dr. Greene: Are they transplantable to normal guinea pigs? And I should like to ask what were the criteria used in calling these tumors adenocarcinoma?

Dr. Blumenthal: The carcinomas were called that, the sarcomas were called that, solely on histological criteria.

Dr. Greene: Do you think that is fair?

Dr. Blumenthal: Well, I think up to a point it is fair. I think that they are undoubtedly very much like human tumors where one can be reasonably certain of malignancy on cytological grounds. In addition, many of these tumors metastasized.

Dr. Joseph Tabachwick: We tried to induce spindle cell sarcomas in guinea pigs by radiation or croton oil and urethane, as has been done for rats, without much success. We did obtain two fibrosarcomas from about 200 animals but it may be that only a few of the animals lived long enough.

How do you keep your animals alive longer than a year or two? Our guinea pigs don't seem to live so long.

Dr. Blumenthal: That is Dr. Roger's department. Dr. Roger's guinea pig colonies are rather famous for their longevity. This is due to a combination of inbreeding guinea pigs in particular for longevity, and the unusual care that he gives them. I think it is important in studying tumors in guinea pigs that one does have guinea pigs in excess of three years, at least if you are going to look for spontaneous tumors. This seems to have been everybody's experience.

Chairman: Do you mind if I ask Dr. Greene a question with regard to the sesame oil?

I believe that it is also used in cooking. I know in Chinese cooking it is used and I seem to recollect it is added to certain prepared food products. Does the Food and Drug Administration have any opinion in that regard, in regard to the use of sesame oil?

Dr. Greene: I don't know. I am not in the Food and Drug Administration. If I was, sesame oil would not be used.

Question: I would like to ask: was the 14 per cent incidence after three years for all strains of guinea pigs, or only for the two specific ones?

Dr. Blumenthal: This was for all of the guinea pigs, so that actually if we took only the susceptible group the percentage would have been even higher.

Question: What age was the guinea pig that you used for the tumor induction? Is there any difference in tumor growth among the various ages that you used?

Dr. Blumenthal: We use guinea pigs of all ages for the induction of tumors. They can readily be induced in guinea pigs of all ages irrespective of strain. The interesting thing, however, is that in young guinea pigs tumors grow much faster and metastasize more readily than in old guinea pigs. Thus if one measures the survival time from the time at which a tumor appears until the death of the animal, the survival time is much shorter in young animals than in older animals. This has some analogy in human cancer.

Question: I noticed in the table the relatively high incidence of metastases to liver and lung. This corresponds to other animals and to humans, but on the other hand, I think 9 per cent of the animals had metastases to the spleen, which is a little unusual. Is the spleen different in this animal with regard to lymphatic drainage or other structures?

Dr. Blumenthal: I am not aware of any differences.

Dr. H. S. N. Greene: May I comment on that question? The spleen of most mammals contains a capsule different from the capsule of the spleen in man. The capsule in man is a fibromuscular one, and I suspect the capsule of an animal is not fibromuscular at all. Thus I suspect the spleen in man, like the heart, is continually in a sort of beating rhythm and therefore metastases do not occur in man.

Question: In regard to your methylcholanthrene administration, did you use any other routes for your induced tumors other than into the abdominal wall?

Dr. Blumenthal: No, that was the only route. This is probably why we didn't have any epithelial tumors, because in all likelihood there was very little methylcholanthrene that came in contact with the epidermis.

Question: What is the induction time in your induced tumors from the injection until the tumor appears?

Dr. Blumenthal: As I indicated, one variable is the age of the animal. Another variable is dosage. There was a considerable range of dosage given to produce tumors in guinea pigs. This ranged from, I think it was, one milligram up to ten. The larger dose would shorten the induction time so that this depends on several variables in the experiment.

I don't know that I can tell you offhand what the shortest induction time was. I don't recall it.

Question: Did you induce any skin tumors?

Dr. Blumenthal: No, we didn't. We didn't have any induced epithelial tumors.

9

SPONTANEOUS LESIONS OF
THE HAMSTER*

ALFRED H. HANDLER

T HE Syrian golden hamster, *Mesocricetus auratus,* is relatively
new to medical research, and thus there is a paucity of information
concerning the pathology of this rodent. An investigation into the
history of the use of hamsters for experimental purposes revealed
that all hamsters currently being raised domestically are descended
from one female and her litter discovered by Israel Aharoni, Cura-
tor of the Zoological Museum, Hebrew University in Jerusalem,
in 1930. The discovery was made in the dry plateau country of
Syria near the city of Allepo. Hamsters were used for several years
in laboratories in Jerusalem mainly in leprosy research before
being shipped to England and ultimately to the United States.
The first hamsters were imported to the United States in 1938
by a United States Public Health Service Station in Louisiana
(59). The majority of Syrian hamsters presently being used in
the United States are descended from this single importation.
Hamsters breed prolifically under laboratory conditions and make
excellent research animals particularly in such areas as vascular
physiology, tissue transplantation, endocrinology, oncology and
oral pathology. Additionally, they are known to be susceptible to
certain pathogenic viruses; such as, poliomyelitis, foot-and-mouth
disease, mumps, influenza, West Nile virus disease, psittacosis and
others (3) including several oncogenic viruses (36); such as,
mouse parotid tumor (polyoma) virus (4A), simian (SV 40)
virus (3A) and human adenovirus (15A).

The original observation that the cheek pouch of the hamster
accepts heterologously transplanted neoplastic tissues, but rejects

*Some of the observations reported herein were made in research supported in
part by Grant C-6516 from the National Cancer Institute, Public Health Service,
Bethesda, Maryland.

adult normal tissues (42, 44), ultimately led to the demonstration, through quantitative titration of cell lines in cheek pouches (45), that a biological difference exists between tissue culture cell lines derived from malignant and non-malignant sources. This demonstration was of interest since studies *in vitro* had failed to reveal significant biochemical or morphological differences between cells derived from normal and from neoplastic tissues (14).

Hamsters are resistant to the toxic effect of colchicine (7, 64), an alkaloid which possesses the ability of arresting cell division at metaphase. Only partial mitotic arrest of bone marrow cells may be observed in hamsters after administration of very high doses of colchicine, 2.4 - 7.2 mg./kg., (7). In contrast, hamsters are as sensitive as other laboratory animals to the effect of other drugs, like vinblastine, which cause metaphase arrest of dividing cells (7).

NEOPLASIA

Gye and Foulds (38) noted in 1939 the occurrence of a spontaneous spindle-cell sarcoma and a melanoma in hamsters, and judged from private communications that spontaneous tumors were not rare. Following this note, however, it was not until 1945 that Ashbel (2) reported that during a period of seven years, thirteen spontaneous tumors were observed in one thousand hamsters examined. These included two polymorphic sarcomas, one carcinoma of the pancreas and ten adrenal cortical hypernephromas. All these tumors were transplantable and metastasized to distant organs. There were no further reports of spontaneous tumors in hamsters until 1952 when Crabb and Kelsall (8) observed a pigmented basal-cell carcinoma, which was transplantable and metastasized. Crabb and Kelsall (9) two years later described a myxosarcoma which arose spontaneously in a male hamster in an inbred colony in 1950. This tumor had been previously noted by Dunham and Stewart in 1953 (12). In the same year, Godglück (30) described a myxofibroma in the spleen of a two-year-old hamster, and Busch (6) noted the first known spontaneous cheek pouch tumor, a transplantable polymorphocellular sarcoma.

Homburger *et al.* (49) observed a leiomyosarcoma in a male hamster. The tumor may have originated spontaneously or may have had some relationship to the subcutaneous implantation of a cholesterol pellet eight months before the tumor was observed.

TABLE I
SUMMARY OF TUMOR TYPES OCCURRING SPONTANEOUSLY IN HAMSTERS* (FORTNER)**

1. *Gastrointestinal Tract*
   Keratotic papilloma
   Adenomatous polyp
   Adenomatous polyp with
      in situ ca.
   Adenocarcinoma
   Leiomyosarcoma

2. *Pancreas*

   Adenoma
   Adenomatous polyp
   Adenocarcinoma
   Cystadenoma

3. *Liver and Biliary Tract*

   In situ carcinoma
   Adenocarcinoma
   Hepatocellular ca.
   Polypoid hyperplasia
   Adenomatous polyp
   Angiosarcoma
   Hemangioma

4. *Lung*
   Adenocarcinoma
   Bronchogenic
      adenocarcinoma

5. *Endocrine*
   Adrenal cortical adenoma
   Adrenal cortical carcinoma
   Thyroid adenoma
   Thyroid adenocarcinoma
   Parathyroid adenoma
   Islet-cell adenoma
   Islet-cell carcinoma
   Ovarian thecoma

6. *Genitourinary Tract*
   Kidney adenocarcinoma
   Prostate adenocarcinoma
   Cowper's gland cystadenocarcinoma
   Uterine endometrial polyp, leiomyoma,
      leiomyosarcoma and adenocarcinoma
   Vaginal keratotic papilloma

7. Melanoma

8. Lymphosarcoma and plasmacytoma

9. Myosarcoma

10. Mesothelioma

11. Undetermined type cancer

Hamster Source: Lakeview Hamster Colony, Newfield, N. J.
*Animal Survival: From 185 to 1,024 days.
**From Fortner, J. G.: *Cancer Research, 21*:1491-1498, 1961.

A large number and spectrum of spontaneous tumors were reported by Fortner *et al.* (16-22). In Table I are summarized the tumor types which they observed. Fortner (17) demonstrated that most of the spontaneous tumors in hamsters arose in the gastrointestinal tract and adrenal cortex. He pointed out that while melanomas of the skin, renal tumors, adenocarcinomas of the lung, tumors of the genital and reticuloendothelial system and a variety of other neoplasms were not infrequent, he had not seen testicular tumors nor squamous cell carcinomas of the skin, lung, bladder, uterine cervix and forestomach. A greater number of spontaneous neoplasms was found in males than in females. The ratio of benign to malignant tumors in both males and females was about 2:1. Fortner also noted that multiple primary tumors may originate in a single animal. Some of the hamsters were found to have as many as four different types of primary tumor. It was suggested that the causative factor for the various spontaneous tumors could be due to an abnormality in the endocrine system. Fortner based this hypothesis on the fact that many of the tumors were of endocrine origin, the types which usually occur during "hormonal" inbalance. Of interest in connection with non-endocrine primary tumors was the observation by Kirkman (56) that tumors of the kidney in hamsters could be induced with estrogens. These renal tumors acted like many forms of endocrine tumors. Fortner *et al.* (19) demonstrated thyroid follicular carcinomas, benign tumors and hyperplasia of the thyroid gland in hamsters fed a diet deficient in iodine. Metastatic cancer of the thyroid was observed only in female hamsters.

The largest number of tumors in hamsters aside from those observed by Fortner and colleagues were reported by Kirkman (57). The types of tumors which were described are summarized in Table II. Ages ranged from newborn to 1,085 days. The incidence of spontaneous tumors was 11.3 per cent or 814 out of 7,200 autopsied hamsters. Kirkman indicated that the incidence

TABLE II
SUMMARY OF TUMOR TYPES OCCURRING SPONTANEOUSLY[1] IN HAMSTERS* (KIRKMAN) **

ADENOMA
    adrenal cortex, thyroid, testicle, parathyroid, pancreas, lung, epididymus, adrenal medulla, exorbital lacrimal gland, duodenum, cheek pouch, thymus
ADENOCARCINOMA
    adrenal cortex, thyroid, basal cell, salivary gland, pancreas, lung, uterus
SARCOMA
    reticulum cell, rhabdomyosarcoma, liposarcoma, fibrosarcoma, leiomyosarcoma
MISCELLANEOUS TUMORS
    hemangioma of spleen, cholangioma, thecoma, synovioma, plasmocytoma, chondroma, neurofibroma, hard fibroma, ganglioneuroma, blue nevi, malignant hepatoma, melanoma, carcinoma of uterus, seminoma, lymphatic leukemia

Hamster Source: Hamster Colony, Anatomy Department Stanford University. Report based on 7,200 autopsied hamsters.

*Animal Survival: Newborn to 1,085 days
**From Kirkman, H.: *Stanford Medical Bulletin*, *20*:163, 1962
[1]See text.

of spontaneous tumors in his studies fell far short of that reported by Fortner (over 60 per cent). If adrenal cortical adenomas (550), many of which were small and detected only by microscopic observation, were deleted, then the incidence was reduced to 3.7 per cent. In addition to the tumors summarized in Table II, Ruffalo and Kirkman (58) recently described two spontaneous, giant cell tumors of tendon sheath. In a personal communication, Kirkman noted that as far as is known these are the only such neoplasms described outside the human species. Greene (32) described a malignant melanoma which occurred in the pigmented spot of the right flank of a two and one-half-year-old male hamster. It appeared as a black rounded mass 1.5 cm. in diameter. Both auxiliary and inguinal nodes were involved. This melanoma has a propensity for amelanotic alteration and sarcomatous transformation after homologous transplantation (for other tumors see Table III, 33). This melanoma and those reported by Fortner and Allen (18) metastasized diffusely after transplantation. Habermann (10A) noted a solitary cystic adenocarcinoma of the mammary gland in an untreated hamster. Greene and Harvey (34) found a lymphoblastic lymphoma which originated in the retroperitoneal space of a two-year-old hamster. We have observed a lymphosarcoma and a reticulum cell sarcoma which arose spontaneously in Albino Syrian hamsters (43). Brindley and Banfield (5) described a spontaneous reticulum-cell sarcoma which appeared on the upper lip of a 732-day-old male hamster. There were no metastases in this animal. These investigators considered this tumor as "contagious" when they demonstrated that a large percentage of normal hamsters placed either in the same cage or in a cage separated only by a screen from the animals inoculated with this reticulum-cell sarcoma, developed laryngeal tumors or systemic tumors with or without laryngeal involvement. Fresh tumor fed to hamsters caused the same results. The tumor has not however, been transmissible with cell-free filtrates. Friedell et al. (27) observed a spontaneous myxofibrosarcoma in the membranous part of the left cheek pouch of an eight-nine-month-old female hamster. This was only the second description of a spontaneous tumor occurring in the hamster cheek pouch. DellaPorta (1A) observed eight tumors in control hamsters used in an investigation on tumor induction with methylcholanthrene. Sherman *et al.* (70) found a spontaneous undifferentiated carcinoma in the right anterolateral cervical triangle of a male hamster. This tumor was probably of salivary gland origin.

Garcia *et al.* (29), Frenkel (25), Russfield (11A), Shubik *et al.* (12A), Tomatis *et al.* (13A), and Dunham and Herrold (2A) noted in some hamsters tumors which occurred without any apparent relationship to treatment with carcinogens and were thus considered to have arisen spontaneously. In a personal communication Toolan (14A) indicated that she had observed twenty-three spontaneous tumors in over several thousand hamsters autopsied.

It is noteworthy, that while Fortner and colleagues and Kirkman have demonstrated large numbers and varieties of spontaneous neoplasms in hamsters (Table I and II), there had been a lesser number of spontaneous tumors reported by all other investigators using hamsters since 1939, (Table III). The reason may lie in the fact that Fortner and Kirkman have observed more hamsters for longer periods or else the reason for the discrepancy may be attributed to some as yet unknown factor in the laboratory or in the constitution of the hamster itself.

PARASITIC, BACTERIAL, FUNGAL AND VIRAL LESIONS

External parasites are known to cause or transmit skin lesions and a variety of inflammatory disorders as well as parasitic and bacterial diseases in laboratory animals (39). Some species of lice, fleas, mites, and bedbugs which are common to mice and rats, and cause alopecia and dermatitis by biting, sucking, or burrowing have also been observed in hamsters (4, 66).

Internal parasites, found in other rodents, are also involved in the causation and transmission of disease in hamsters. Habermann *et al.* (41) noted that a heavy infestation of the cestode, *Hymenolepis diminuta* (Rudolphi, 1819), Figure 1, caused marked catarrhal enteritis in hamsters. *Hymenolepis diminuta* infestation was also observed in our laboratories in hamsters purchased from several commercial breeders. The enteritis was either acute, as shown in Figure 2 in an isolated section of intestine, or chronic and produced both gastroenteritis and enterocolitis. *Hymenolepis nana*, the dwarf tapeworm, Figure 3, has also been isolated from hamsters (73). Soave (71) found a heavy infestation of this parasite in a shipment of twenty-five hamsters in which all died from intestinal impaction and obstruction. *S. enteriditis* and *S. typhimurium* have been isolated from hamsters. In 1958, Habermann and Williams (40) reported *S. enteriditis* infestation in the ham-

TABLE III
NUMBER AND TYPES OF SPONTANEOUS TUMORS* REPORTED IN HAMSTERS

Gye and Foulds	1939	2	Spindle Cell Sarcoma
			Melanoma
Ashbel	1945	13	Polymorphic Sarcoma (2)
			Carcinoma of Pancreas (1)
			Adrenal Cortical
			Hypernephroma (10)
Crabb and Kelsall	1952	1	Basal Cell Carcinoma
Godgluck	1953	1	Myxofibroma
Busch	1953	1	Polymorphocellular Sarcoma
Crabb and Kelsall	1954	1	Myxosarcoma
Homburger *et al.*	1957	1	Leiomyosarcoma
Greene[1]	1958	1	Melanoma
Habermann	—	1	Adenocarcinoma of Mammary Gland
Greene and Harvey	1960	1	Lymphoblastic Lymphoma
Handler *et al.*	1960	2	Lymphosarcoma
			Reticulum Cell Sarcoma
Friedell *et al.*	1960	1	Myxofibrosarcoma
Brindley and Banfield	1961	1	Reticulum Cell Sarcoma
DellaPorta	1961	8	Squamus Cell Papilloma of
			Forestomach (2)
			Angioma of Liver (1)
			Papilloma of Forstomach (1)
			Carcinoma of Salivary Gland (1)
			Plasmacytoma (1)
			Reticulum Cell Sarcoma (2)
Sherman *et al.*	1963	1	Undifferentiated Carcinoma
Toolan	1963	23	Ovarian Carcinoma (1)
			Epidermoid Carcinoma (1)
			Epidermoid Papilloma (1)
			Lyomyosarcoma (1)
			Reticulum Cell Sarcoma (1)
			Adrenal Carcinoma (1)
			Melanoma (2)
			Angiosarcoma (1)
			Adenocarcinoma (5)
			Lymphosarcoma (3)
			Fibrosarcoma (1)
			Liposarcoma (1)
			Undifferentiated sarcoma (1)
			Rhabdomyosarcoma (1)
			Plasma Cell Myeloma (1)
			Myxosarcoma (1)

*Tumors described by Fortner *et al.* and Kirkman are reported in Tables I and II and are excluded from this listing

[1] In personal communication Greene reported several additional spontaneous tumors in hamsters including: malignant hepatoma, leukemia, lymphomas and melanotic and amelanotic melanomas

ster. The lesions of Salmonellosis in hamsters are not unlike those found in the mouse, rat, guinea pig, or rabbit. Innes *et al.* (50) described an epizootic infection in a hamster colony caused by *S. enteriditis* in which the most pronounced lesion was phlebothrom-

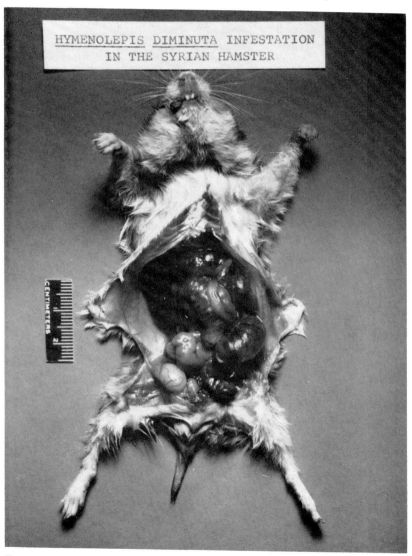

HYMENOLEPIS DIMINUTA INFESTATION
IN THE SYRIAN HAMSTER

FIGURE 1. Marked catarrhal enteritis due to infestation with the cestode *Hymenolepis diminuta* in the Syrian hamster.

bosis. The disease was acute and frequently fatal. There were some bronchopneumonic liver and splenic lesions.

According to Griesemer (35) Bartonellosis, a severe disease in rats, is rare in the hamster. It is produced by an organism resembling *Haemobartonella muris*. The Haemobartonellae are parasites of erythrocytes but not of other tissue cells and are transmitted by Arthropods. The organisms are polymorphous but are mostly rod or coccoid forms. Lesions and symptoms of this disease, particularly in splenectomized animals, are generally those found in acute hemolytic anemia.

In another report by Habermann (39), it was indicated that protozoa may cause diarrhea and catarrhal enteritis in hamsters. Sheffield and Beveridge (69) in investigating a fatal diarrhea called "wet tail," Figure 4, showed that healthy as well as sick hamsters had infestations of several species of protozoa, such as *Trichomonas muris, Giardia muris*, and *Balantidium coli*. Diarrhea in "wet tail" causes the caudal area to become excoriated, and the animals become lethargic, irritable, anorexic, and emaciated. Death usually occurs in from forty-eight hours to a week following onset of symptoms. Autopsies performed on hamsters dying of "wet tail" revealed that the ileum, jejunum, colon, and rectum contained yellow semi-fluid material and some gas. Many of the hamsters had inflammatory lesions of the ileum and/or in the cecum. In some instances the caecal mucosa was ulcerated. In our own laboratories, post-mortem observations of hamsters dying of "wet tail" were in general agreement with those described above. There was, however, marked *Trichomonas* infestation in the intestine with hemorrhagic areas starting at the junction of the intestine and cecum which progressed upward toward the stomach. In some of the animals there was thickening of the walls of the lower portion of the small intestine which contained a thick, white, caseous material. There was ulceration and hemorrhage in the ascending and transverse colon. In both laboratories heavy growths

FIGURE 2. Enterocolitis in an isolated section of hamster intestine, caused by *Hymenolepis diminuta* infestation.

FIGURE 3. Scolex and beginning of strobila *(left)* and proglottids *(right)* of the dwarf tapeworm, *Hymenolepis nana,* isolated from a hamster. x45.

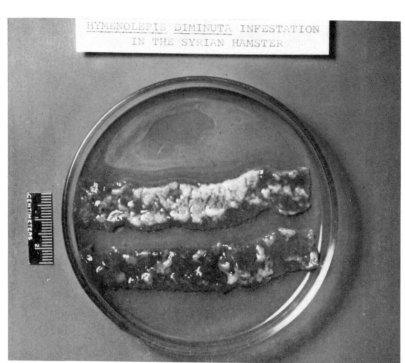

HYMENOLEPIS DIMINUTA INFESTATION
IN THE SYRIAN HAMSTER

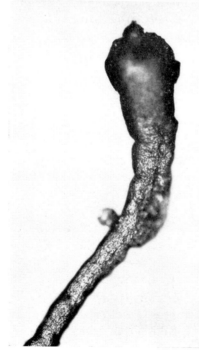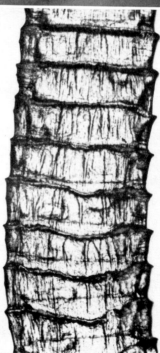

of *Escherichia coli* were found in the gut contents of affected hamsters in contrast to only a few *E. coli, Staphylococci,* and *Bacilli* in healthy animals. Sheffield and Beveridge suggested that *E. coli* might be the cause of the fatal diarrhea since neomycin sulfate appears to be effective in the prophylaxis of "wet tail" and *in vitro* inhibits the growth of *E. coli* strains isolated from hamsters. They indicated that "wet tail" in hamsters resembled "infantile diarrhea" in mice, scouring in piglets and chickens, white scours in calves, and mucoid enteritis of rabbits. Fulton and Jaymer (28) and Neal (62) reported that a previously unclassified strain of amoeba had been isolated from the hamster's caecum. According to Soave (71), this amoeba is non-pathogenic.

Pearson and Eaton (64) isolated a virus from hamsters and mice which produced pneumonia with regularity. It was demonstrated by cross immunity and neutralization tests that this virus was related to *mouse pneumonia virus* (PVM). Pseudo-tuberculosis primarily affects the digestive system (4). In its chronic form, lesions resemble those of tuberculosis with small caseating nodules. The causative agent is *Pasteurella pseudo-tuberculosis.* Infection in hamsters is rare and progresses slowly. Lesions are found in the spleen, liver, lungs, and intestinal walls. There is generally intermittent diarrhea in affected animals.

Leptospirosis is a common cause of infection of the kidneys in all rodents (4, 25).

ORAL PATHOLOGY

Caries, Figure 5, a disease of poorly developed and poorly calcified teeth, has been studied extensively in hamsters. Arnold, in 1942 (1), described the presence of carious lesions in the molars of hamsters. This observation was confirmed by several investigators (10, 63). Lesions generally commence with changes in translucency of enamel and then produce surface depressions and fissures. The lesions may begin at the lateral surface at the contact of two teeth which may both become involved. Acid dissolves the cement substance of the enamel and an area of erosion and decalcification is produced. Disintegration gradually progresses into the dentine with eventual exposure of the pulp. It is accompanied by putrefactive bacterial infection, inflammation, and ultimately complete necrosis. Studies by Keyes have indicated that under certain laboratory conditions caries must be considered infectious and transmissible (52, 53). Caries can be induced in normal hamsters by inoculation with pure cultures of cariogenic microflora or by adding microflora to the drinking water (54). Keyes (51, 52) demonstrated that hamsters with low caries potential develop tooth decay if caged with hamsters with a high potential for caries.

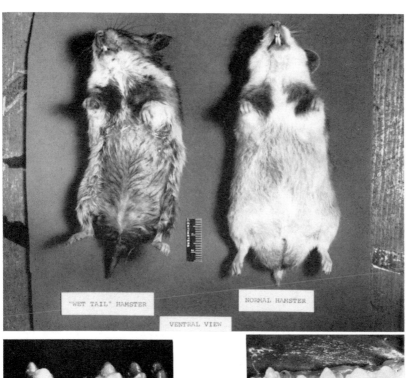

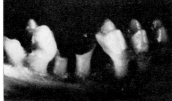

FIGURE 4. Diarrhea causing the caudal area to be moistened in a hamster with "wet tail" left. Contrast with a normal hamster *(right)*.
FIGURE 5. Dental caries in the hamster (through the courtesy of P. H. Keyes).
FIGURE 6. Periodontal disease in a hamster harboring Nocardia (through the courtesy of P. H. Keyes).

The normal animals become infected with cariogenic strepto-cocci by coprophagy. Inoculation into the mouth and cheek pouch-es with fecal material from caries-active hamsters also produced rampant caries. Rampant dental caries can be induced in golden and albino hamsters by feeding a high-carbohydrate low-fat diet (51). Harris and Nizel (46) showed that diets low in phosphorus content may be cariogenic in hamsters. Caries and general perio-dontal disease have been observed in hamsters with hypervitamino-sis D (13). Vitamin A deficient hamsters also have increased sus-ceptibility to caries. Salley *et al.* (67, 68) suggested that since saliva plays an important role in cleansing of teeth, vitamin A deficiency resulting in salivary gland lesions probably accounts for the increase in caries susceptibility.

In 1959, Gorlin and Chaudhry (31) noted a tumor-like growth in the submaxillary gland of a hamster which was diagnosed as "foci of necrosis in the gland." Microscopically these were foci of purulent material in which *Actinomyces bovis* were demon-strated. Keyes (55) indicated that active periodontal disease, Fig-ure 6, occurs if dietary factors are favorable and if the animals harbor certain filamentous bacteria classified as *Nocardia*. Gupta *et al.* (37) noted that when hamsters are stressed there is an in-crease in periodontal calcified tissue lesions over those found in non-stressed animals. Microscopically there is widening of bone marrow spaces with osteoporosis of alveolar bone.

As shown in Figure 7, Keyes (55) has described a type of papillomatous lesion spread over the tongue, cheeks, palate and

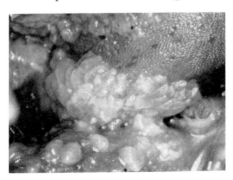

Figure 7. Papillomatous lesion infiltrating tongue, cheeks, palate, and lips (through the courtesy of P. H. Keyes).

lips. The lesion was not malignant and etiologic factors are unknown.

MUSCULAR DYSTROPHY

West and Mason (74) showed that hamsters maintained from weaning on vitamin E deficient diet developed dystrophy of skeletal muscles. Lesions are pleomorphic and may be characterized by alignment of muscle nuclei in chain-like rows within the fiber, focal degeneration of myofibrils, formation of contraction clots and coagulation necrosis. In final stages there is conversion of myofibrils to a granular mass in which the nuclei have degenerated. Homburger *et al.* (48) observed muscular lesions in an inbred strain of hamsters. The earliest pathological changes occurred at thirty-three days of age, by eighty-five days myopathy was fully evident, and far advanced by 120 days of age, at which time an unsteady gait was noted. By 220 days of age, the animals die of cardiac necrosis. West *et al.* and Homburger *et al.* noted sarcoplasmic basophilia due to ribonucleic acid in some of the dystrophic fibers. From genetic studies on this disease, Homburger suggested a simple recessive mode of transmission.

OSTEOARTHRITIS

Sokoloff (72) noted that hamsters are susceptible to spontaneous osteoarthritis, which is, however, rarely observed in animals under two years of age. The disease in hamsters is similar to that described in the mouse with deformity mainly about the knee. There is separation at the zone of calcification of the cartilage with sclerosis and dislocation of bone, fibrillation of ligaments and fibrosis of the synovial membrane.

MISCELLANEOUS PATHOLOGY

Dam and Christensen (11) and subsequently Fortner (15) observed gallstones in the gall bladders of hamsters fed "cholesterol-free" and very nearly fat-free diet. There appeared also to be an increase in gallstone formation in animals whose diet was deficient in either vitamin A or D. The gallstones were composed principally of crystalline cholesterol and were embedded in a mucoid mass in the lumen of the gall bladder.

Follis (5A, 6A) showed the hamster to be the only laboratory animal which reacts to iodine deficiency followed by iodine supplementation by developing a colloid goiter similar to those occurring under similar conditions in man.

The following types of lesions, in addition to neoplasms, were seen by Fortner (16) in hamsters maintained under ordinary laboratory conditions for twenty to twenty-three and one-half months: "gastrointestinal ulcers; renal changes of amyloid nephrosis and nephrocalcinosis; perivascular inflammation; hyaline necrosis of arterioles; thrombosis of peripheral vessels and of the cardiac auricular appendage; endocardial alterations; myocardial necrosis and fibrosis; fluid accumulation in the subcutaneous tissues and in the pleural and peritoneal cavities; hepatic alterations consisting of central and periportal vascular inflammation and amyloid deposition, bile duct proliferation, cyst formation, increased hepatic cellular glycogen or fat accumulation, and multiple focal areas of necrosis; fat deposition in the pancreatic acinar cells; severe damage or complete destruction of the adrenal cortical zona reticularis and fasiculata by lipid or amyloid congestion and/or hemorrhage; ovarian luteinization and testicular atrophy." Among other lesions Frenkel *et al.* observed a dissecting aneurysm of the aorta (26), islet cell hyperplasia (24), and para-amyloid deposits in the spleen, liver, kidney, adrenal and thyroid gland (23). Herrold and Dunham (47) often observed in untreated hamsters pathological changes in the nasal cavity that varied from mild inflammation to acute suppuration with necrosis and hemorrhage. Dunham and Herrold (2A) described the frequent occurrence of amyloid in the liver, kidney and spleen of aging hamsters; and Russfield (11A) felt that amyloidosis seemed to be the cause of death of hamsters in most of her long term experiments.

We have seen several examples of hind limb paralysis in young adult male and female hamsters. Animals die in from two days to two weeks following the onset of symptoms. There do not appear to be unusual lesions in these hamsters except in a few instances as shown in Figure 8, where lesions in the brain were consistent with those of lymphocytic choriomeningitis. This is currently under investigation. Other spontaneous lesions in hamsters observed in these laboratories and studied microscopically by Doctors A. B.

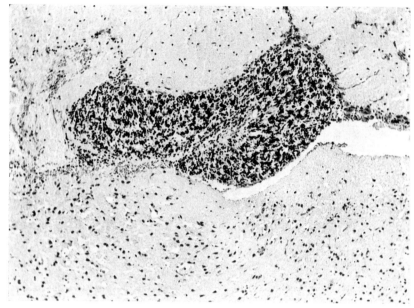

FIGURE 8. Lesion in the hamster brain consistent with that of lymphocytic choriomeningitis. Hematoxylin and eosin. x250.

Russfield and S. S. Epstein are generally similar to those reported by other investigators. A few of these lesions are illustrated in Figures 9-17.

SPONTANEOUS DIABETES MELLITUS IN THE CHINESE HAMSTER

The Chinese hamster, *Cricetulus griseus,* a species that is phylogentically different from the Syrian hamster, was reported by Meier and Yerganian (61) to be susceptible to spontaneous diabetes mellitus in some intensively inbred strains. Although according to Meier (60) diabetes mellitus has been observed in cattle, horses, pigs, sheep, dogs and cats, there was no mention of spontaneous diabetes in rodents of this hereditary type as seen in the Chinese hamster. Only certain inbred lines are affected and the condition probably is transmitted by a recessive gene. Normal blood glucose levels average 110 ± 6 mg. per 100 ml. Diabetic levels are between 200 and 800 mg./per 100 ml. This disease in Chinese hamsters

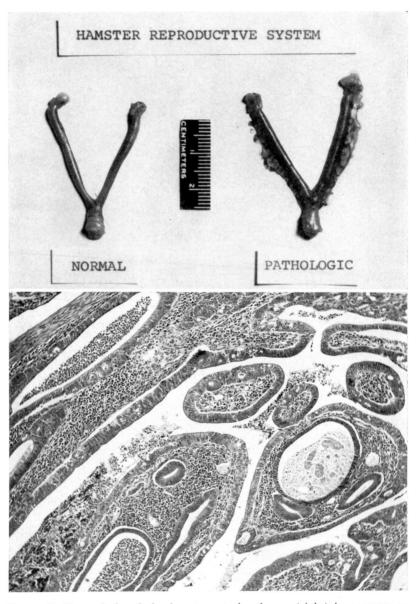

FIGURE 9. Hyperplasia of the hamster uterine horns *(right)* in contrast to "normal" hamster uterine horns *(left)*.

FIGURE 10. Hamster uterus having marked endometrial hyperplasia with pyometra. Hematoxylin and eosin. x150.

is pancreatogenic with degranulation, hydropic degeneration, and deficiency of beta cells. Green *et al.* (9A) showed the a_2 portion of the serum protein in diabetic hamsters to be elevated to 12-30 per cent as composed to 5-10 per cent in normal hamsters. Green *et al.* (8A) noted that animals with high a_2 levels but not showing early symptoms of diabetes did develop active diabetes

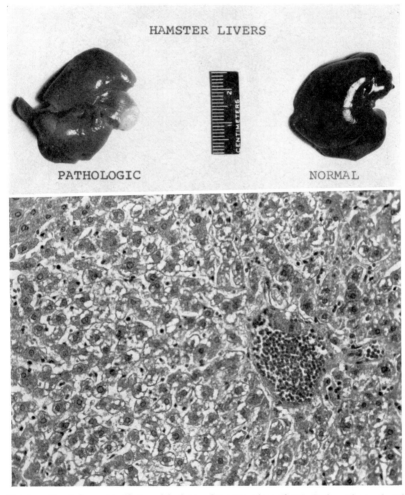

FIGURE 11. A hamster liver with fatty degeneration *(left)*. It is pale and soft with swollen, rounded egdes. This contrasts with the "normal" liver *(right)*. FIGURE 12. Liver in Figure 11, indicating fatty distention with lobular congestion and destruction of sinusoids. Hematoxylin and eosin. x550.

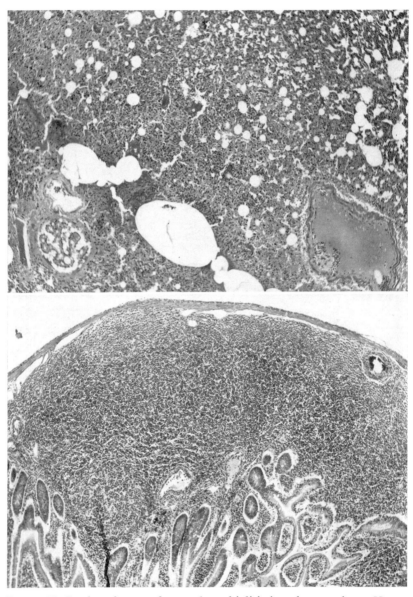

FIGURE 13. Patchy edema and acute bronchiolitis in a hamster lung. Hematoxylin and eosin. x135.

FIGURE 14. Marked lymphoid hyperplasia in the gut of a hamster in which
tapeworms were found. Hematoxylin and eosin. x125.

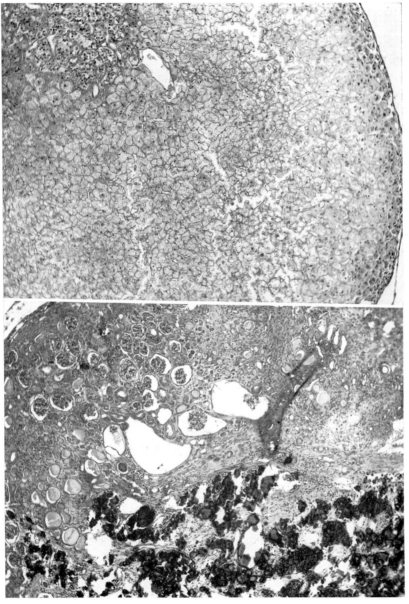

FIGURE 15. An adrenal with amyloid-like degeneration. Amyloid-like material also has been seen in the hamster liver and kidney. Hematoxylin and eosin. x140.

FIGURE 16. Hamster pyelonephritis with marked renal calcification. Hematoxylin and eosin. x135.

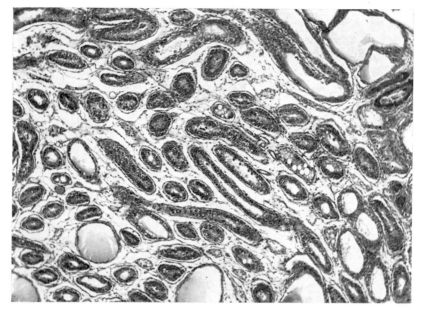

FIGURE 17. Atrophic testis in a hamster. Hematoxylin and eosin. x135.

upon aging. Green and Yerganian (7A) indicated that the slope, type and pattern of serum protein on starch gel can be used to distinguish between diabetic and non-diabetic hamsters.

ACKNOWLEDGMENTS

I am indebted to Dr. Agnes B. Russfield for providing and interpreting some of the histological preparations which were illustrated; to Dr. Samuel S. Epstein for microscopic study and interpretation of spontaneous lesions; to Dr. P. H. Keyes for providing illustrations of oral pathology; to John N. Carabitses for technical assistance in the preparation of photographs; and to several members of the technical staff of the Children's Cancer Research Foundation for assistance in the preparation of this manuscript.

REFERENCES

1. ARNOLD, F. A.: The production of carious lesions in the molar teeth of hamster. Treasury Weekly, *Public Health Rep., 57:* 1597, 1942.

2. ASHBEL, R.: Spontaneous transmissible tumours of the Syrian hamster. *Nature, 155*:607, 1945.

3. ASHBEL, R.: Development of tumors in hamsters and rats following the injection of mycobacteria. *Pubbl. Staz. Zool. Napoli, 28*: 12, 1956.

4. BJOTVEDT, G., and TUFTS, J.: *Manual for Laboratory Animal Care,* Ralston Purina Company, 1963.

5. BRINDLEY, D. C., and BANFIELD, W. G.: A contagious tumor of the hamster. *J. Nat. Cancer Inst., 26*:949, 1961.

6. BUSCH, G.: Uber einen übertragbaren Spontantumor beim syrischen Goldhamster. *Z. Krebsforsch., 59*:485, 1953.

7. CARDINALI, G., CARDINALI, G., HANDLER, A. H., and AGRIFOGLIO, M. F.: Comparative effects of colchicine and vincaleukoblastine on bone marrow activity in Syrian hamsters. *Proc. Exp. Biol. Med., 107*:891, 1961.

8. CRABB, E. D., and KELSALL, M. A.: A malignant basaloma transplantable in hamsters. *Cancer Res., 12*:256, 1952.

9. CRABB, E. D., and KELSALL, M. A.: A myxosarcoma HS-5, transplantable in hamsters. *Proc. Amer. Assoc. Cancer Res., 1*:10, 1954.

10. DALE, P. D., LAZONSKY, J. P., and KEYES, P. H.: Production and inhibition of dental caries in Syrian hamsters. *J. Dent. Res., 23*: 445, 1944.

11. DAM, H., and CHRISTENSEN, F.: The alimentary production of gallstones in hamsters. *Acta Path. Microbiol. Scand., 30*:236, 1952.

12. DUNHAM, L. J., and STEWART, H. L.: *J. Nat. Cancer Inst., 13*:1342, 1953.

13. FAHMY, H., ROGERS, W. E., MITCHELL, D. F., and BREWER, H. E.: Effects of hypervitaminosis D on the periodontium of the hamster. *J. Dent. Res., 40*:870, 1961.

14. FOLEY, G. E., and HANDLER, A. H.: Differentiation of "normal" and neoplastic cells maintained in tissue culture by implantation into normal hamsters. *Proc. Soc. Exp. Biol. Med., 94*:661, 1957.

15. FORTNER, J. G.: Experimental studies of gallstone formation. *Surgery, 36*:932, 1954.

16. FORTNER, J. G.: Spontaneous tumors, including gastrointestinal neoplasms and malignant melanomas in the Syrian hamster. *Cancer, 10*:1153, 1957.

17. FORTNER, J. G.: The influence of castration on spontaneous tumorigenesis in the Syrian (Golden) hamster. *Cancer Res., 21*:1491, 1961.

18. FORTNER, J. G., and ALLEN, A. C.: Hitherto unreported malignant melanomas in the Syrian hamster: An experimental counterpart of the human malignant melanomas. *Cancer Res., 18:*98, 1958.

19. FORTNER, J. G., GEORGE, P. A., and STERNBERG, S. S.: The development of thyroid cancer and other abnormalities in Syrian hamsters maintained on an iodine deficient diet. *Surg. Forum, 9:*646, 1959.

20. FORTNER, J. G., GEORGE, P. A., and STERNBERG, S. S.: Induced and spontaneous thyroid cancer in the Syrian (Golden) hamster. *Endocrinology, 66:*364, 1960.

21. FORTNER, J. G., MAHY, A. G., and COTRAN, R. S.: Transplantable tumors of the Syrian (Golden) hamster. Part II: Tumors of the hematopoietic tissues, genitourinary organs, mammary glands and sarcomas. *Cancer Res., Cancer Chemotherapy Screening Data X, 21:*199, 1961.

22. FORTNER, J. G., MAHY, A. G., and SCHRODT, G. R.: Transplantable tumors of the Syrian (Golden) hamster. Part I: Tumors of the alimentary tract, endocrine glands and melanomas. *Cancer Res., Cancer Chemotherapy Screening Data X, 21:*161, 1961.

23. FRENKEL, J. K.: Hormonal effects on a sarcoid-like response with Schaumann bodies and amyloid in golden hamsters infected with photochromogenic mycobacteria. *Amer. J. Path., 34:*586, 1958.

24. FRENKEL, J. K.: Pancreatic islet cell hyperplasia in hamsters treated with cortisone and chlorothiazide (DIURIL). *Fed. Proc., 19:* No. 1, Pt. 1, 1960.

25. FRENKEL, J. K.: Personal communication, 1963.

26. FRENKEL, J. K., RASMUSSEN, P., and SMITH, O. D.: Synergism of cortisol (F) and desoxycorticosterone (DOC) in the production of dissecting aortic aneurysms in hamsters. *Fed. Proc., 18:* No. 1, 1959.

27. FRIEDELL, G. H., OATMAN, B. W., and SHERMAN, J. D.: Report of a spontaneous myxofibrosarcoma of the hamster cheek pouch. *Transplant. Bull., 7:*97, 1960.

28. FULTON, J. D., and JAYMER, L. P.: Natural amoebic infections in laboratory rodents. *Nature, 161:*66, 1948.

29. GARCIA, H., BARONI, C., and RAPPAPORT, H.: Transplantable tumors of the Syrian Golden hamster (Mesocricetus auratus). *J. Nat. Cancer Inst., 27:*1323, 1961.

30. GODGLÜCK, G.: Eine primäre Geschwulst der Milz bei einen syrischen Goldhamster. *Mschr. Veterinarmedizin, 8:*31, 1953.

31. GORLIN, R. J., and CHAUDHRY, A. P.: A note on the occurrence of actinomyces bovis in the hamster. *J. Dent. Res., 38:*842, 1959.

32. GREENE, H. S. N.: A spontaneous melanoma in the hamster with a propensity for amelanotic alteration and sarcomatous transformation during transplantation. *Cancer Res., 18:*422, 1958.

33. GREENE, H. S. N.: Personal communication, 1963.

34. GREENE, H. S. N., and HARVEY, E. K.: The inhibitory influence of a transplanted hamster lymphoma on metastasis. *Cancer Res., 20:*1094, 1960.

35. GRIESEMER, R. A.: Bartonellosis. *J. Nat. Cancer Inst., 20:*949, 1958.

36. GROSS, L.: *Oncogenic Viruses.* Pergamon Press, 1961.

37. GUPTA, O. P., BLECHMAN, H., and STAHL, S. S.: Effects of stress on the periodontium of the hamster. *J. Dent. Res., 38:*724, 1959.

38. GYE, W. E., and FOULDS, L.: A note on the production of sarcomata in hamsters by 3:4-Benzpyrene. *Amer. J. Cancer, 35:*108, 1939.

39. HABERMANN, R. T.: Spontaneous diseases and their control in laboratory animals. *Public Health Rep., U. S. Department of Health, Education, and Welfare, 74:*165, 1959.

40. HABERMANN, R. T., and WILLIAMS, F. P., JR.: Salmanellosis in laboratory animals. *J. Nat. Cancer Inst., 20:*933, 1958.

41. HABERMANN, R. T., WILLIAMS, F. P. JR., and THORP, W. T. S.: *Public Health Service Publications No. 343,* U. S. Dept. of Health, Education, and Welfare, National Institutes of Health, Bethesda, Maryland.

42. HANDLER, A. H.: Transplantation of heterospecific tumor tissue into the cheek pouch of the golden hamster. *Mesocricetus Auratus.* Doctoral dissertation, Boston University, 1951.

43. HANDLER, A. H., ADAMS, R. A., and FARBER, S.: Further studies on the growth of homologous and heterologous lymphoma and leukemia transplants in Syrian hamsters. *Acta Union Intern. Contre Le Cancer, 26:*1175, 1960.

44. HANDLER, A. H., DAVIS, S., and SOMMERS, S. C.: Heterotransplantation experiments with human cancers. *Cancer Res., 16:*32, 1956.

45. HANDLER, A. H., and FOLEY, G. E.: Growth of human epidermoid carcinomas, strains KB and HeLa, in hamsters from tissue culture inocula. *Proc. Soc. Exp. Biol. Med., 91:*237, 1956.

46. HARRIS, R. S., and NIZEL, A. E.: Effect of food, ash, phosphate and trace minerals upon hamster caries. *J. Dent. Res., 38:*1142, 1959.

47. HERROLD, K. M., and DUNHAM, L. J.: Induction of tumors in the Syrian hamster with diethylnitrosamine N-nitrosodiethylamine. *Cancer Res., 23:*773, 1963.

48. HOMBURGER, F., NIXON, C. W., HARROP, J., WILGRAM, G., and BAKER, J. R.: Further morphologic and genetic studies on dystrophy-like primary myopathy of Syrian hamsters. *Fed. Proc., 22:*195, 1963.

49. HOMBURGER, F., TREGIER, A., and BORGES, P. R. F.: A transplantable leiomyosarcoma (HT-1) of the hamster. *Cancer Res., 17:* 659, 1957.

50. INNES, J. R. M., WILSON, C., and Ross, M. A.: Epizootic Salmonella enteriditis infection causing septic pulmonary phlebothrombosis in the hamster. *J. Infect. Dis., 98:*133, 1956.

51. KEYES, P. H.: Dental caries in the Syrian hamster. VIII. The induction of rampant caries activity in albino and golden animals. *J. Dent. Res., 38:*525, 1959.

52. KEYES, P. H.: The infectious and transmissible nature of experimental dental caries. *Arch. Oral Biol., 1:*304, 1960.

53. KEYES, P. H.: Questions raised by the infectious and transmissible nature of experimental caries. Conference on Oral Biology. *J. Dent. Res., 39:*1086, 1960.

54. KEYES, P. H., and FITZGERALD, R. J.: Dental caries in the Syrian hamster - IX. *Arch. Oral Biol., 7:*267, 1962.

55. KEYES, P. H.: Personal communication, 1963.

56. KIRKMAN, H.: Estrogen-induced tumors of the kidney in the Syrian hamster. *Nat. Cancer Inst. Monogr. #1,* Bethesda, Maryland, U. S. Department of Health, Education and Welfare, 1959.

57. KIRKMAN, H.: A preliminary report concerning tumors observed in Syrian hamsters. *Stanford Med. Bull., 20:*163, 1962.

58. KIRKMAN, H.: Personal communication, 1963.

59. MARSH, A. F.: *The Hamster Manual.* Gulf Hamstery, 1951.

60. MEIER, H.: Diabetes mellitus in animals, a review. *Diabetes, 9:* 485, 1960.

61. MEIER, H., and YERGANIAN, G. A.: Spontaneous diabetes mellitus in chinese hamsters Cricetulus griseus. 1. Pathological findings. *Proc. Soc. Exp. Biol. Med., 100:*810, 1959.

62. NEAL, R. A.: Entamoeba species from the Syrian hamster. *Nature, 159:*502, 1947.

63. ORLAND, F. J.: A study of the Syrian hamster, its molars and their lesions. *J. Dent. Res., 25:*445, 1946.

64. ORSINI, M. W., PANSKY, B.: The natural resistance of the Golden hamster to colchicine. *Science, 115*:88, 1952.

65. PEARSON, H. E., and EATON, M. D.: A virus pneumonia of Syrian hamsters. *Proc. Soc. Exp. Biol. Med., 45*:677, 1940.

66. RATCLIFFE, H. L.: Disease control and colony management of infrahuman primates at the Philadelphia Zoological Gardens. *Proc. Animal Care Panel, 4*:8, 1954.

67. SALLEY, J. J., and BRYSON, W. F.: Vitamin A deficiency in the hamster, 35th Gen. Meeting, I. A. D. R., Atlantic City, Reprinted abstracts, 1957.

68. SALLEY, J. J., BRYSON, W. F., and ESHLEMAN, J. R.: The effect of chronic Vitamin A deficiency on dental caries in the Syrian hamster. *J. Dent. Res., 38*:1038, 1959.

69. SHEFFIELD, F. W., and BEVERIDGE, E.: Prophylaxis of wet tail in hamster. *Nature, 196*:294, 1962.

70. SHERMAN, J. D., RIGBY, P. G., HACKETT, R. L., and FRIEDELL, G. H.: A new spontaneous hamster carcinoma associated with a positive erythroagglutination reaction and anemia. *Cancer Res.,* in press.

71. SOAVE, ORLAND A.: Diagnosis and control of common diseases of hamsters, rabbits and monkeys. *J. Amer. Vet. Med. Ass., 142:* 285, 1963.

72. SOKOLOFF, L.: Joint diseases of laboratory animals. *J. Nat. Cancer Inst., 20*:965, 1958.

73. STUMKARD, H. W.: The Syrian hamster, Cricetus auratus, host of hymenolepis nana. *J. Parisit., 31*:151, 1945.

74. WEST, W. T., and MASON, K. E.: Histopathology of muscular dystrophy in the vitamin E deficient hamster. *Amer. J. Anat., 102*:323, 1958.

ADDENDUM

1A. DELLAPORTA, G.: Induction of intestinal, mammary, and ovarian tumors in hamsters with oral administration of 20-'Methylcholanthrene. *Cancer Res., 21*:575, 1961.

2A. DUNHAM, L. J., and HERROLD, K. M.: Failure to produce tumors in the hamster cheek pouch by exposure to ingredients of betel quid; histopathologic changes in the pouch and other organs by exposure to known carcinogens. *J. Nat. Cancer Inst., 29*:1047, 1962.

3A. EDDY, B. E., BORMAN, G. S., GRUBBS, G. E., and YOUNG, R. D.:

Identification of the oncogenic substance in rhesus monkey kidney cell cultures as simian virus 40. *Virology, 17*:65, 1962.

4A. EDDY, B. E., STEWART, S. E., YOUNG, R., and MIDER, G. B.: Neoplasms in hamsters induced by mouse tumor agent passed in tissue culture. *J. Nat. Cancer Inst., 20*:747, 1958.

5A. FOLLIS, R. H., JR.: Experimental colloid goiter produced by thiouracil. *Nature* (Lond.) *193*:1817, 1959.

6A. FOLLIS, R. H., JR.: Experimental colloid goiter in the hamster *Proc. Soc. Exp. Biol. Med., 100*:203, 1959.

7A. GREEN, M. N., and YERGANIAN, G.: Abstracts 1963 Annual meeting of the American Diabetes Association, Atlantic City, New Jersey.

8A. GREEN, M. N., YERGANIAN, G., and GAGNON, H. J.: Prediction of spontaneous hereditary diabetes mellitus in Chinese hamsters by means of elevated Alpha-2 serum levels. *Nature, 197*:396, 1963.

9A. GREEN, M. N., YERGANIAN, G., and MEIER, H.: Elevated a-2-serum proteins as a possible genetic marker in spontaneous hereditary diabetes mellitus of the Chinese hamster, Cricetulus griseus. *Experientia, 16*:503, 1960.

10A. See 4A.

11A. RUSSFIELD, A. B.: Personal communication, 1963.

12A. SHUBIK, P., PIETRO, G., and DELLAPORTA, G.: Studies of skin carcinogenesis in the Syrian golden hamster. *Cancer Res., 20*: 100, 1960.

13A. TOMATIS, L., DELLAPORTA, G., and SHUBIK, P.: Urinary bladder and liver cell tumors induced in hamsters with O-Aminoazotoluene. *Cancer Res., 21*:1513, 1961.

14A. TOOLAN, H. W.: Personal communication, 1964.

15A. TRENTIN, J. J., YABE, Y., and TAYLOR, G.: The quest for human cancer viruses. A new approach to an old problem reveals cancer induction in hamsters by human adenovirus. *Science, 137*:835, 1962.

DISCUSSION

Question: Would you comment further on "wet tail."

Dr. Handler: This "wet tail" condition in hamsters must be given serious consideration. It has in many instances affected so many of the breeding stock that some commercial breeders have been driven out of business. We have been in constant contact with Mr. Samuel Poiley of the National Institutes of Health in regard to this matter. We have been assured that an investigation into cause and therapy of "wet tail" is being made.

The highest incidence of "wet tail" occurs in the United States in the summer months in contrast to a report that most animals are affected in Europe in the winter.

We have witnessed entire shipments of hamsters die in as short a time as one or two days following their arrival in the laboratory.

Dr. F. Homburger: In talking about "wet tail" we must consider that its devastating spread throughout commercial hamster colonies may often be a consequence of messy and stingy operation due to the fact that producers are expected to sell a sixty-five-cent hamster. This cannot be done. While it appears from your presentation of the literature that hamsters can be very sickly animals, this need not be the case. The hamster is extremely sensitive to stress and must be protected accordingly. It is quite possible, as we have demonstrated during the past six years, to operate a closed hamster colony relatively free from "wet tail" and parasitic infestations.

I would like to make another comment and that is that people do not seem to learn from the experience that has been accumulated since 1926 on the use of the inbred mouse. When a new species such as the hamster comes into use we still tend to use random bred animals with the unfortunate result that nobody knows in the end what he has really dealt with. These animals vary tremendously, depending on genetic factors.

Over the last six years, we have developed some sixteen inbred strains of hamsters with Dr. Whitney and Dr. Nixon, and anatomic studies of these animals have shown marked differences between the strains in organ weights, in fertility, and in fecundity. We don't know yet about longevity and aging changes because we haven't been able to accumulate enough aging animals, though of course, we want to do this. With Dr. Harris, of M.I.T., a caries-susceptible strain was developed and recently we encountered a new strain of hamsters with the recessive dystrophy-like myopathy.

This is a useful tool because dystrophy and cardiac myopathy occur in 100 per cent of animals of the affected strain. Yet one may carry on the strain in a vigorous hybrid, as a sort of reservoir, which can be perpetuated indefinitely.

Such things are only possible by systematic inbreeding and development of pure inbred lines. This is predictable. It has been done with mice, and I don't see why a greater effort is not being spent on doing it with hamsters. It may well be possible that we may come up with a resistant strain where "wet tail" will be no problem any more, even in a casually run operation.

Dr. Walter Fleischmann: I would like to ask Dr. Handler regarding an observation we have made. We have been working with the resistance of the hamster, which seems to be very marked in the Chinese hamster, but in doing excretion studies we were never able to obtain a clear urine using a syringe and withdrawing samples from the bladder. It has always been turbid. We have never seen very much under the microscope, some amorphous material with no leucocytes or anything else. I wondered whether anybody else has had this experience and knows what it may be due to.

Dr. Handler: We have not investigated the hamster urine *per se*. Grossly it is a strange, thick, milky fluid. There is, however, something about the hamster kidney that is strange. In using urethane as an anesthetic in hamsters, we found a tremendous amount of blood in the urine and the kidneys were badly damaged. Later, we observed that almost any marked stress appeared to affect the kidney.

Dr. F. Homburger: In our study on myoglobin in hamster urine, we observed normally a high proteinuria and a viscous urine. The only way we have found practical to make large urine collections is to hydrate the hamsters continuously by forcing them to drink from an eyedropper. This permits large quantities of urine to be collected reasonably quickly.

Dr. Geo. F. Wilgram: I would like to ask two questions:

Would you comment on the frequently observed thrombosis and its origin in the hamster? What do you think is the mechanism?

And secondly, you mentioned viral diseases in the hamster. Would you enlarge upon that?

Dr. Handler: I don't think I would like to say anything about the thrombosis. I have never seen it. Have you seen thrombosis in the hamster, Dr. Wilgram?

Dr. Wilgram: Dr. Fortner has.

Dr. Handler: I have a number of references on viruses in hamsters, and I could give them to you. Also, I recall Dr. Fortner has observed a few instances of inclusion disease involving the pancreas.

Dr. Elihu Bond: I am interested in "wet tail" disease of hamsters. We have seen some chronic cases and have been able to transmit this disease. We believe it is of viral origin. It seems to start in the serosa and progress inward. It doesn't seem to be a type of infection that first affects the mucosa and works outward. It apparently is very similar to terminal ileitis in man, with the same kind of chronic inflammation.

Dr. Bart Watanic: Regarding transmission of "wet tail," we can usually get the sick hamsters. They send to us material for examination and then we transmit it from these by contact and by injection of infectious material intraperitoneally, or by feeding it by tube.

Dr. Helene W. Toolan: We have a very large colony of hamsters. We have now autopsied over 3,000 animals beyond the age of two and a half years. We are very fortunate in that these animals, which were all born in our laboratory, have been completely free of "wet tail." In animals that are over two and a half years old we have an incidence of 7 per cent of tumors, so that by now we have collected quite a few. Many are of the types that you mentioned. Three were renal cortical tumors and seven were melanomas.

I don't think that tumors in the hamsters are as rare as one probably supposes, provided that the animals are kept longer.

One of the interesting things that we see in these very ancient hamsters of three years or more is a very large percentage of hernias. Many of them have died of strangulated hernia, despite the very thin and delicate condition of the tissues in old age.

Dr. Charlie N. Barron: I keep hearing about the disease "wet tail." I wish that this term could be dropped, because a hamster can get his tail wet by sticking it in a glass of water. To me it is just a sign of diarrhea and why shouldn't one expect to call it that?

When you encounter one of these diseases, let's investigate it for both its clinical picture *and* its morphological picture and try to name it accordingly.

Question: I would like to ask a little more about the melanomas. You mentioned that you had observed an amelanotic melanoma.

Chairman: Dr. Greene did.

Dr. Wilgram: May I ask whether in genetic studies this amelanotic melanoma could be made to pigment after successive generations, or what were the criteria for making the diagnosis of amelanotic melanoma?

Chairman: Dr. Greene, would you care to comment?

Dr. H. S. N. Greene: Yes, Amelanotic melanoma derived from a melanoma continues in a pigmented area until it finally becomes a perfectly pigmented tumor. The truly amelanotic melanoma is serially transplanted in hamsters for a great many generations without any pigment formation whatsoever.

It is of considerable interest, I think, that although these tumors are similar without the pigment, yet their biological behavior is as different as is possible, one invading rapidly, the other invading slowly, one metatasizing profusely, the other metastasizing very little.

I have found no experiments to try to modify the amelanotic melanoma into a melanotic melanoma other than the natural, whatever it is, condition.

10

SPONTANEOUS LESIONS OF THE RAT
KATHARINE C. SNELL

Human beings and rats have quite different tumor patterns. If we examine tables of cancer frequency in the United States (1), we see that the most common tumors are, in decreasing order, as follows: skin, breast, stomach, large intestine, cervix, rectum, lung, hematopoietic tissue, prostate, and bladder. With the exception of tumors of the mammary gland, very few of the others on this list occur in any appreciable number in the rat. This does not mean that cancer is infrequent in the rat, since this species develops many spontaneous tumors, chiefly of the endocrine and reproductive organs. A comparison of tumor patterns may, however, be unwarranted since the laboratory rat lives a carefully controlled existence, while man is exposed to nearly all the conditions that we outlaw when setting up criteria for tumors that we are willing to call spontaneous. In spite of the difference in tumor patterns, the rat, when exposed to appropriate carcinogens, develops numerous tumors equivalent to those found in man; hence the rat is a valuable species for the study of carcinogenesis. But if it is to be used for such studies we must know the tumors the untreated rat develops and the variations that appear among different strains. Moreover, not only must we know the tumor frequency, but we must also be aware of the various inflammatory diseases and congenital abnormalities that are likely to occur. We must be able to recognize normal structures such as the pineal body, the extraorbital lachrymal glands (Fig. 1, (2,3)), and the rete ovarii (4-7), that have sometimes been mistaken for tumors. We should be familiar with non-neoplastic but grossly tumor-like lesions such as infarcted mesenteric fat (Figs. 2 and 3) or liver.

Spontaneous lesions may be defined as those for which we do not know a cause, or more specifically, as those occuring in animals not subjected to any experimental procedure such as inocula-

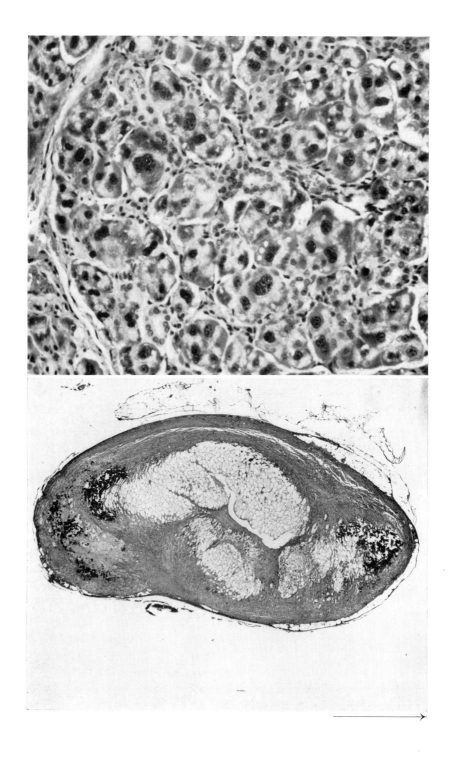

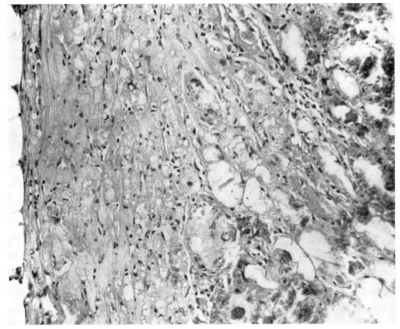

FIGURE 3. A higher power view of infarcted omental fat illustrated in Figure 2. Note coagulation necrosis in the center. The remainder consists of necrotic fat cells, calcareous deposits, hyalinized connective tissue, a few inflammatory cells, and phagocytes containing pigment and lipoidal material. x210.

tion with microorganisms, irradiation, imbalanced diet, transplantation of normal or tumor tissue, or exposure to any chemical, physical, or biological carcinogens. These conditions apply to the NIH inbred rats from which most of this information has been gathered and to a few NIH Sprague-Dawley rats whose tumors are illustrated. Added is information obtained from some of the

FIGURE 1. Extraorbital lachrymal gland having marked irregularity in size of nuclei and variation in mitochondrial content of the cytoplasm. These bizarre cells of the normal extraorbital lachrymal gland have led the inexperienced to a misdiagnosis of carcinoma of the mammary gland. x275. This illustration and those that follow were taken from sections stained with hematoxylin and eosin unless otherwise specified.

FIGURE 2. Infarcted omental fat found near the left ovary. Grossly, this nodule was firm and dark yellow. x19.

publications dealing with wild rats, with rats used as controls, with one group of germ-free rats, and with experimental rats when the authors stated that the tumors and other lesions were almost certainly unrelated to the treatment.

Table I lists references to studies in which large numbers of rats were examined (8-19). It gives the strain, number of rats, number with tumors, and special experimental conditions.

In the Laboratory of Pathology at the National Cancer Institute we have been making a survey of spontaneous tumors and other lesions that occur in six inbred strains of rats. The strains of rats used were: ACI (AxC 9935/N or Irish); BUF (Buffalo, BFO); F344 (Fischer), OM (OM/N, Inbred Osborne-Mendel); M520 (Marshall 520); and WN (WTR, Inbred Wistar). The plan of study was to set aside male and female rats of each strain and to kill and necropsy a pre-determined group at three-month intervals after they had reached the age of twelve months. Both non-breeders and retired breeders were included. Breeding female rats that developed mammary tumors before they were twelve months old were removed from the breeding colony and are not included in this survey. Three male and three female rats that had not been bred and three male and three female retired breeders of each strain were killed at twelve months. Similar groups of seventy-two rats were later killed and necropsied at fifteen, eighteen, twenty-one, twenty-four and twenty-seven months. A few hardy rats lived to be necropsied at thirty months of age. A rat that became ill before its scheduled killing date was included in the group corresponding most closely to its actual date of death. Additional rats are still being added to various groups. We have now examined 488 rats, or about eighty of each strain. All six strains of rats examined were inbred by strict brother-sister mating for well over twenty generations. The origin and outstanding characteristics of these and other strains can be found in a publication by George Jay (20).

A complete necropsy was performed on each rat. Pieces of tissue for histologic study were taken from subcutaneous tissues, salivary glands, esophagus, stomach, intestines, liver, spleen, pancreas, kidneys, adrenal glands, sex organs, lungs, heart, thymus,

lymph nodes, eyes, ears, brain, vertebral column, sternum, and the pituitary, adrenal, thyroid, and parathyroid glands. The stomach and intestines were always opened and examined.

LESIONS OTHER THAN TUMORS

While the spontaneous lesions of rats may vary considerably among different strains, certain pathologic conditions appear in many or all strains. The most frequently encountered are as follows.

(1) Pulmonary disease, including inflammatory lesions diagnosed as bronchiectasis, bronchitis, peribronchial inflammation, pneumonitis, or chronic murine pneumonia (21-23).

(2) Otitis media (24, 25), sometimes extending to involve the inner ear and brain.

(3) Chronic cecitis, often leading to ulceration of the cecum (Figs. 4 & 5) and usually accompanied by a reactive hyperplasia

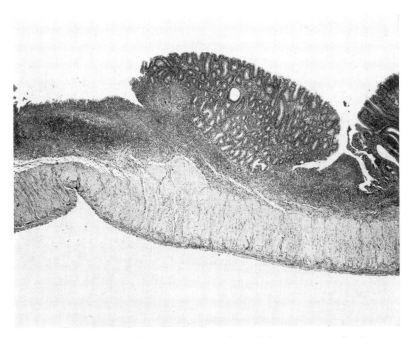

FIGURE 4. Cecum with cecitis. Note ulceration of the mucosa and submucosa. x35.

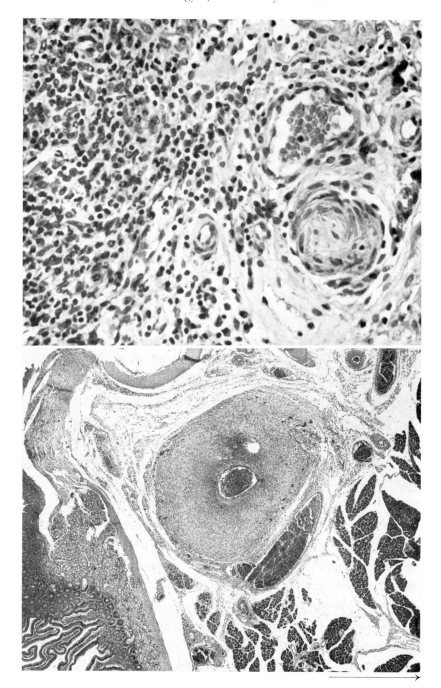

or progressive cystic dilation and fibrosis of the cecal lymph nodes (26).

(4) Miscellaneous diseases including chronic nephritis (27), polyarteritis (Fig. 6) (28), prostatitis, endometritis, cervicitis, interstitial myocarditis (29), arteriosclerosis (30), sialodacryoadenitis (31), rhinitis and sinusitis (32, 33), and hydronephrosis. Myocarditis is frequently encountered in F344 and OM rats (Fig. 7), and hydronephrosis in Slonaker-Addis rats (34). The histology of various organs in senile rats has been studied by several investigators (35-40).

(5) Congenital abnormalities, including defective or supernumerary organs or appendages, persistence or misplacement of embryonic structures, and unusual development or lack of development of parts of the genitourinary system. The first category includes deformed or absent appendages, accessory spleen or adrenal glands, diaphragmatic hernia, and dextroposition of the aorta. Under persistence or misplacement of embryonic remnants we include such anomalies as nests of squamous cells from the thyroglossal duct or ultimobranchial bodies found within the thyroid gland (41), thyroid tissue near the thymus or along the aorta, Harderian gland tissue within the extraorbital lachrymal gland (Fig. 8), and ganglion cells within the adrenal medulla (Fig. 9), representing survival and development of primitive cells from the coeliac plexus (42). Abnormalities of the genito-urinary organs are exemplified by the development of a ventral prostate in some female rats (Fig. 10) and by defects in the kidneys and sex organs of ACI rats. A female prostate is not uncommon in OM rats and occurs in about 50 per cent of a strain used at Northwestern University (43). About 20 per cent of ACI rats have one kidney, usually the right, missing or replaced by a cyst (44). There is no significant difference between the sexes in the frequency

FIGURE 5. Cecitis. A higher power view of the base of the ulcer illustrated in Figure 4. Inflammatory cells consist of lymphocytes, plasma cells, mononuclear cells and a few polymorphonuclear leukocytes and eosinophils. In the lower portion of the field there is perivascular fibrosis and thrombosis of a small arteriole. x340.

FIGURE 6. Mesenteric artery in region of pancreas and duodenum with periarteritis. The pancreatic tissue is atrophic. x25.

with which the abnormality occurs. The homolateral ureter, uterine horn, vas deferens, epididymis, and vesicular gland may be absent, atrophic, incomplete, or cystic. In the male the homo-lateral testis is usually atrophied and sometimes undescended. In the rats that we have examined, both adrenal glands and both ovaries, in the females, have been present and normal.

TUMORS

Skin and Subcutaneous Tissues

Squamous cell and basal cell carcinomas and, less frequently, papillomas of the skin have been mentioned in most tabulations of spontaneous tumors of rats. The majority were located on the face, paws, or tail. Carcinoma of the preputial gland has also been reported (10). Two skin tumors occurred in our F344 rats. One was a hair follicle tumor in the left axilla of a twenty-four-month-old male, and the other, a squamous cell carcinoma in the perineal region of a twenty-one-month-old female.

Subcutaneous fibromas of the left axilla were found in a F344 male of eighteen months and in a WN male of twenty-one months. An F344 male rat of twenty-four months had a large fibrosarcoma (Fig. 11) that apparently had originated in the right axilla and invaded the chest wall. Subcutaneous tumors of these types, as well as hemangioendotheliomas (45), lymphangiomas (45), and lipomas (10, 46), have also been reported, but rather infrequently.

Bone and Cartilage

None of the untreated rats we examined had a tumor origi-nating in bone or cartilage, and very few such tumors have been reported. Bullock and Curtis (10) described an osteochondro-sarcoma, an osteosarcoma, and an osteoma, all of the leg; they also found two intrathoracic osteochondrosarcomas, one of which was

→

FIGURE 7. Interventricular system of a heart with interstitial myocarditis. Note degeneration and fibrosis of the myocardial fibers and infiltration of inflammatory cells. Six-month-old OM strain male. x210.
FIGURE 8. Extraorbital lachrymal gland containing a group of pale Harderian gland acini with pigment. x430.

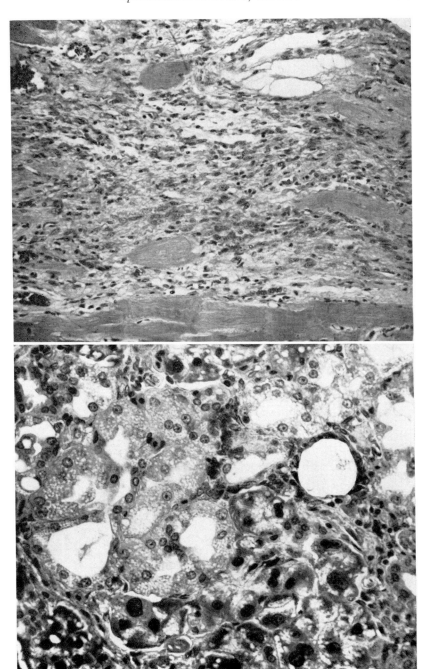

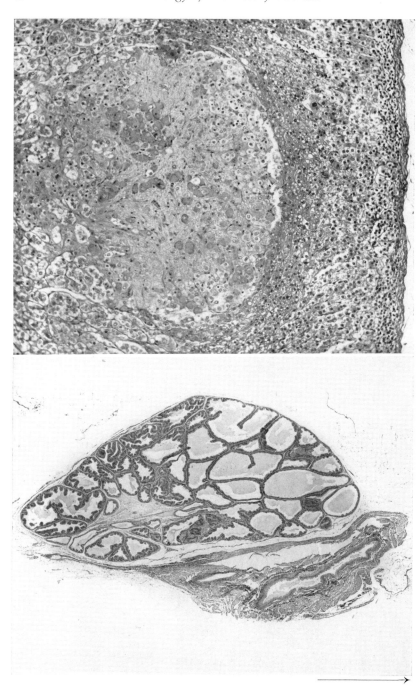

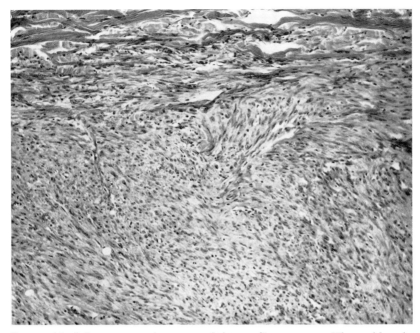

FIGURE 11. Subcutaneous tissue containing a fibrosarcoma. The epidermis, which is not shown, lies above the heavy subepidermal collagen at the upper part of the field. x135.

thought to be primary in the lung. Ratcliffe (12) noted six osteogenic sarcomas, one of the costochondral junction, one each of the tibia and humerus, and three of the femur. Guèrin described an osteogenic sarcoma of the right hind paw (14). Schulze (47) reported an osteoma in the cranial cavity, and Arai (48), an osteogenic sarcoma of the base of the skull which extended along the right optic nerve from the optic foramen to the sella turcica.

Muscle

A myoblastic sarcoma, probably originating in the posterior abdominal wall, was reported by Guèrin (14), and a chondro-

FIGURE 9. Adrenal gland with an area of proliferated ganglion cells in the medulla. The cortex is secondarily compressed. x125.

FIGURE 10. Ventral prostate of a female rat. When present, this structure usually consists of a single lobe located in the midline adjacent to the neck of the bladder. x19.

rhabdomyosarcoma of the sternum by Bullock and Curtis (49). This latter tumor grew in transplant; both the primary tumor and the transplants gave rise to metastases containing striated muscle. Sugiura (50) reported upon a transplantable myosarcoma primary in the periosteal area of the vertebrae.

Adipose Tissue

Several types of tumors arising from fatty tissue have been noted in various organs and tissues of the rat. We found a lipoma of the kidney in a BUF female of thirty months. Gilbert and Gillman (17) also reported a lipoma of the kidney. Crain (16) and Guérin (14) have each described a lipoma of the spermatic cord. Lipomas have also been found in the thoracic region (14, 10, 8), within the abdominal cavity (10), and in the subcutaneous tissue (10, 18, 46). Liposarcomas, one intrathoracic and one located along the dorsal spine, were reported by Guérin (14), who also reported one lipoblastoma of the cervico-dorsal region.

Vascular System

Two rats included in our study had hemangiomas of the liver. One was a WN female, and the other a BUF male, both twenty-seven months old. We found a hemangioendothelioma of a lymph node in a F344 female and of the spleen in an old OM female. The only lymphangioma we have noted was in the liver of an old BUF male breeder.

In the wild rats he examined, McCoy (8) found one angiosarcoma of the neck, one of the testis, and one attached to the right femur. Guérin (14) reported a "histio-endothelial sarcoma" in the subcutaneous tissue of the inguinal region of one rat. A hemangioendothelioma and a lymphangioma, both in the neck region, were listed by Olcott (45). Tiberiça (51) observed two hemangioendotheliomas of the mesentery with metastases to the mediastinum. Thompson and his associates (19) described a cavernous hemangioendothelioma of the oviduct.

Hematopoietic Neoplasms

Tannenbaum and Maltoni (52) pointed up the difficulty in evaluating the literature dealing with hematopoietic neoplasms when they wrote: "The terminology of neoplastic diseases of the lymphoreticular system, in the mouse as well as in man, abounds in ambiguity and confusion." They go on to say that those engaged primarily in animal experimentation have adopted various generic nomenclatures such as leukemia, malignant tumors of the lymphoreticular system, and malignant lymphoma, irrespective of whether or not malignant cells are found in the peripheral blood. We agree with these remarks and have found the diversity in terms a handicap in reviewing the literature, since the same disease may appear under a number of different names.

In our laboratory we classify those neoplasms of hematopoietic tissue without leukemic cells in the peripheral blood as lymphosarcoma, reticulum cell sarcoma, or plasma cell myeloma. When malignant white blood cells are found in the blood, we diagnose leukemia, with the subdivisions of granulocytic, lymphocytic, or unclassified types. Even after careful study it is often difficult to classify a neoplasm within this group. Furthermore, the line between inflammation and tumor is often indistinct, and it is probable that inflammatory lesions such as cecitis have more than once been diagnosed as neoplastic.

We seldom see lymphosarcomas or reticulum cell sarcomas in our untreated rats. Lymphosarcoma of the lung (Figs. 12 and 13) of the type described by Nelson and Morris (53) in untreated OM rats and by Moon and his associates (54) in rats treated with growth hormone occurred in only two of our rats, both of the WN strain. One was a twenty-four-month-old male and the other an eighteen-month-female. One BUF male eighteen months old had a lymphosarcoma confined to the cecum and bone marrow, and another BUF male twenty-four months old had a generalized lymphosarcoma (Fig. 14) that involved the lung, liver, spleen, lymph nodes, bone marrow, kidneys, heart, pancreas, sex organs, alimentary tract, and brain. This tumor was transplanted for several generations. Reticulum cell sarcoma of the colon occurred in a M520 male of twenty-one months (Figs. 15 and 16). One BUF male rat thirty months old had a thymoma (Fig. 17) with metastasis to the brain.

Most of the authors who have enumerated tumors of rats have listed neoplasms designated as lymphosarcoma, reticulum cell

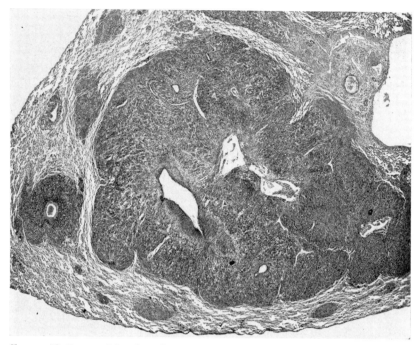

FIGURE 12. Lung with a lymphosarcoma distributed chiefly around blood vessels and bronchi. In this rat the lymphosarcoma was confined to the lung. ×19.

sarcoma, reticulohistiocytic neoplasm, or malignant lymphoma as occurring in the mesenteric or cecal lymph nodes, the mediastinal lymphoid tissue, thymus, or lung. The number and types of hematopoietic neoplasms reported from different colonies vary widely even within the same strain. Bullock and Curtis (10) reported that an unusually large number of their rats had lymphosarcoma of the cecal lymph nodes, while in the thymus of Copenhagen rats they found two lymphosarcomas, one sarcoma, and

——————————————→

FIGURE 13. Lung. A higher power view of the lymphosarcoma illustrated in Figure 12. The characteristics of the neoplastic cells are evident. ×160.
FIGURE 14. Mesenteric lymph node with lymphosarcoma. In this rat lymphosarcoma was found in nearly all tissues and organs. Everywhere it was composed of sheets of heavily stained neoplastic cells interspersed with large phagocytic cells that contained engulfed nuclear debris. This histologic pattern is like that of the so-called "African lymphoma" in children. ×880.

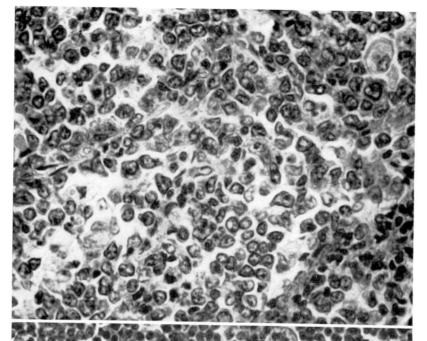

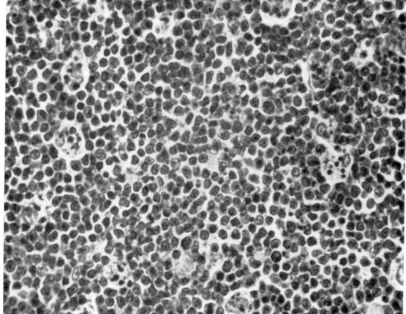

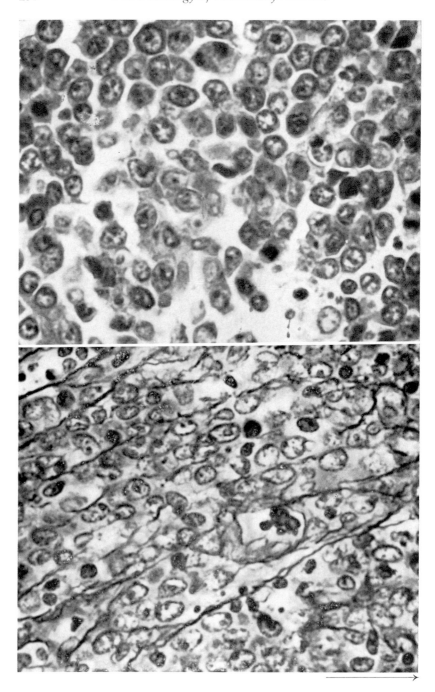

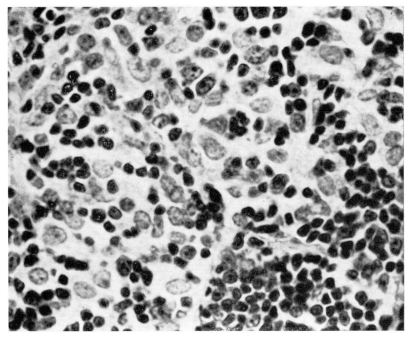

FIGURE 17. A high power view of a thymoma. The appearance of the small dark cells and the pale epithelioid cells and their relation to each other is demonstrated. x 880.

three carcinomas. Similar findings have been made by others (16, 17, 56, 57). After many failures, Curtis and Dunning (55) succeeded in transplanting successfully two lymphosarcomas originating in the cecal lymph nodes. Pollard and Teah (58) recently reported lymphosarcomas of the thymus in three twenty-five-month-old germ-free Wistar rats. Jenney (59) diagnosed reticulum cell sarcoma of the mesentery of the ileocecal junction in twelve of eighty-three Wistar rats. Saxton, Sperling, Barnes, and McKay (13) stated that fifty-nine of their 198 control rats had lymphosarcoma of the lung. One lymphoid and three epithelial tumors of the thymus were reported by Ratcliffe (12), while

FIGURE 15. Colon showing reticulum cell sarcoma. x880.
FIGURE 16. Colon, illustrating distribution of reticular fibers in reticulum cell sarcoma in Figure 15. Wilder's silver. x 880.

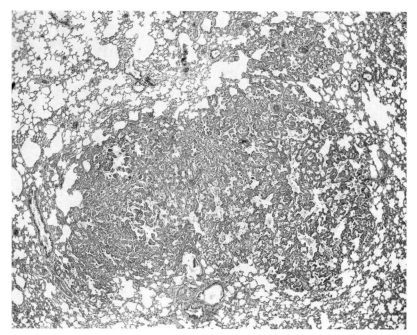

FIGURE 18. Lung with alveologenic carcinoma. The tumor is composed of cuboidal cells in a papillary glandular arrangement. It is similar to the common pulmonary tumor of the mouse. x 35.

Stoerk, Guérin and Guérin (60) described ten thymic tumors composed of both lymphocytes and epithelial cells.

We have diagnosed leukemia in one rat in each of the inbred F344, BUF, and ACI strains, but found no leukemia in the OM or M520 rats. About 14 per cent of WN rats over eighteen months of age have granulocytic leukemia. The greater tendency for Wistar rate to develop leukemia was also noted by Kim, Clifton and Furth (18), who reported leukemia in six of eighty-three rats of an inbred Wistar line similar to ours.

FIGURE 19. Lung with an adenomatous polyp in a dilated bronchus. x 22.
FIGURE 20. An area of adenomatosis in a lung. The lesion is well circumscribed and the pleural surface somewhat depressed. Mucus is present chiefly as fine cytoplasmic droplets at the free margin of the cell. The lumens of some of the glands contain mucus and cellular debris. x 56.

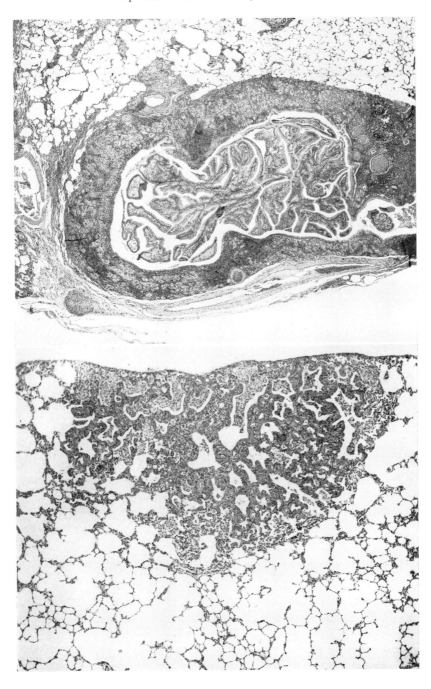

To our knowledge, spontaneous leukemia in the rat was not reported until 1936, when Wilens and Sproul (61) described twelve cases in Osborne-Mendel rats over twenty months old. All but one of these neoplasms were granulocytic in type. Other cases of spontaneous leukemia in rats have been reported (45, 48, 62-67). Some of these were transplantable. Engelbreth-Holm (68) has made an extensive review of leukemia in animals.

Lung

In 1952, Horn and Stewart (69) published a description of an alveologenic carcinoma found in a twelve-month-old M520 male rat of our NIH series of untreated controls. Since that time we have found three similar tumors, all in rats twenty-one months old. One was in a WN female, and the other two in F344 rats, one a male and one a female (Fig. 18). These tumors resembled the common pulmonary tumor of the mouse, displaying a papillary glandular pattern. We have observed bronchial polyps in two F344 male rats (Fig. 19) and pulmonary adenomatosis in an ACI female (Figs. 20 and 21).

Others have remarked upon the infrequency of spontaneous pulmonary neoplasms in the rat. Only four pulmonary tumors were recorded by Bullock and Curtis (10); these were an osteochondrosarcoma, a squamous-cell carcinoma, a polymorphous-cell tumor, and a fibrosarcoma. Saxton and associates (13) found two adenomas of the lung in Osborne-Mendel rats. Guérin (14) reported eight epithelial tumors arising from the lung or bronchi, as well as two sarcomas. Olcott (45) also reported a sarcoma in a Sherman-Mendel rat. No primary pulmonary tumors were found in the other series of rats listed in Table I.

————————————————————→

Figure 21. A higher power view of a portion of the area of adenomatosis illustrated in Figure 20. The distribution of mucus within the cells is shown. Periodic acid-Schiff. x 780.

Figure 22. Submaxillary gland. There is a tumor of the capsule of the gland; it is composed of tightly-packed mesenchymal-type cells interspersed with cysts of various sizes. Immature vascular structures distended with blood are seen in the lower right corner. In the upper right portion of the illustration is a remnant of submaxillary gland. x 50.

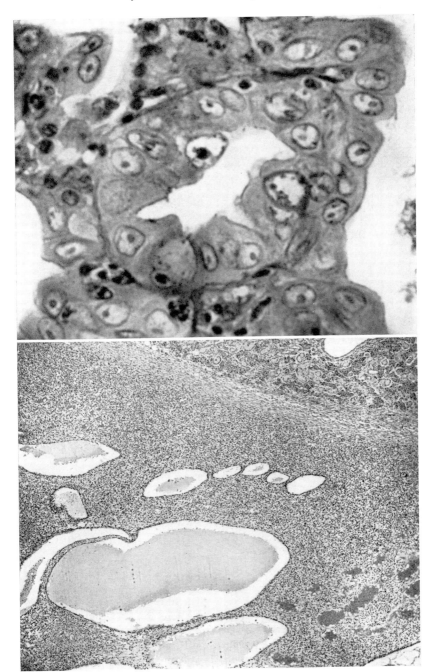

Salivary Glands

Spontaneous tumors of the salivary glands occur infrequently in rats of any age. Davis, Stevenson and Busch (15), Ratcliffe (12), Gilbert and Gillman (17), and McEuen (70) each reported one carcinoma of the submaxillary gland, and Guérin (14) described five "epitheliomas." Curtis and associates (11) reported a parotid gland adenoma. The two sarcomas reported by McCoy (8) and by Wooley and Wherry (9) and the myxoma noted by Olcott (45) in the salivary gland region involved, and may have originated in, the salivary glands. A sarcoma of the submaxillary gland of a Sprague-Dawley rat described by Thompson and his associates (19) is similar to two spontaneous tumors we have seen, one in a twenty-four-month ACI female and the other in a BUF male of twenty-two months (Fig. 22). These tumors are also like the sarcomas induced in younger rats by the administration of N,N', 2-7 fluorenylenbisacetamide (71). We have noted adenoma-like hypertrophic glandular lesions in the parotid glands of many rats, particularly in rats of the ACI, F344, and BUF strains. These lesions consist of a circumscribed focus of from a few to several greatly enlarged acini that compress the surrounding tissue.

Alimentary Tract

The only tumor of the stomach we observed was a sarcoma of the forestomach in a twenty-four month F344 male (Fig. 23). We found a small carcino-sarcoma of the ileum in a thirty-month ACI female. One OM male and one female had adenomatous polyps of the cecum, and another OM male had multiple tumors, either fibromas or neuromas, also of the cecum. A rectal polyp in an ACI male was histologically malignant but failed to grow after transplantation.

The rarity of tumors of the alimentary tract is indicated by

———————————→

FIGURE 23. Wall of forestomach containing a sarcoma. In some areas this tumor penetrated all layers of the stomach and extended onto the peritoneum. x 70.

FIGURE 24. Pancreas containing a small islet cell adenoma. x 140.

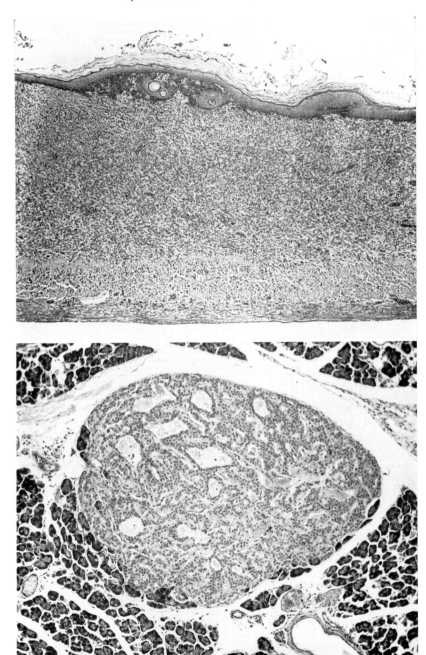

the meager number reported in the literature. We have found descriptions of one squamous cell carcinoma of the tongue (13) and a similar tumor of the esophagus (16). Squamous-cell carcinomas of the forestomach have been noted in three instances (13, 14, 19). Bullock and Curtis (10) described nine sarcomas; six of these involved the glandular stomach, and three involved both forestomach and glandular stomach. They found but one adenocarcinoma of the glandular stomach. Crain (16) has recently described two carcinomas originating in the glandular stomach. The only other tumor of the stomach that we have found reported in the literature is a polypoid adenoma, location unspecified, listed by Saxton and associates (13). An adenocarcinoma of the ileum was reported by Thompson and co-workers (19). Three cases of carcinoma of the colon have been reported in two series of necropsies (16, 72), while Bullock and Curtis (10) described one gelatinous carcinoma, two fibromas, and seven sarcomas of the cecum. Crain (16) found one lipoma between the mucosa and the muscularis in the wall of the large intestine.

Pancreas

We have observed only two islet cell tumors, one in a twenty-four-month-old WN male (Fig. 24) and the other in an ACI female of twenty-one months. Rosen and his associates while studying the effects of ionizing irradiation or neutron exposure on Sprague-Dawley rats paid particular attention to the pancreas. Among their control animals they found islet cell adenomas in four of forty-one rats in one series (73) and in seven of forty-one in another (74). Islet cell adenomas in Sprague-Dawley rats were also reported by Berdjis (75) and by Thompson and his associates (19), while Bagg and Hagopian (76) and also Gilbert and Gillman (17) noted similar tumors in Wistar rats.

We found a single acinar cell carcinoma; this was in a thirty-month-old M520 female. The only other tumors of this type we

--→

Figure 25. A small sarcoma in a kidney. Dilated calyces can be seen on the right of the illustration. x 26.

Figure 26. A higher power view of the sarcoma of the kidney illustarted in Figure 25 showing tumor cells encircling a glomerulus. x 340.

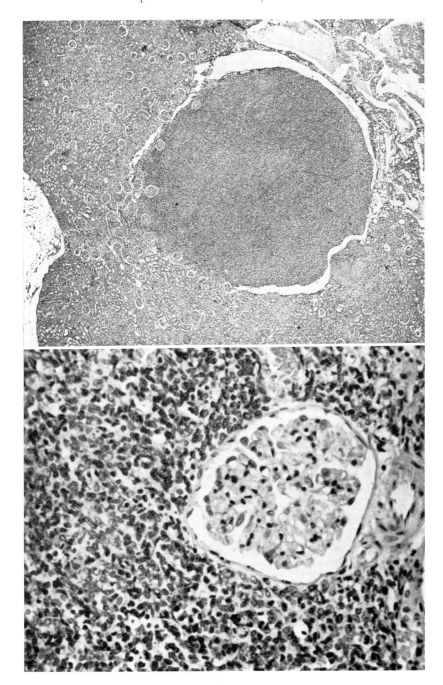

know to have been reported were in one rat of Gilbert and Gillman's series (17) and in one of the rats examined by Loeb (77).

Liver

In contrast to the ease with which tumors of the liver can be induced by a variety of carcinogens, the spontaneous occurrence of hepatomas is exceptional. We have observed only two. Both were small and well-differentiated, and both were in M520 female rats twenty-seven months of age.

The few spontaneous tumors of hepatic cell origin reported include two hepatomas in the Osborne-Mendel rats of Saxton and his associates (13), one hepatoma, one adenocarcinoma, and five cystadenomas in the rats examined by Bullock and Curtis (10), and one hepatoma in the OM rats of Nelson and Morris (53).

Urinary Tract

We have found but one tumor of the kidney; this was a sarcoma in a twenty-four-month BUF male (Figs. 25 and 26). A number of embryonal carcinomas and a few adenomas and sarcomas of the kidney have been described in various strains of rats (8-10, 12, 14, 16, 19, 45, 48, 78-80), but in general renal tumors are uncommon. We have never seen a spontaneous tumor of the bladder. Bullock and Rohdenburg (46), in a review of tumors described by others, mention a carcinoma of the bladder, and Wooley and Wherry (9) and Guérin (14) each reported a papilloma.

Testis

Hyperplasia of the interstitial cells of the testis occurs in ACI and F344 rats killed as early as fifteen months. After eighteen months, 80 per cent of ACI rats show hyperplastic nodules (Fig. 27) but very few large tumors, whereas many of our F344 rats in this age range have tumors that nearly replace one or both testes

————————————→

FIGURE 27. Testis containing one large and several small tumor-like nodules of proliferated interstitial cells. x 20.

FIGURE 28. Testis containing a tumor that measured 2 x 1.3 x 1.3 cm. The remaining testicular tubules are compressed and atrophied. x 28.

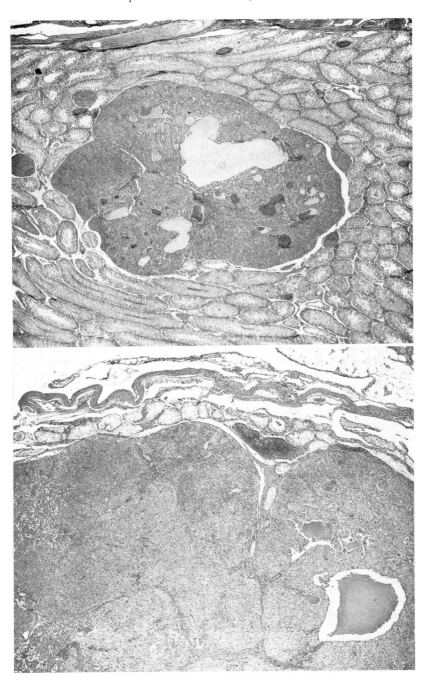

(Figs. 28 and 29). We have seen interstitial cell tumors in two ACI rats twenty-one and twenty-four months old, but none in the BUF, OM, or WN strains. A testis with such a tumor is enlarged to as much as twice its normal size. The tumors are yellowish-brown and have somewhat the consistency of brain tissue. Interstitial cell tumors do not invade nor metastasize and we have not been able to transplant one successfully. Iglesias, however, reported the transplantation of a tumor of this type that originated in an ACI rat (81). He stated that the tumor had no hormonal action in castrated male hosts.

One interstitial cell tumor was described by Bullock and Curtis (10), another by Saxton and his co-workers (13), three by Guérin (14), and two by Berdjis (75). Gilbert and Gillman (17) as well as Crain (16) referred to a high incidence of interstitial cell tumors in Wistar rats. However, in the inbred WN rats used at NIH, interstitial cell testicular tumors have not been noted. One fifteen-month-old Wistar rat in our series had a fibrosarcoma of the testis and scrotal sac, probably similar to two tumors reported by Ratcliffe (12) and the two reported by Bullock and Curtis (10).

We have occasionally seen in histologic sections a small, papillary adenomatoid tumor situated along the genital omentum and on the serosal surface of the testis or epididymis of one or both sides (Fig. 30). We have never tried to transplant such tumors, but histologically they appear benign. They may be found in rats of a number of strains, but most often in ACI, BUF, and OM.

Ovary

About a third of our OM rats over eighteen months of age develop granulosa cell tumors (Fig. 31), but we have seen only a few in ACI, M520, and WN strain rats and none in the BUF and

————————————————————→

FIGURE 29. A section from the margin of the interstitial cell testicular tumor shown in Figure 28. A testicular tubule is present on the left. The tumor is composed of cords of polyhedral cells with one or two prominent nuclei and abundant homogeneous, somewhat vacuolated cytoplasm. x 275.

FIGURE 30. Testis with papillary mesothelioma of the genital omentum and tunica vaginalis testis. x40.

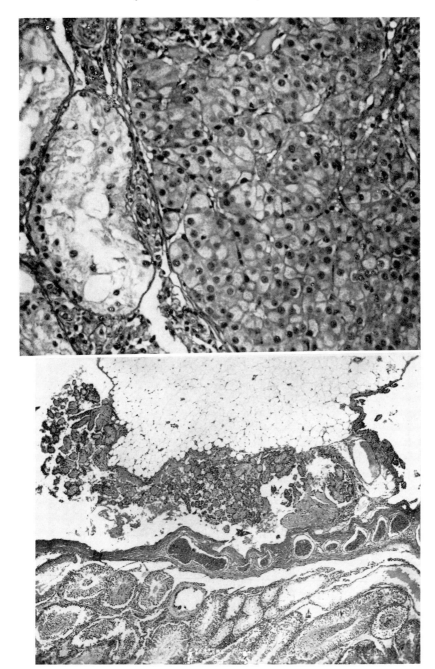

F344 rats. Metastasis to the regional lymph nodes and spleen has occasionally occurred. Rats with granulosa cell tumors may have concomitant hyperplasia of the endometrium (Fig. 32) and mammary tissue and mucification of the vagina. A few OM rats have had papillary cystadenocarcinoma of the ovary (Fig. 33). Simple cysts may sometimes be found in all our six strains.

Other authors have reported granulosa cell tumors (17, 19, 82), fibromas (16, 10, 13), adenomas (13, 75), sarcomas (10) and carcinomas (16, 10, 12, 83).

Uterus and Vagina

(a) Uterine Horns

Nearly two-thirds of our F344 rats and one-third of our M520 rats over twenty-one months of age have tumors of endometrial origin. A few OM, ACI, and BUF rats but no WN rats have tumors of this type. In the F344 and M520 rats, more tumors occur in virgins than in breeders, but in the other strains there is no significant difference evident by mating history.

The majority of the tumors are adenomatous polyps (Figs. 34-37), but a few are angiosarcomas. We transplanted one of the latter and found that the histologic pattern of the transplant was similar to that of the original tumor. Adenocarcinoma of the endometrium (Fig. 38) was found in two ACI and in one BUF rat; these tumors extended through the wall of the uterus. Two areas of squamous cell carcinoma were present in a dilated, squamous-cell-lined uterine horn of a twenty-seven-month BUF rat. We found but one myoma; this occurred in a F344 rat twenty-four months of age (Fig. 39). According to the literature, as well

--->

FIGURE 31. Ovary virtually replaced by granulosa cell tumor with a folliculoid pattern. Granulosa cell tumors may have various combinations of folliculoid and sarcomatoid cells and may have much diversity of structure from part to part. x 210.

FIGURE 32. Uterus with cystic hyperplasia of the endometrium and inflammatory reaction. The lesion in some animals assumes a more polypoid appearance. In this and other rats, uterine hyperplasia may be associated with granulosa cell tumors of the ovary. x 37.

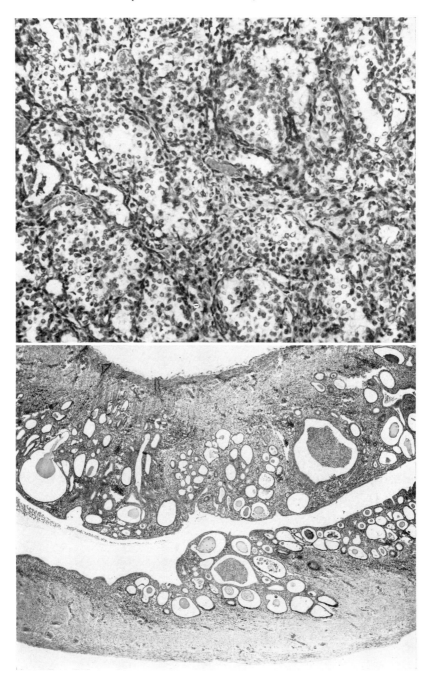

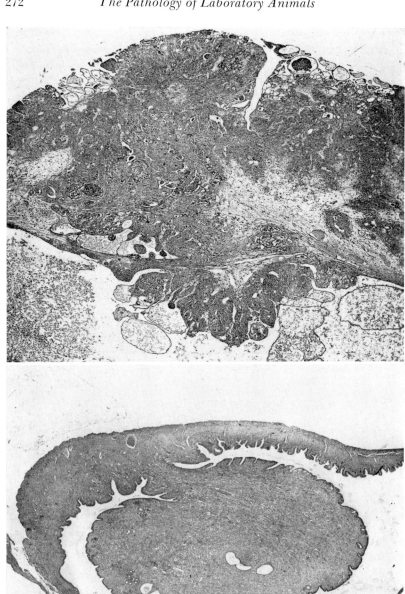

as to our own observations, the uterine horns are a rather common site for neoplastic growths. Forty-eight tumors of a variety of types were reported by Bullock and Curtis (10), ten by Ratcliffe (12), twelve by Crain (16), three by Thompson and associates (19), twenty by Gilbert and Gillman (17), thirty-one by Schultze (47), and forty-five by Guérin (14). Pollia (84), Singer (85) each described a transplantable uterine sarcoma, and Guérin and Guérin (86), a transplantable carcinoma.

(b) Cervix

The cervix, in contrast to the uterine horns, is a rare site for tumor development. Only one of our rats, an OM breeder of twenty-seven months, had a cervical polyp. Tumors of the cervix described in the literature include two fibrovascular polyps in the Sprague-Dawley rats of Thompson and his co-workers (19) and one fibroendothelioma in the Wistar rats of Gilbert and Gillman (17).

(c) Vagina

Three sarcomas (10, 17, 12), three carcinomas (17, 12), and two fibromas (12) have been reported. We have found no tumors of the vagina in our NIH rats.

Mammary Gland

Tumors of the mammary gland have been so thoroughly described and discussed that little further comment is needed except to cite the recent review of the subject made by Noble and Cutts (87).

A few references dealing with the normal development of the mammary gland (88-90) are included here.

We have found a few fibroadenomas (Fig. 40) and carcinomas (Fig. 41) in the old female breeder and non-breeder rats of all

---

FIGURE 33. Cystadenocarcinoma of an ovary. The growth has a papillary glandular pattern; tumor tissue forms a part of the wall of the cyst and also covers a portion of the surface. x 26.

FIGURE 34. Uterus. An angiomatous adenomatous polyp occupies part of the distended uterine cavity. The epithelium covering the polyp is continuous with that lining the uterus. x 10.

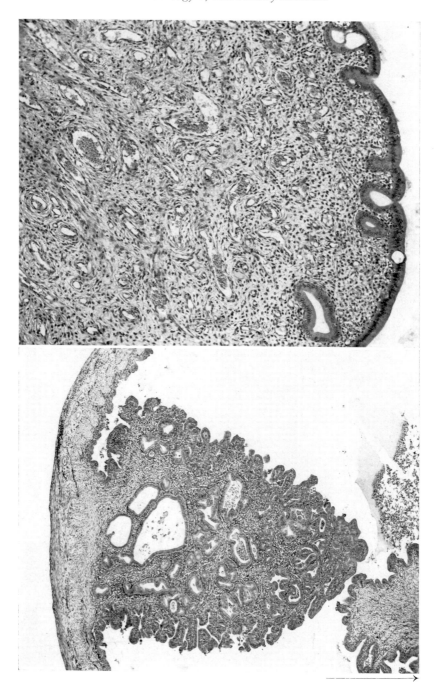

our strains. More mammary gland tumors occur in the WN rats than in rats of other strains. Among their germ-free Wistar rats, Pollard and Teah (58) found eighteen mammary tumors, but they found no tumors in germ-free rats of the Fischer or Sprague-Dawley strains.

Pituitary Gland

The incidence of tumors of the anterior lobe of the pituitary gland probably varies directly with the number of skulls opened and the number of pituitary glands examined grossly and histologically. Pituitary adenomas were probably first noted by Fischer in 1926 (91). One of the first careful studies of the rat's pituitary gland was made by Wolfe, Bryan, and Wright (92). In rats eighteen months of age or older, these authors encountered pituitary adenomas or early adenomatous changes in 10 per cent of breeders and non-breeders of their Albany strain female rats, in 68 per cent of Wistar female breeders, in 29 per cent of Vanderbilt female breeders, and in 12 per cent of Vanderbilt males. The Vanderbilt strain was started from Osborne-Mendel stock. Wolfe and Wright (93) have also published a study of the cytology of pituitary gland tumors. Saxton and his co-workers (13) found that ninety-two of their rats of the Yale line of the Osborne-Mendel strain had chromophobe adenomas. Kim, Clifton, and Furth (18) reported pituitary tumors in twenty of eighty-three rats of a line of the Wistar strain, the WF. Crain (16), Thompson and his associates (19), Schulze (47), Arai (48), Berdjis (75) and Oberling, Guérin, and Guérin (94) have also noted adenomas of the pituitary gland.

In these various series of necropsies, as in ours, the incidence of pituitary gland tumors rises in the older age groups. We have found them in few rats younger than eighteen months. About one-third of ACI and M520, one-fourth of F344 and OM, three-fourths of BUF, and nearly all WN female rats have pituitary

FIGURE 35. A higher power view of the adenomatous polyp illustrated in Figure 34. x 135.

FIGURE 36. Uterus showing an adenomatous polyp which is quite different from the one illustrated in Figures 34 and 35. x 50.

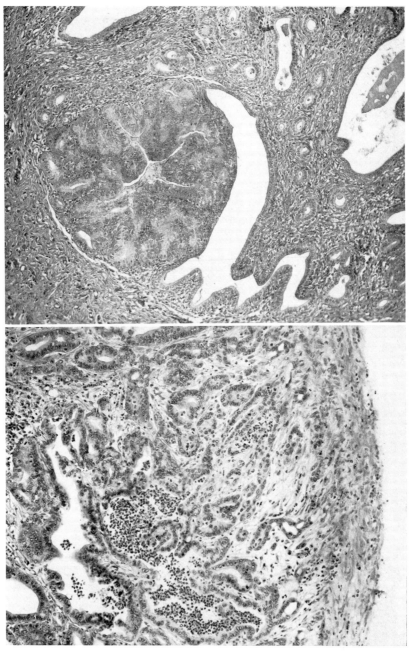

Figure 37. Uterus containing a small adenoma of the endometrium. x 125.
Figure 38. An adenocarcinoma with marked inflammatory reaction in a uterus. In a nearby area this tumor extended completely through the wall of the uterus. x 135.

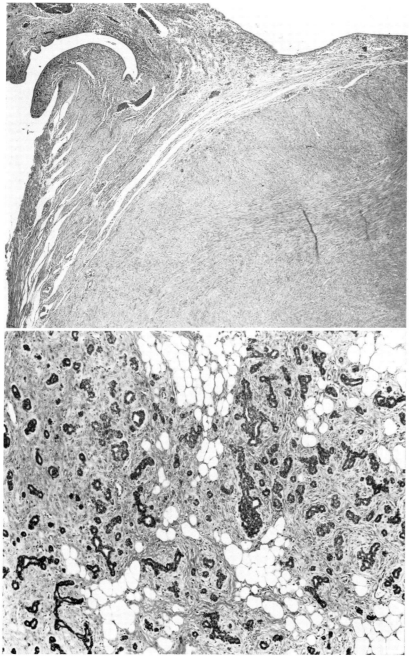

FIGURE 39. Uterus with a myoma of the myometrium. x 35.
FIGURE 40. Mammary gland replaced by a fibroadenoma with proliferated duct structures and a large amount of connective tissue. x 100.

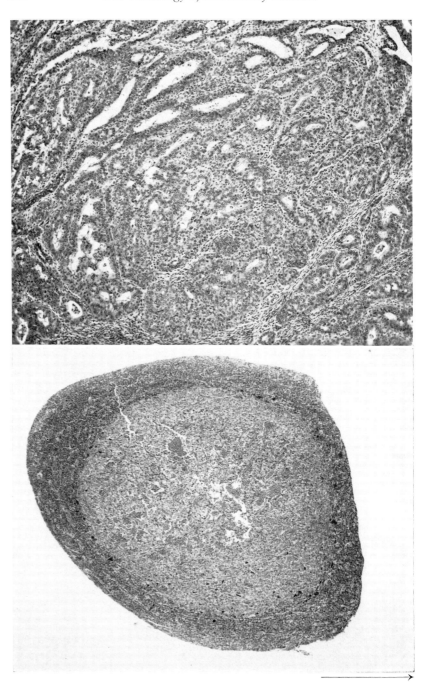

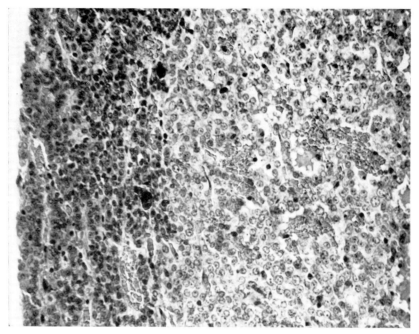

FIGURE 43. A higher power view of the chromophobe adenoma illustrated in Figure 42. The tumor lies in the right portion of the field and is composed of uniform cells. The more angiomatous portion of the tumor is in the center. The pituitary tissue on the left is compressed. x 210.

tumors after they are eighteen months old. This is about half as many as we have found in males, except for the F344 strain, in which we have noted no sex difference. There is no statistical difference between the incidence of pituitary tumors in breeders or non-breeders of any strain. The tumors are classified simply as "chromophobe adenomas" when they are composed of well demarcated nodules of hypertrophied chromophobe cells compressing the surrounding tissue (Figs. 42 and 43). When, in addition, there are many dilated blood channels and hemorrhage,

---

FIGURE 41. Mammary gland replaced by an adenocarcinoma. The tumor cells, arranged in a papillary pattern, are low columnar or cuboidal with a well-defined cell membrane, finely granular cytoplasm, and round nuclei. x 70.

FIGURE 42. Anterior lobe of pituitary gland with a chromophobe adenoma that is partially angiomatous. x 65.

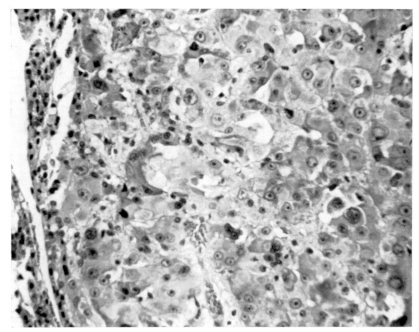

FIGURE 44. Carcinoma of the anterior lobe of the pituitary gland. Note the great variations in size, shape and staining of the cells as compared with the adenoma illustrated in Figures 42 and 43. x 290.

the term "angiomatous adenoma" is used. Mitotic figures as well as giant cells with bizarre, hyperchromatic nuclei are observed in some tumors. The term "adenoma" is probably used too generally to describe these neoplasms; many are actually carcinomas (Figs. 44 and 45) that invade surrounding structures and grow upon transplantation. Some pituitary tumors, especially in old females, are associated with hyperplasia or tumors of the mammary gland, a condition noted by Guérin (14) and also by Kim, Clifton, and Furth (18).

————————————→

FIGURE 45. Section through brain and nasopharynx. There is a large carcinoma replacing the pituitary gland and producing secondary dilatation of the left lateral ventricle. x 8.

FIGURE 46. Adrenal gland with an adenoma of the cortex. x26.

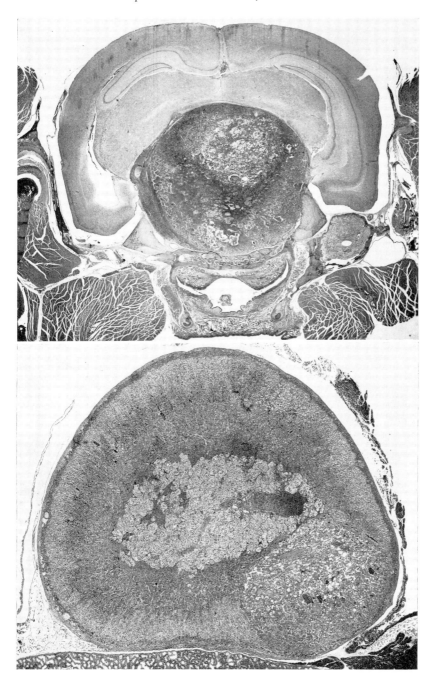

Adrenal Gland

(a) Cortex

Inbred strains of rats differ in their propensity to develop tumors of the cortex of the adrenal gland. Although we have never seen a cortical adenoma or carcinoma in our ACI strain, they must occur in some lines, for Iglesias and Mardoncs (95) have carried one in transplant for many years. F344 and WN rats rarely show adrenal cortical adenomas or even hyperplastic cortical nodules. After the rats are eighteen months old, we have found adrenocortical adenomas in about one-fifth of the M520 males and two-fifths of the M520 females and in one-third of the BUF males and in two-thirds of the BUF females. OM rats are particularly prone to develop hyperplastic nodules or small adenomas between twelve and eighteen months, and nearly all (73 per cent of males and 95 per cent of females) OM rats over eighteen months of age have adenomas or carcinomas (Figs. 46 and 47). Some of these are transplantable and hormonally-active (96, 97). They appear to be similar to the tumors studied by Cohen, Furth, and Buffett (98), which, though derived from radiothyroidectomized WF rats, were believed to be of spontaneous origin.

(b) Medulla

We rarely see pheochromocytomas or preneoplastic nodules in the adrenal medulla of our rats until the animals are at least twenty-one months old. They are found more often in males and occur in about 40 per cent of males of the BUF, F344, and WN strains, rarely in ACI, and not at all in OM rats. In old males of the M250 strain, we find well-defined pheochromocytomas in

————————————————————→

FIGURE 47. Right adrenal gland with a carcinoma of the cortex. This tumor grew upon transplantation. The tumor tissue is separated from the capsule by a thin layer of zona glomerulosa. The cytoplasm of the tumor cells is homogeneous or finely granular and contains vacuoles; the nuclei are small and round with one to three nucleoli. x 360.

FIGURE 48. Adrenal gland with a pheochromocytoma. x 16.

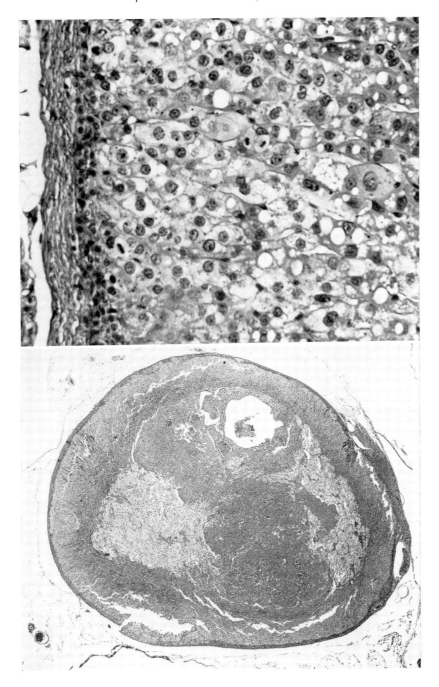

about two-thirds of the animals (Fig. 48). These tumors enlarge the adrenal gland and compress the cortex to a thin rim. In other rats, especially in females, it is difficult to differentiate small tumors and nodules of atypical cells considered to be precursors of pheochromocytomas. We have not tried to determine whether any of the pheochromocytomas were functional. There are abundant descriptions of pheochromocytomas in rats of various strains. Gillman, Gilbert, and Spence (99) reported that in different groups of Wistar rats pheochromocytomas occurred in from 82 to 85.5 per cent of males and in from 50 to 76 per cent of females. Yeakel (100) described adrenal medullary hyperplasia in thirteen of eighteen male and in three of nineteen female rats of the Wistar and Norway strains. Nodular hyperplasia and tumors of the adrenal medulla have been observed also by Saxton and his associates (13), Guérin (14), Crain (16), and Thompson and his associates (19).

Thyroid and Parathyroid Glands

Adenomas of the thyroid gland occur in a few of our F344, OM, and WN rats (Fig. 49). We found one carcinoma of the thyroid gland with metastases to the mediastinal lymph nodes in an old WN female (Figs 50 and 51) and are still carrying this tumor in transplant. It was of the solid type with very little colloid. We have also carried in transplant a papillary adenocarcinoma containing a great deal of a colloid-like material; this tumor originated in an old OM female (Fig. 52). Thompson and coworkers (19) described nine "light cell adenomas" of the thyroid gland which they thought resembled thyroid tumors induced by iodine deficiency (101, 102), although the diet of their rats contained sufficient iodine. Tumors of the thyroid gland appear with high frequency in old Long-Evans strain rats (103). In one ex-

---------------------------------------→

Figure 49. Thyroid gland containing an adenoma. x 43.
Figure 50. Thyroid gland, trachea, and esophagus. There is a carcinoma of the left lobe of the thyroid gland with invasion of blood vessels and perivascular structures and metastases to cervical and mediastinal lymph nodes. x 17.

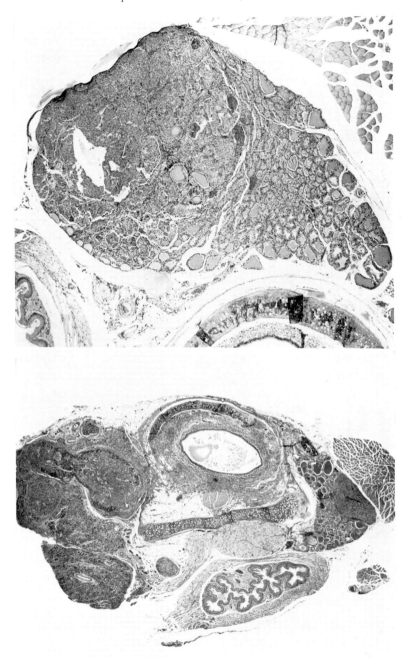

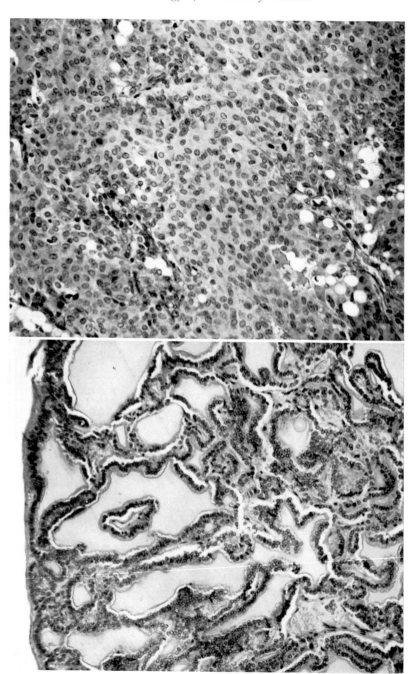

periment, Lindsay and his associates (104) found one adenoma and eleven alveolar carcinomas among thirty-nine untreated controls. Gilbert and Gillman (17) reported that 10 per cent of their Wistar rats had thyroid carcinomas. Others have reported only a few adenomas, carcinomas, or sarcomas of the thyroid gland (10, 14, 47, 48, 75, 77, 91, 105), but some investigators admit that the thyroid glands were seldom examined histologically.

We have only two adenomas of the parathyroid gland in our collection; one occurred in a M520 male rat twenty-four months old (Figs. 53 and 54), and the other in a WN male of twenty-one months. Since neither rat had any pathologic changes in kidneys or bone indicative of deranged calcium metabolism, we assume that these parathyroid adenomas were non-functional. Spontaneous adenomas of the parathyroid gland have also been noted by a few others (14, 48, 75, 104).

Brain, Spinal Cord, Cranial Nerves, and Pineal Body

There are only a few spontaneous intracranial tumors reported; however, this paucity may be misleading, for the brain and adjacent structures were frequently not examined at necropsy. The possible oversight of these tumors is pointed out by Bullock and Curtis, who wrote: "Since the routine autopsies rarely included the brain and spinal cord because of the absence of clinical manifestations of the presence of neoplasms in these organs, it is possible that the nervous system gave origin to tumors which were never discovered" (10).

Sokoloff (106) found a glioma in an Osborne-Mendel rat eighteen months old, and Highman and Altland (107) described a glioma in the pons of a Sprague-Dawley rat maintained under conditions of high altitude. Other reports include a ganglioneuroma of the optic nerve in one female of the Copenhagen line

FIGURE 51. A higher power view of the carcinoma of the thyroid gland illustrated in Figure 50. The histologic pattern is that of a solid carcinoma. x 260.

FIGURE 52. Thyroid gland replaced by a papillary, colloid-containing carcinoma. x 210.

2331 examined by Bullock and Curtis (10), one perineural sarcoma of the eighth nerve and one glioblastoma of the brain in each of two Osborne-Mendel rats studied by Saxton and his associates (13), and one meningioma in the Wistar rats of Gilbert and Gillman (17). In 10,000 rats necropsied, Guérin (14) observed one meningioma, two gliomas, and one glioependymoma. Thompson and his co-workers (19) have recently described an ependymoma, a meningioma, a papilloma of the choroid plexus, and a tumor of the pineal body in Sprague-Dawley rats allowed to live out their life span. We have never seen a tumor of the central nervous system or pineal body in any of our untreated rats.

Ear

Squamous cell carcinoma arising from the external auditory canal or ceruminous (Zymbal's) glands has seldom been noted in untreated rats, although such tumors are easily induced by a variety of carcinogens. Tannenbaum and Maltoni (52) described three tumors of Zymbal's gland in control Sprague-Dawley rats. The failure of many investigators to take routine sections through the ears may account for the failure to identify tumors in this area, although even with routine ear sections we have found only a few tumors. Three squamous cell carcinomas of the ear canal occurred in OM rats and two in M520 rats (Fig. 55), all over twenty-one months of age. In addition, we found one squamous papilloma of the ceruminous gland in a twenty-four-month-old ACI male. A dermoid cyst occurred in another twenty-four-month ACI male rat (Figs. 56 and 57). Serial sections indicated that this cyst probably originated in the middle ear, destroyed the inner ear, and compressed and distorted surrounding structures. The cyst was filled with hairs, but only a few hair follicles were found in its wall.

FIGURE 53. Parathyroid gland adenoma. x 28.

FIGURE 54. A higher power view of the parathyroid adenoma illustrated in Figure 53 showing the cellular characteristics and pattern of growth. x 340.

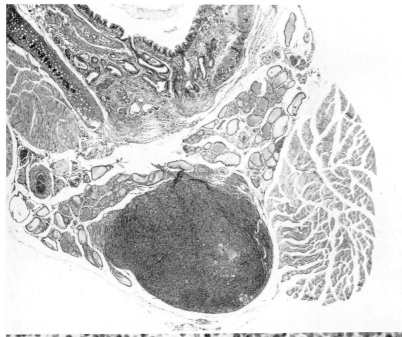

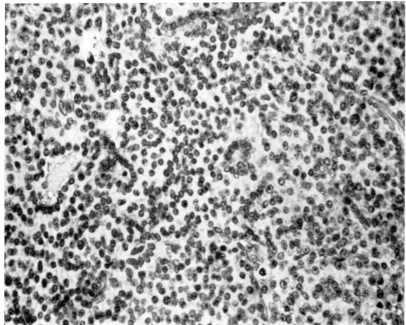

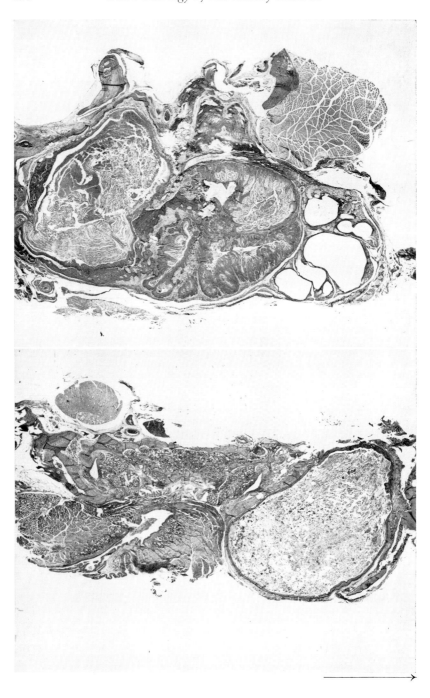

5. GREENE, R. R., BURRILL, M. W., and IVY, A. C.: The effects of postnatal androgenic treatment in the female rat. *Anat. Rec.*, *83*:19–29, 1942.

6. ENGLE, E. T.: Tubular adenomas and testis-like tubules of the ovaries of aged rats. *Cancer Res.*, *6*:578–582, 1946.

7. RAYNAUD, A.: Formations syncytiales observées dans les ovaires de jeunes rats. *Ann. Endocr.*, *8*:141–164, 1947.

8. McCOY, G. W.: A preliminary report on tumors found in wild rats. *J. Med. Res.*, *16*:285–296, 1909.

9. WOOLLEY, P. G., and WHERRY, W. B.: Notes on twenty-two spontaneous tumors in wild rats, (*M. Norvegicus.*) *J. Med. Res.*, *25*:205–216, 1911.

10. BULLOCK, F. D., and CURTIS, M. R.: Spontaneous tumors of the rat. *J. Cancer Res.*, *14*:1–115, 1930.

11. CURTIS, M. R., BULLOCK, F. D., and DUNNING, W. F.: A statistical study of the occurrence of spontaneous tumors in a large colony of rats. *Amer. J. Cancer*, *15*:67–121, 1931.

12. RATCLIFFE, H. L.: Spontaneous tumors in two colonies of rats of the Wistar Institute of Anatomy and Biology. *Amer. J. Path.*, *16*:237–254, 1940.

13. SAXTON, J. A., JR., SPERLING, G. A., BARNES, L. L., and McCAY, C. M.: The influence of nutrition upon the incidence of spontaneous tumors of the albino rat. *Acta Un. Int. C. Cancr.*, *6*: 423–431, 1948.

14. GUÉRIN, M.: *Tumerus Spontanées des Animaux de Laboratorie (Souris-Rat-Poule).* Paris, Legrand, 1954.

15. DAVIS, R. K., STEVENSON, G. T., and BUSCH, K. A.: Tumor incidence in normal Sprague-Dawley female rats. *Cancer Res.*, *16*:194–197, 1956.

16. CRAIN, R. C.: Spontaneous tumors in the Rochester strain of the Wistar rat. *Amer. J. Path.*, *34*:311–335, 1958.

17. GILBERT, C., and GILLMAN, J.: Spontaneous neoplasms in albino rats. *S. Afr. J. Med. Sci.*, *23*:257–272, 1958.

18. KIM, U., CLIFTON, K. H., and FURTH, J.: A highly inbred line of Wistar rats yielding spontaneous mammo-somatotropic pituitary and other tumors. *J. Nat. Cancer Inst.*, *24*:1031–1055, 1960.

19. THOMPSON, S. W., HUSEBY, R. A., FOX, M. A., DAVIS, C. L., and HUNT, R. D.: Spontaneous tumors in the Sprague-Dawley rat. *J. Nat. Cancer Inst.*, *27*:1037–1057, 1961.

20. Jay, G. E.: "Genetic Strains and Stocks" in *Methodology in Mammalian Genetics*. W. Burdette, Ed. San Francisco, Holden-Day, Inc., 1963.

21. Innes, J. R. M., McAdams, A. J., and Yevich, P.: Pulmonary disease in rats: A survey with comments on "chronic murine pneumonia." *Amer. J. Path., 32:*141–159, 1956.

22. Newberne, P. M., Salmon, W. D., and Hare, W. V.: Chronic murine pneumonia in an experimental laboratory. *A.M.A. Arch. Path., 72:*224–233, 1961.

23. Passey, R. D., Leese, A., and Knox, J. C.: Bronchiectasis and metaplasia in the lung of the laboratory rat. *J. Path. Bact., 42:* 425–434, 1936.

24. Nelson, J. B., and Gowen, J. W.: The incidence of middle ear infection and pneumonia in albino rats at different ages. *J. Infect. Dis., 46:*53–63, 1930.

25. Nelson, J. B.: The bacteria of the infected middle ear in adult and young albino rats. *J. Infect. Dis., 46:*64–75, 1930.

26. Stewart, H. L., and Jones, B. F.: Pathologic anatomy of chronic ulcerative cecitis: A spontaneous disease of the rat. *Arch. Path., 31:*37–54, 1941.

27. Wilgram, G. F., and Ingle, D. J.: Renal-cardiovascular pathologic changes in aging female breeder rats. *A.M.A. Arch. Path., 68:*690–703, 1959.

28. Wilens, S. L., and Sproul, E. E.: Spontaneous cardiovascular disease in the rat. II. Lesions of the vascular system. *Amer. J. Path., 14:*201–216, 1938.

29. Wilens, S. L., and Sproul, E. E.: Spontaneous cardio-vascular disease in the rat. I. Lesions of the heart. *Amer. J. Path., 14:* 177–199, 1938.

30. Hueper, W. C.: Spontaneous arteriosclerosis in rats. *Arch. Path., 20:*708, 1935.

31. Innes, J. R. M., and Stanton, M. F.: Acute disease of the submaxillary and harderian glands (sialo-dachryoadenitis) of rats with cytomegaly and no inclusion bodies. With comments on normal gross and microscopic structure of the exocrine glands in the head and neck of rats. *Amer. J. Path., 38:*455–468, 1961.

32. Kelemen, G., and Sargent, F.: Nonexperimental pathologic nasal findings in laboratory rats. *Arch. Otolaryng., 44:*24–42, 1946.

33. Kelemen, G.: The junction of the nasal cavity and the pharyngeal tube in the rat. *Arch. Otolaryng., 45:*159–168, 1947.

34. SELLERS, A. L., ROSENFELD, S., and FRIEDMAN, N. B.: Spontaneous hydronephrosis in the rat. *Proc. Soc. Exp. Biol. Med., 104:* 512–515, 1960.

35. ANDREW, W.: Age changes in the vascular architecture and cell content in the spleens of 100 Wistar Inst. rats, including comparisons with human material. *Amer. J. Anat., 79:*1–74, 1946.

36. ANDREW, W. and ANDREW, N. V.: Age changes in the deep cervical lymph nodes of 100 Wistar Institute rats. *Amer. J. Anat., 82:*105–165, 1948.

37. HARRIS, C., and BURKE, W. T.: The changing cellular distribution in bone marrow of the normal albino rat between one and fifty weeks of age. *Amer. J. Path., 33:*931–951, 1957.

38. SIMMS, H. S., and BERG, B. N.: Longevity and the onset of lesions in male rats. *J. Geront., 12:*244–252, 1957.

39. ANDREW, W., and PRUETT, D.: Senile changes in the kidney of Wistar Institute rats. *Amer. J. Anat., 100:*51–80, 1957.

40. EVETITT, A. V., and WEBB, C.: The blood picture of the aging male rat. *J. Geront., 13:*255–260, 1958.

41. VAN DYKE, J. H.: Behavior of ultimobranchial tissue in the postnatal thyroid gland: the origin of thyroid cystadenomata in the rat. *Anat. Rec., 88:*369–391, 1944.

42. BACHMANN, R.: "Die Nebenniere" in *Handbuch der Mikroskopischen Anatomie des Menschen*. E. W. von Mollendorff, Ed. Berlin, Gottingen, Heidelberg, Springer, 1954.

43. BURRILL, M. W., and GREENE, R. R.: Androgen production during pregnancy and lactation in the rat. *Anat. Rec., 83:*209–227, 1942.

44. DERINGER, M. K., and HESTON, W. E.: Abnormalities of urogenital system in strain A X C Line 9935 rats. *Proc. Soc. Exp. Biol. Med., 91:*312–314, 1956.

45. OLCOTT, C. T.: A transplantable nephroblastoma (Wilms' tumor) and other spontaneous tumors in a colony of rats. *Cancer Res., 10:*625–628, 1950.

46. BULLOCK, F. D., and ROHDENBURG, G. L.: Spontaneous tumors of the rat. *J. Cancer Res., 2:*39–61, 1917.

47. SCHULZE, E.: Spontantumoren der Schädelhöhle und Genitalorgane bei Sprague-Dawley und Bethesda—Black Ratten. *Z. Krebsforsch., 64:*78–82, 1960.

48. ARAI, M.: Uber die spontanen Geschwulste bei weissen Ratten. *Gann, 34:*137–143, 1940.

49. BULLOCK, F. D., and CURTIS, M. R.: A transplantable metastasizing chondro-rhabdo-myosarcoma of the rat. *J. Cancer Res.,* 7:195–207, 1922.

50. SUGIURA, K.: Studies upon a new transplantable rat tumor. *J. Cancer Res., 12:*143–159, 1928.

51. TIBIRIÇA, P.: Curieuse apparition de néoplasmes sur des rats en expérience. *Compt. Rend. Soc. Biol., 118:*177–178, 1935.

52. TANNENBAUM, A., and MALTONI, C.: Neoplastic response of various tissues to the administration of urethan. *Cancer Res., 22:* 1105–1112, 1962.

53. NELSON, A. A., and MORRIS, J. M.: Reticulum cell lymphosarcoma in rats. *Arch. Path., 31:*578–584, 1941.

54. MOON, H. D., SIMPSON, M. E., LI, C. H., and EVANS, H. M.: Neoplasms in rats treated with pituitary growth hormone. I. Pulmonary and lymphatic tissues. *Cancer Res., 10:*297–308, 1950.

55. CURTIS, M. R., and DUNNING, W. F.: Transplantable lymphosarcomata of the mesenteric lymph nodes of rats. *Amer. J. Cancer, 40:*299–309, 1940.

56. McEUEN, C. S.: The occurrence of lymphosarcoma in rats. *Amer. J. Cancer, 36:*383–385, 1939.

57. FARRIS, E. J., and YEAKEL, E. H.: Spontaneous and transplanted reticulum cell sarcomas in Wistar rats. *Amer. J. Path., 20:* 773–781, 1944.

58. POLLARD, M., and TEAH, B. A.: Spontaneous tumors in germ-free rats. *J. Nat. Cancer Inst., 31:*457–465, 1963.

59. JENNEY, F. S.: Reticulum cell sarcoma of the rat transferred through twelve successive passages in animals of related stock. *Cancer Res., 1:*407–409, 1941.

60. STOERK, H., GUÉRIN, M., and GUÉRIN, P.: Tumeurs lymphoepithéliales du thymus chez le rat. *Bull. Ass. Franç. Cancer, 33:* 141–151, 1946.

61. WILENS, S. L., and SPROUL, E. E.: Spontaneous leukemia and chloroleukemia in the rat. *Amer. J. Path., 12:*249–258, 1936.

62. RASK-NIELSEN, R.: Experimental studies on a transplantable aleukemic myelomatosis in white rats. *Acta. Path. Microbiol. Scand., 15:*285–300, 1938.

63. OBERLING, C., GUÉRIN, M., and GUÉRIN, P.: Leucémies spontanées et transplantables du rat. *Bull. Ass. Franç. Cancer, 28:*214–242, 1939.

64. ROUSSY, G., GUÉRIN, M., and GUÉRIN, P.: Étude d'un chlorome transplantable chez le rat. *Bull. Acad. Med. (Par.)*, *125*:223–226, 1941.

65. LEWIS, M. R.: A transplantable rat lymphoma. *Science*, *118*:355–357, 1953.

66. IGLESIAS, R., and MARDONES, E.: Two instances of spontaneous transplantable leukemias in A x C rats. *Proc. Amer. Assoc. Cancer Res.*, *2*:121, 1956.

67. DUNNING, W. F., and CURTIS, M. R.: A transplantable acute leukemia in an inbred line of rats. *J. Nat. Cancer Inst.*, *19*: 845–853, 1957.

68. ENGELBRETH-HOLM, J.: *Spontaneous and Experimental Leukaemia in Animals.* Translated by C. L. Heel. Edinburgh & London, Oliver & Boyd, Ltd., 1942.

69. HORN, H. A., and STEWART, H. L.: Spontaneous pulmonary tumor in the rat: report of a lesion. *J. Nat. Cancer Inst.*, *12*: 743–749, 1952.

70. McEUEN, C. S.: Occurrence of cancer in rats treated with oestrone *Amer. J. Cancer*, *34*:184–195, 1938.

71. SNELL, K. C., STEWART, H. L., MORRIS, H. P., WAGNER, B. P., and RAY, F. E.: Atrophy, proliferative lesions, and tumors of the salivary glands of rats ingesting N-2-fluorenylacetamide or N,N'-2,7-fluorenylenebisacetamide. *Nat. Cancer Inst. Monogr.*, *5*:55–83, 1961.

72. WILLIS, R. A.: Carcinoma of the intestine in rats. *J. Path. Bact.*, *40*:187–188, 1935.

73. ROSEN, V. J., JR., CASTANERA, T. J., JONES, D. C., and KIMELDORF, D. J.: Islet-cell tumors of the pancreas in the irradiated and nonirradiated rat. *Lab. Invest.*, *10*:608–616, 1961.

74. ROSEN, V. J., JR., CASTANERA, T. J., KIMELDORF, D. J., and JONES, D. C.: Pancreatic islet cell tumors and renal tumors in the male rat following neutron exposure. *Lab. Invest.*, *11*:204–210, 1962.

75. BERJIS, C. C.: Protracted effects of repeated doses of x-ray irradiation in rats. *Exp. Molec. Path.*, *2*:157–172, 1963.

76. BAGG, H. J., and HAGOPIAN, F.: The functional activity of the mammary gland of the rat in relation to mammary cancer. *Amer. J. Cancer*, *35*:175–187, 1939.

77. LOEB, L.: Further investigations in transplantation of tumors. *J. Med. Res.*, *8*:44–73, 1902.

78. LILLIE, R. D., and ENGLE, J. L.: Renal adenosarcoma in a white rat. *Arch. Path., 19:*687–689, 1935.
79. EKER, R.: Familial renal adenomas in Wistar rats. A preliminary report. *Acta Path. Microbiol. Scand., 34:*554–562, 1954.
80. BABCOCK, V. I., and SOUTHAM, C. M.: Transplantable renal tumor of the rat. *Cancer Res., 21:*130–131, 1961.
81. IGLESIAS, R.: Paradoxical actions of steroids on three transplantable ovarian and testicular tumours of the A x C rat. *Acta. Un. Int. C. Cancr., 16:*189–192, 1960.
82. IGLESIAS, R., STERNBERG, W. H., and SEGALOFF, A.: A transplantable functional ovarian tumor occurring spontaneously in a rat. *Cancer Res., 10:*668–673, 1950.
83. SYMEONIDIS, A., and MORI-CHAVEZ, P.: A transplantable ovarian papillary adenocarcinoma of the rat with ascites implants in the ovary. *J. Nat. Cancer Inst., 13:*409–429, 1952.
84. POLLIA, J. A.: A transplantable uterine rat sarcoma of 100 per cent transmissibility. *Amer. J. Cancer, 32:*545–548, 1938.
85. SINGER, C.: A transplantable sarcoma arising in the uterus of a rat. *J. Path. Bact., 18:*495–497, 1913–14.
86. GUÉRIN, M. and GUÉRIN, P.: Epithélioma de l'utérus du rat, lymphotrope et transplantable. *Bull. Ass. Franç. Cancer, 23:* 632–646, 1934.
87. NOBLE, R. L., and CUTTS, J. H.: Mammary tumors of the rat: A review. *Cancer Res., 19:*1125–1139, 1959.
88. MAEDER, L. M. A.: Changes in the mammary gland of the albino rat during lactation and involution. *Amer. J. Anat., 31:*1–26, 1922.
89. TURNER, C. W., and SCHULTZE, A. B.: A study of the causes of the normal development of the mammary glands of the albino rat. *Mo. Agri. Res. Bull.,* No. 157, 1931.
90. WARBRITTON, V. and REECE, R. P.: Mammary glands of the rat during growth and senescence. *Exp. Med. Surg., 5:*33–46, 1947.
91. FISCHER, O.: Über hypophysengeschwülste der weissen ratten. *Virchows Arch. Path. Anat., 259:*9–29, 1926.
92. WOLFE, J. M., BRYAN, W. R., and WRIGHT, A. W.: Histologic observations on the anterior pituitaries of old rats with particular reference to the spontaneous appearance of pituitary adenomata. *Amer. J. Cancer, 34:*352–372, 1938.
93. WOLFE, J. M., and WRIGHT, A. W.: Cytology of spontaneous adenomas in the pituitary gland of the rat. *Cancer Res., 7:*759–773, 1947.

94. OBERLING, C., GUÉRIN, P., and GUÉRIN, M.: Les tumeurs hypophysaires spontanées chez le rat. *Bull. Ass. Franç. Cancer, 37:* 83–96, 1950.

95. IGLESIAS, R., and MARDONES, E.: Spontaneous and transplantable functional tumour of the adrenal cortex in the A x C rat. *Brit. J. Cancer, 12:*20–27, 1958.

96. SNELL, K. C., and STEWART, H. L.: Variations in histologic pattern and functional effects of a transplantable adrenal cortical carcinoma in intact, hypophysectomized, and newborn rats. *J. Nat. Cancer Inst., 22:*1119–1155, 1959.

97. JOHNSON, D. F., SNELL, K. C., FRANCOIS, D., and HEFTMANN, E.: In vitro metabolism of progesterone-4-^{14C} in an adrenocortical carcinoma of the rat. *Acta Endocr., 37:*329–335, 1961.

98. COHEN, A. I., FURTH, J., and BUFFETT, R. F.: Histologic and physiologic characteristics of hormone-secreting transplantable adrenal tumors in mice and rats. *Amer. J. Path., 33:*631–651, 1957.

99. GILLMAN, J., GILBERT, C., and SPENCE, I.: I. Phaeochromocytoma in the rat; pathogenesis and collateral reactions and its relation to comparable tumours in man. *Cancer 6:*494–511, 1953.

100. YEAKEL, E. H.: Medullary hyperplasia of the adrenal gland in aged Wistar albino and gray Norway rats. *Arch. Path., 44:* 71–77, 1947.

101. BIELSCHOWSKY, F.: Chronic iodine deficiency as cause of neoplasia in thyroid and pituitary of aged rats. *Brit. J. Cancer, 7:*203–213, 1953.

102. AXELRAD, A. A., and LEBLOND, C. P.: Induction of thyroid tumors in rats by a low iodine diet. *Cancer, 8:*339–367, 1955.

103. LINDSAY, S., POTTER, G. D., and CHAIKOFF, I. L.: Thyroid neoplasms in the rat: A comparison of naturally occurring and I^{131}-induced tumors. *Cancer Res., 17:*183–189, 1957.

104. LINDSAY, S., SHELINE, G. E., POTTER, G. D., and CHAIKOFF, I. L.: Induction of neoplasms in the thyroid gland of the rat by x-irradiation of the gland. *Cancer Res., 21:*9–16, 1961.

105. SLYE, M., HOLMES, H. F., and WELLS, G. H.: The comparative pathology of cancer of the thyroid, with a report of primary spontaneous tumors of the thyroid in mice and in a rat. Studies on the incidence and inheritability of spontaneous tumors in mice. XXII. *J. Cancer Res., 10:*175–193, 1926.

106. SOKOLOFF, L.: Personal communication.

107. Highman, B., and Altland, P. D.: Acclimatization response and pathologic changes in rats at an altitude of 25,000 feet. *Arch. Path., 48:*503–515, 1949.

DISCUSSION

Question: Dr. Snell, in regard to pituitary adenomas, were there other types of adenomas?

Dr. Snell: I am a bit afraid to answer that. I have recently seen in the F344 rats tumors that I think are probably basophilic adenomas but I cannot be sure until I have special stains. So far as I am concerned right now most of the tumors are chromophobe adenomas.

Dr. Charlotte L. Maddock: We have picked up a spontaneous rat sarcoma in the inbred W/Fu strain . . . . and also an interstitial cell tumor in that line.

Dr. Snell: I am glad to know this. The paper about tumors in that strain was mostly based on females and I didn't have any information about other strains of Wistar, at least in this country.

Dr. Maddock: I wondered whether your interstitial cells had any hormones? We have never been able to see that they had.

Dr. Snell: In Chile, Dr. Iglesias has one from an ACI rat growing in transplant. It has no effect on castrated male hosts, and I presume that the tumors are all very much alike.

Question: What is the cause of testicular atrophy in the rats? Second, discuss adrenocortical nodular hyperplasia and hemorrhage. And third, please discuss mucoid pneumonia.

Dr. Snell: That is quite an order.

I know that most of our old rats do have atrophy of the testicular tubules and whether it is simply cessation of pituitary and other hormonal activity, I cannot say.

We often see nodular hyperplasia of the adrenal cortex especially in the OM rats under twelve months of age. I feel fairly certain that adenomas and possibly carcinomas develop from these hyperplastic nodules because in many animals we have observed what we consider to be transition stages between hyperplasia and neoplasia.

And then you wanted to know about the hemorrhage. Sometimes there is hemorrhage and what we might even call angiomatous adenoma as well as areas of vacuolated cells within the cortex. I am not sure, but I think that some of these may also be pre-neoplastic.

Question: Does the rat have a true mucoid pneumonia? We often suspected this is a progression of mucoid bronchitis.

Dr. Snell: I am sorry, I am unable to answer that.

Chairman: Would anyone in the audience like to speak to this point?

Dr. C. E. Brown: I think many members of the audience will recall the bronchiectatic and mucoid lesions that older rats develop and I think perhaps this varies a good bit from strain to strain and locality to locality.

A number of years ago, while working with Wistar rats in Philadelphia I saw a number of these lesions. As a matter of fact, it seemed to me the very old rats would die of this.

Dr. Sexton, of this city, wrote a paper describing a so-called bronchiectatic pneumonia of older rats. Recently while working with another strain in Philadelphia I haven't seen this at all. We assumed at that time that that is a common way old rats die, but apparently that is not so.

Dr. Snell: We see much less inflammatory disease of any type than we did, say, ten years ago. I think it is all a matter of better environmental conditions.

Dr. J. M. King: In many older rats one sees focal gray areas on the surface of the lung with or without murine pneumonia. It just appears to be foam cell accumulations. Do you have an explanation for this?

Dr. Snell: No, I don't. Someone was speaking of this yesterday and I think the answer was the same, that we didn't know why they occurred.

Sometimes there are similar areas that we call lipoidal pneumonia, but I don't believe that has really been studied. If so, I have missed the references to it.

Dr. King: I believe that with rabbits one gets the same type of lesion on high cholesterol diets and this is also seen in ferrets and in dogs. In rats it is usually in the diaphragmatic (inferior) lobes. I think it can easily be caused by stress—and I hate the term because it is so invidious—because these lesions can be caused by a lipemia which develops as the result of stress and you can actually kill rabbits with lipid pneumonia in this sense.

The only cases I have seen of it in ferrets or mink were in animals which were challenged in vaccination studies with distemper, or something similar.

Dr. Jean Weston: This reminds me of something I saw many years ago and which made me realize that under certain circumstances the lung may be an excretory organ. We were giving long-term administration of a drug which accumulated in the macrophages in the reticuloendothelial tissues. When rats died the people in the laboratory were diagnosing deaths as due to pneumonia. When we did autopsies on some of these animals we found that grossly the lung looked like pneumonia but we also found, when we took sections, that the pulmonary macrophages were filled with this drug. Macrophages were storing it wherever they could. They finally invaded the lung because this drug was not metabolized in the body, and was not excreted through the urine. In regard to this mucoid pneumonia, was there something in the body that the macrophages were trying to get rid of which could not be degraded and taken care of by the usual routes or is this true mucin? Actually in our cases there were so many of these macrophages that it was obviously impossible for the animal to get a good oxygen exchange, and was indeed a death from pneumonia because the other organs showed no real pathologic changes.

Question: Would you discuss focal areas of fat in the rat kidney?

Dr. A. A. Nelson: We have seen these lipomatous hamartomas, or whatever you wish to call them, in rats. I have the feeling that they are one end of a spectrum that can range from simple fat to liposarcoma.

In regard to mucoid-laden macrophages—with the feeding of atropine or chloramine to rats there were encountered large collections of foamy macrophages in the alveoli, which to my mind were nothing like the segmental or patchy mucinous pneumonia discussed here. They were diffuse, that is, they were scattered all over the lung in patches and not in one segment.

11

SPONTANEOUS LESIONS OF MICE

THELMA B. DUNN

A NUMBER OF QUALITIES possessed by the inbred mouse make it a valuable laboratory animal and often the animal of choice in many types of experiment.

1. Mice are relatively inexpensive to purchase and to maintain. A rough estimate is that three mice can be purchased for the price of one rat, and seven can be maintained in the space needed for a rat. In comparison with a hamster, guinea pig or rabbit, five, ten, or fifty can be maintained.

2. The mouse has a short life span. Most experiments involving mice can be completed within two years. In cancer experiments in particular, where it is often required that the animal live out its natural life span, this will extend to about twenty-four months with the mouse as compared with thirty months for the rat, four years for the guinea pig, and eight years for the rabbit.

3. A voluminous literature has been accumulated on the normal and pathologic anatomy, physiology, endocrinology, and many biochemical reactions of the mouse. This provides the investigator with a reliable background of knowledge from which to begin his own research.

4. The mouse is the smallest of the commonly used laboratory animals. Many consider this a handicap, but one can learn to do surgical procedures and autopsies under a dissecting microscope. Because of its small size, a complete histological survey is easily accomplished, and obtaining serial sections on many organs is feasible.

5. Many inbred strains have been developed, and most of them are readily available. This is perhaps the most important reason for using mice in laboratory investigations. When inbred mice are used, groups of identical individuals can be subjected to variations in environment or experimental procedure and any al-

terations observed can be directly compared with untreated controls. The pathologist, especially, can benefit from this opportunity. When the same number of controls is carried, microscopic slides from a control and experimental group can be examined side-by-side. When this practice is followed, it is almost impossible to confuse a spontaneous with an induced lesion.

Mice from a single inbred strain are in effect replications of a single individual. Mice from another inbred strain will represent a different individual. Each inbred strain has its own characteristics which must be recognized. The assumption that non-inbred mice are preferable in some experiments, "because they are more like human beings," shows a deplorable ignorance of the purpose of inbred strains in research. Human beings are not good experimental animals. One of the greatest difficulties in clinical research is to determine what are normal controls. Advantage should be taken of precise controls that inbred mice offer (1).

Many inbred strains of mice have special features which make them desirable and dependable for particular studies, and choosing the right inbred strain is a crucial decision in any experiment using mice. It is often desirable to carry out an experiment with several well chosen inbred strains, because each strain has features that fit it for different research projects.

The incidence of a variety of tumors in inbred strains is well documented (2), and "high" and "low" cancer strains are in constant use. Many mutant strains are known, and new ones are being developed (3). Some of these mutants, such as the obese, the muscular dystrophic, and the pituitary dwarf offer opportunities for well controlled studies on pathologic conditions that duplicate diseases in man.

It is only fair to point out some disadvantages in the use of mice in laboratory investigations. There are very few. One is the rapid postmortem autolysis that renders some tissues useless for histologic study if secured more than an hour after death. To combine a study on survival time with a study on pathologic anatomy and necropsy findings is usually unprofitable, and it is better at the beginning of the experiment to include enough animals so that some can be set apart for predetermined killing. The identification of blood-forming cells and the diagnosis of neoplasms is especially difficult and hazardous if autolysis has occurred. Another handicap with mice is the recognition of alterations in the pituitary gland even when the tissues are immediately fixed upon death. The different types of cells of the pituitary gland of the mouse are less distinctive than the corresponding cells in the rat or in man. It has been my experience that with routine sections of the pituitary gland in the mouse, only extreme alterations are recognized.

I have divided the abnormalities to be discussed into several groups to show: (A) Sexual dimorphism; (B) Endocrine peculiarities; (C) Reactions to the growth of certain tumors; and (D) Strain variations and geriatric lesions.

(A) *Sexual Dimorphism.* Although male and female mice may look much the same from the outside, they have many internal secondary sex characteristics. These have attracted the interest of the endocrinologists, because they can be altered by sex hormones.

The submaxillary gland of the male mouse has a terminal duct composed of columnar epithelial cells packed with cytoplasmic granules that are intensely eosinophilic (4). The same segment of the submaxillary gland of the female is composed of low cuboidal, non-granulated cells (Fig. 1, A and B). The submaxillary gland is a sensitive indicator of testerone since the male characteristic does not appear unless this hormone is active. The sublingual gland also shows a sex difference, but this difference is so slight that it is inapparent unless a hormonal stimulus is introduced (5) or histochemical studies are made (6).

The adrenal cortex in the female mouse is richer in lipoid than in the male (7). For this reason, the female gland on gross observation is relatively large, pale and opaque. Another sex difference revealed by the adrenal gland is the so-called X zone which I will describe and illustrate later.

Perhaps the most striking example of sexual dimorphism appears in the kidney. In the male, cuboidal epithelial cells line the parietal layer of Bowman's capsule (Fig. 2) whereas in the female the lining cells are flattened squamous cells (8). This secondary male character is not found in castrated male mice unless testosterone has been administered to them. Sexual dimorphism of the kidney is also found in the distribution of alkaline phosphatase in the tubular epithelium (9). The sex difference in the kidney appears to be the result of inbreeding, because it was not present in a group of wild mice studied recently (10. This sex difference can also be detected by examining the urine of male and female mice, and a difference in function is perhaps responsible for the difference in susceptibility of males and females to some toxic agents. For example, a given dose of chloroform is considerably more

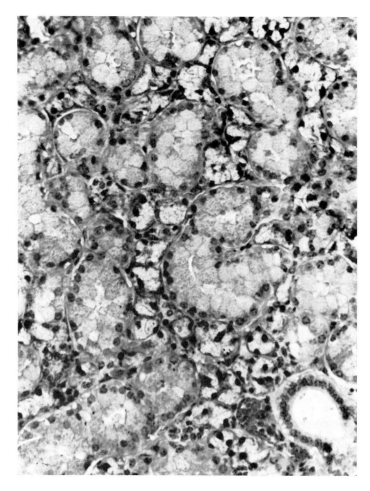

FIGURE 1. (A and B) Submaxillary gland. (A) Male. Epithelium of terminal tubule is composed of tall columnar cells filled with eosinophilic granules.

lethal to male than to female mice, and the male mice that survive exposure to chloroform often develop calcific deposits in the outer cortex of the kidney (11) (Fig. 3). In our laboratory we take strict precautions in the use of chloroform around mice.

Sexual dimorphism of the bony pelvis also occurs in mice (12).

The Harderian gland of the strain C3H female is reported to be more heavily pigmented than in the male, and to show a greater intensity of red fluorescence. These differences are more pronounced at seventy-five days of age than at 250 (13).

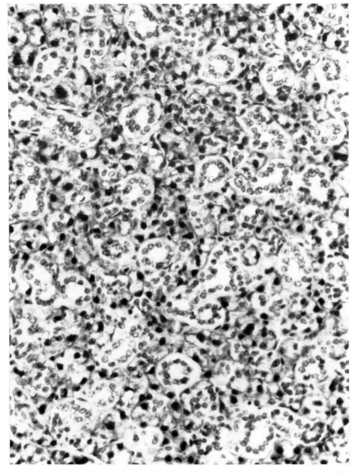

(B). Female. Epithelium of terminal tubules is lined by low cuboidal epithelium. Hematoxylin and eosin. x340.

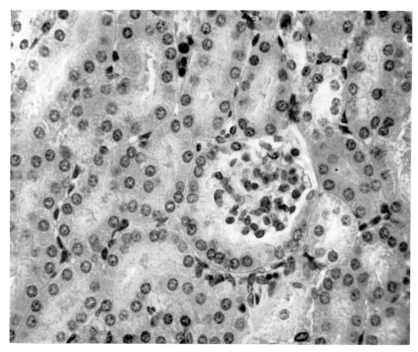

Figure 2. Glomerules from kidney of male. Parietal layer of Bowman's capsule is lined by cuboidal epithelium. In the female, the lining cells are flattened as in man and other species. Hematoxylin and eosin. x520.

(B) *Endocrine Peculiarities.* The first that will be mentioned is the occurrence of microscopic cysts lined by flattened or cuboidal cells, sometimes cilated, that are frequently found in the thyroid gland (14), the pituitary gland, and the thymus (15). These microscopic cysts occur less frequently in the parathyroid gland and very rarely in the adrenal gland (16). The cysts of the thyroid gland are the most carefully studied. They contain a pale foamy substance, unlike the smooth eosinophilic colloid of the normal follicle (17), even though they often communicate with normal follicles (Fig. 4). Presumably these cysts are embryonic remnants, and their presence in the mouse suggests that the Creator did not finish off this species very well. Additional evidence for a lack of finish in the endocrine organs is the frequent appearance of thymus tissue within the thyroid gland either replacing the parathyroid gland or being incorporated along with parathyroid gland tissue (Fig. 5). This anomaly is regularly present in strain BALB/ c (18) and its presence may account for the failure of members of this strain to show the effects of neonatal thymectomy as regularly as do members of some other inbred strains (19).

The follicles of the thyroid glands of old mice, particularly mice of strain C3H, often contain birefringent crystals (20) (Fig.

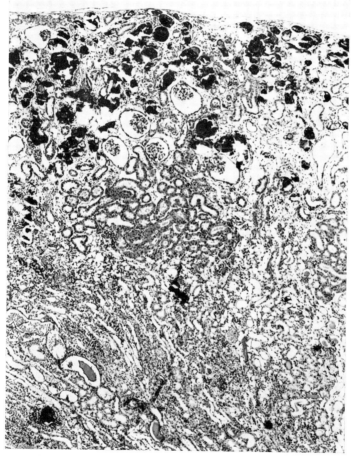

FIGURE 3. Kidney cortex of male strain C3H mouse three months after exposure to chloroform vapor. Heavy deposits of calcium are seen in the outer cortical area. In female mice similarly exposed, a few calcium flecks were found at the cortico-medullary junction. Hematoxylin and eosin. x68.

6). These we think are identical to the crystals of calcium oxalate that may be present in the thyroid gland of man (21). We have not found reports of similar crystals in any other species.

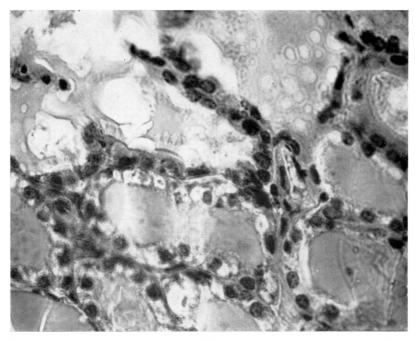

FIGURE 4. Thyroid gland, showing follicles containing a pale, foamy, colloid with some ciliated lining cells. Hematoxylin and eosin. x500.

Dendritic melanocytes are often present in the stroma of the parathyroid glands of mice that are heavily pigmented such as members of strain C58 (22) (Fig. 7). Melanocytes may also be found in the heart valves and meninges in these mice.

The adrenal gland of the mouse has a number of unusual features that make it attractive for studies in endocrinology (23). The sexual dimorphism in the lipoid content of the cortex has already been discussed. Two other features that show a sex difference are the so-called X zone, and the accumulation of ceroid-containing cells designated as "brown degeneration." The X zone is a wide zone of small cells lying between the cortex and medulla in the young mouse (24) (Fig. 8). This zone disappears by rapid degeneration of the cells in the male at the time he reaches sexual maturity, and more slowly in the female at the time of first pregnancy. In some strains of mice, notably strain A, when degeneration of the X zone is rapid, it may be replaced by a wide zone of adipose cells (Fig. 9). The lesion of "brown degeneration" consists of the deposition of brown pigmented ceroid-containing cells between the cortex and medulla of the adrenal gland. It is regularly present in old mice of some inbred strains. Estrogens, especially when administered to males, produces a larger lesion at an earlier

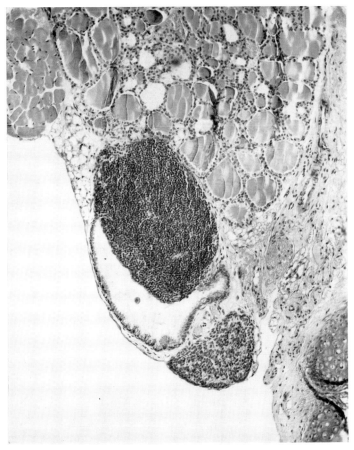

FIGURE 5. Thymus tissue within the parathyroid area, adjacent to thyroid tissue above. A cyst lined by ciliated epithelium lies below, and a small mass of parathyroid tissue below the cyst. Hematoxylin and eosin. x125.

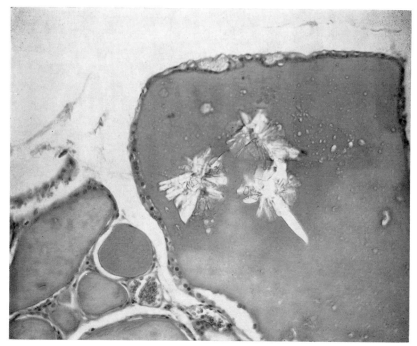

FIGURE 6. Crystals within a large thyroid follicle of a female strain C3H mouse
aged nine months. Hematoxylin and eosin. x210.

age (25). The periodic acid-Schiff reaction reveals the lesion of
brown degeneration clearly because the ceroid cells are intensely
fuchsinophilic (Fig. 10).

The adrenal gland of old mice commonly contains patches of
spindle cells resembling scars just beneath the capsule (26). In
tumor bearing and gonadectomized mice the number and extent
of these patches is increased. Mast cells which are not commonly
found in the adrenal gland, may appear in considerable numbers
within these patches.

Accessory nodules of adrenal tissue are not uncommon (27)
(Fig. 11) and the possibility of such accessory tissue must be elimi-
nated before adrenalectomy can be considered complete.

If the adrenal is fixed in Zenker's solution, reducing bodies,
probably a precipated catecholamine can be seen in the medulla
(28) (Fig. 12).

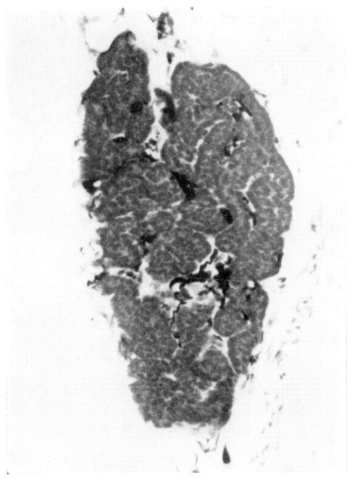

FIGURE 7. Dendritic melanocytes in the stroma of a parathyroid gland from a strain C58 mouse. Toluidine blue. x400.

(C) *Alterations Accompanying the Growth of Certain Tumors.* Physiologic and anatomic changes in mice bearing hormonally active tumors are frequently described. The alterations can usually be explained as the result of the functional activity of an endocrine neoplasm, and need not cause much perplexity (29). However, some tumors that are not known to exert an endocrine effect may produce pathologic alterations in the host mouse. An

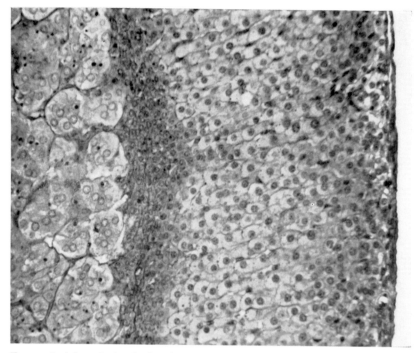

FIGURE 8. Adrenal gland, showing X zone composed of small dark cells lying between cortex and medulla. Strain C3H female, age three months. Hematoxylin and eosin.

extreme elevation of the granulocytes in the circulating blood with extensive extramedullary granulocytopoiesis develops in mice bearing transplants of the myoepithelioma of the submaxillary gland, and certain other neoplasms such as fibrosarcomas or squamous cell carcinoma will produce this effect (30) (Fig. 13). Mice with ovarian tumors develop hypervolemia (31) and a number of other seemingly unrelated neoplasms may produce an extreme dilatation of blood vessels (Fig. 14). We have found very active erythrocytopoiesis in the spleens of mice bearing transplanted reticulum cell sarcomas, and BALB/c mice bearing one line of a transplantable adrenal cortical tumor showed a great increase in reticulocytes in the peripheral blood (Fig. 15) and extramedullary erythrocytopoiesis. Furth described a dilation of the biliary tract in mice transplanted with a pituitary tumor (32). A biochemical

FIGURE 9. Adrenal gland, showing degenerating X zone. Fat stain shows lipoid laden cells of cortex, and adipose-type cells of degenerating X-zone lying between cortex and medulla. Fat droplets have been lost from many cells. Oil red 0. x125.

study of the tumors that produce these curious effects might disclose some hitherto unknown endocrine or enzyme factor not recognized in the normal organ, but present in the neoplastic tissue.

(D) *Lesions Related to Strain and Age.* It would be tedious to list all of the lesions related to inbreeding and age. The careful investigator should be aware that these lesions exist, and that he can avoid errors in diagnosing them if he carries an adequate num-

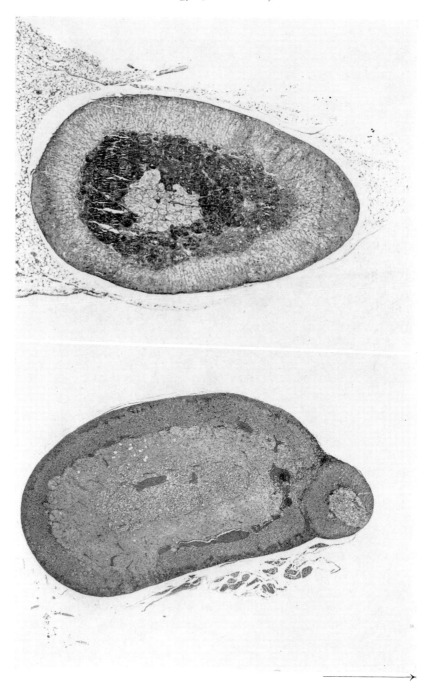

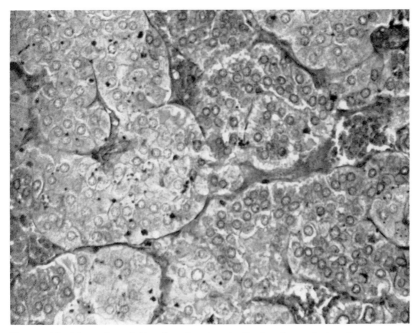

Figure 12. Adrenal medulla after fixation in Zenker-formol, showing precipitated dark brown granules. Note that cells of the medulla are not uniformly pigmented or chromated, after this fixation. Hematoxylin and eosin. x340.

ber of controls, and performs autopsies at different age periods. A few illustrations are as follows: The number of mast cells in the spleen is very high in strain A mice and increases with age, while almost none are found in strain I mice (33). Retinal dystrophy (34) is regularly found in strain C3H mice and in the inbred Swiss strain carried at the National Cancer Institute. It has also been observed in some members of non-inbred Swiss and wild house mice (10) (Fig. 16 A and B), but has not been observed in other inbred strains at the National Cancer Institute. So-called "mesenteric disease," a non-neoplastic enlargement with

Figure 10. Adrenal gland, showing "brown degeneration," a zone of ceroid cells lying between cortex and medulla. Periodic-acid-Schiff. x55.

Figure 11. Accessory adrenal. Broken line defines limit of medulla, which is separated from cortex by a wide zone of ceroid cells. Ceroid cells are also present in the medulla of the accessory adrenal. Hematoxylin and eosin. x37.

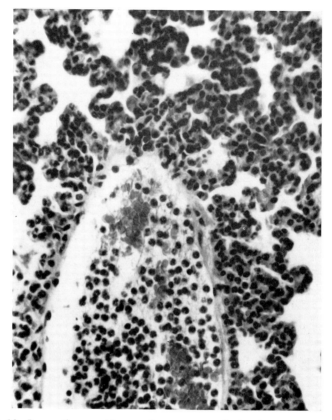

FIGURE 13. Lung tissue with a pulmonary vessel. Leukemoid reaction was produced by a transplanted myoepithelioma. Note enormous numbers of mature and disintegrating granulocytes in the vessel and within alveolar walls. Hematoxylin and eosin. x520.

many small cystic dilations in the mesenteric lymph node, is commonly found in old strain C3H mice and occasionally in other strains of mice (35) (Fig. 17). Fat infiltration and parenchymatous atrophy of the pancreas, leaving the islets surrounded by adipose tissue has been found in old mice of several strains (1). Crystalline deposits have been described in the lung (36). We have seen them often in old inbred mice, and they were especially frequent in old wild mice (10) (Fig. 18). Amyloidosis, almost unheard of in rats, is very common in mice. A primary, idiopathic type of amyloidosis is especially common in strain A mice, and

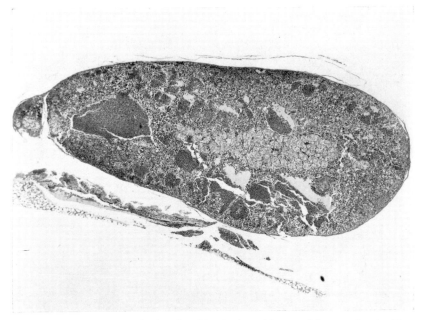

FIGURE 14. Adrenal gland, showing histologic evidence of hypervolemia. Vessels of the adrenal cortex are greatly distended. Mouse was bearing a transplanted mammary tumor. Hematoxylin and eosin. x55.

often produces a form of renal disease (37) (Fig. 19). Secondary amyloidosis often accompanies inflammatory conditions (38), or tumor growth and is readily produced by repeated injections of protein substances (39). Although many studies have been made of amyloidosis (40), I believe that there is still much that could be learned about this degenerative disease from studies on inbred mice. If someone will find out why amyloidosis is so rare in rats, and so frequent in mice, he will have gone a long way in explaining this metabolic puzzle.

Finally, the reader should realize that while the inbred mouse has been the animal of choice in cancer research, it can also be useful in many investigations not related to cancer.

REFERENCES

1. DUNN, T. B.: The importance of differences in morphology in inbred strains. *J. Nat. Cancer Inst.*, 15:573-585, 1956.

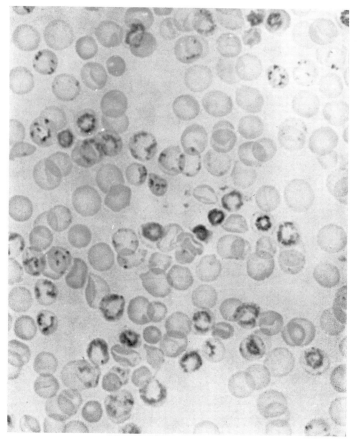

FIGURE 15. Peripheral blood with erythrocytes stained to demonstrate reticulo-cytes. These were increased 50 per cent or more in some mice bearing an adrenal cortical tumor. New methylene blue N stain. x1180.

2. COMMITTEE ON STANDARDIZED GENETIC NOMENCLATURE FOR INBRED STRAINS OF MICE. Second listing. *Cancer Res., 20:*145-160, 1960.
3. GRÜNEBERG, H.: *The Genetics of the Mouse.* Second edition. The Hague, Nijhoff, 1962.

FIGURE 16. A and B. A. Normal retina from a wild mouse. Note rod layer next to pigmented choroid, and thick layer of rod nuclei. B. Retinal dystrophy in a wild mouse. Note absence of rod layer, and only a few scattered rod nuclei. Hematoxylin and eosin. x470.

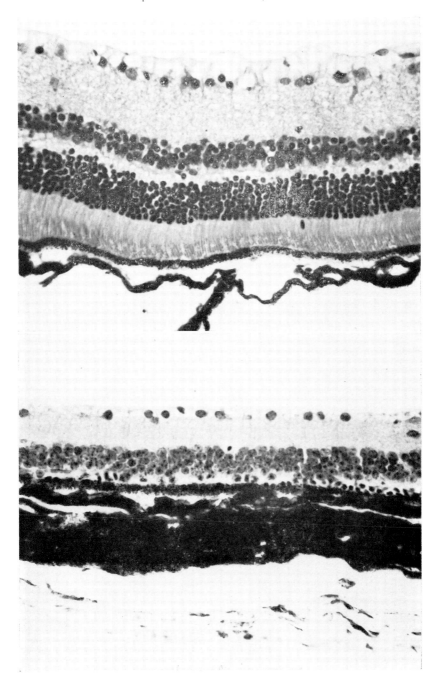

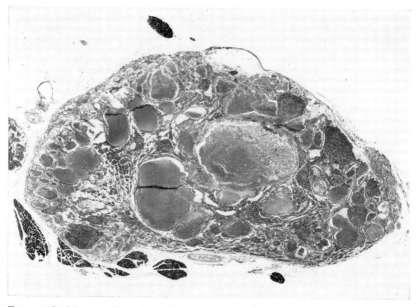

FIGURE 17. Mesenteric node with "mesenteric disease" in a strain C3H male mouse age two years. Note dilated vascular channels. This condition appears frequently in old strain C3H mice. Hematoxylin and eosin. x20.

4. LACASSÁGNE, A.: Dimorphisme sexuel de la glande sous - maxilliare chez la souris. *Compt. rend. Soc. biol., 133*:180-181, 1940.

5. LACASSÁGNE, A. ET CAUSSEL, R.: Dimorphisme sexuel de la glande retrolinguale chez la souris. *C.R. de la Soc. de Biol., 135*:25, 1941.

6. SPICER, S. S.: The use of various cationic reagents in histochemical differentiation of mucopolysaccharides. *Amer. J. Clin. Path., 36*:393-407, 1961.

7. DEANESLEY, R.: Adrenal cortex difference in male and female mice. *Nature, 141*:79, 1938.

8. CRABTREE, E. E.: The structure of Bowman's capsule as an index of age and sex - variation in normal mice. *Anat. Rec., 79*:395-413, 1941.

9. DUNN, T. B.: Some observations on the normal and pathologic anatomy of the kidney of the mouse. *J. Nat. Cancer Inst., 9*: 285-301, 1949.

10. DUNN, T. B., and ANDERVONT, H. B.: Histology of neoplasms and some non-neoplastic lesions found in wild mice. *J. Nat. Cancer Inst., 31*:873-901, 1963.

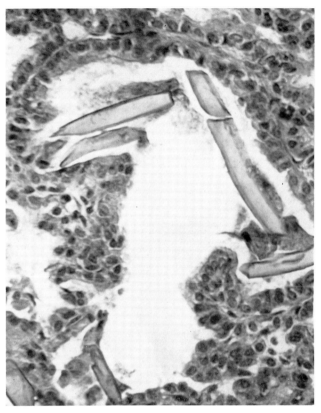

FIGURE 18. Bronchus containing numerous crystals from an old wild mouse. Hematoxylin and eosin. x380.

11. DERINGER, M. K., DUNN, T. B., and HESTON, W. E.: Results of exposure of strain C3H mice to chloroform. *Proc. Soc. Exp. Biol. Med., 183*:474-479, 1953.

12. GARDNER, W. U.: Sexual dimorphism of the pelvis of the mouse, the effect of estrogenic hormones upon the pelvis and upon the development of scrotal hernias. *Amer. J. Anat., 59*:458-483, 1936.

13. STRONG, L. C.: Sex differences in pigment of Harderian glands of mice. *Proc. Exp. Biol. Med., 50*:123-125, 1942.

14. DUNN, T. B.: Ciliated cells of the thyroid of the mouse. *J. Nat. Cancer Inst., 4*:555-557, 1944.

15. FEKETE, E.: *Histology.* Chapter 3 in Biology of the Laboratory Mouse. G. D. Snell, Ed. New York, Dover Publications, 1941.

16. DUNN, T. B., and GREEN, A. W.: Cysts of the epididymis, cancer of the cervix, granular cell myoblastoma, and other lesions after estrogen injections in newborn mice. *J. Nat Cancer Inst., 31:* 425-455, 1963.

17. GORBMAN, A., and BERN, H. A.: *A Textbook of Comparative Endocrinology.* New York, Wiley, 1962.

18. GREEN, A. W.: Unpublished observations.

19. LAW, L. W.: Unpublished observations.

20. DUNN, T. B.: Unpublished observations.

21. RICHTER, M. N., and McCARTY, K. S.: Anisotropic crystals in the human thyroid gland. *Amer. J. Path., 30:*545-554, 1954.

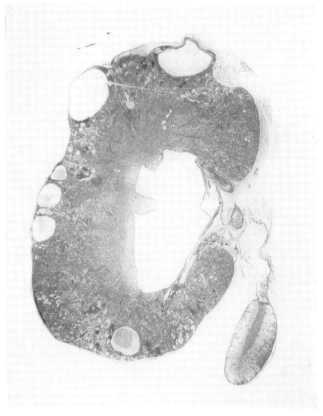

FIGURE 19. Kidney and adrenal in strain A mouse. Note necrosis of tip of papilla, cystic dilatation of glomeruli, and areas of fibrosis in kidney. Amorphous eosinophilic amyloid replaces inner zones of the adrenal cortex. Hematoxylin and eosin. x12.

22. DUNN, T. B.: Melanoblasts in the stroma of the parathyroid glands of strain C58 mice. *J. Nat. Cancer Inst.*, *10*:725-733, 1949.

23. CHESTER JONES, I.: Variations in the mouse adrenal cortex with special reference to the zona reticularis and to brown degeneration, together with a discussion of the cell migration theory. *Quart. J. Micr. Sc.*, *89*:53-74, 1948.

24. HOWARD - MILLER, E.: A transitory zone in the adrenal cortex which shows age and sex relationships. *Amer. J. Anat.*, *40*:251-295, 1927.

25. CRAMER, W., and HORNING, E. S.: Adrenal changes associated with oestrin administration and mammary cancer. *J. Path. Bact.*, *44*: 633-642, 1937.

26. WHITEHEAD, R.: Abnormalities of the mouse suprarenals. *J. Path. Bact.*, *35*:415-418, 1932.

27. HUMMEL, K.: Accessory adrenal cortical nodules in the mouse. *Anat. Rec.*, *132*:281-295, 1958.

28. SPICER, S. S., and DUNN, T. B.: Reducing bodies in the adrenal medulla fixed with Zenker-formol. *J. Nat. Cancer Inst.*, *25*:1451-1459, 1960.

29. GARDNER, W. U., PFEIFFER, C. A., and TRENTIN, J. J.: *Hormonal Factors in Carcinogenesis.* Chapter 6 in Physiopathology of Cancer. Edited by F. Homburger. Second edition, Hoeber-Harper, 1959.

30. BATEMAN, J. C.: Leukemoid reactions to transplanted mouse tumors. *J. Nat. Cancer Inst.*, *11*:671-687, 1951.

31. FURTH, J., and MOSHMAN, J.: On the specificity of hypervolemia and congestive changes in tumor-bearing mice. *Cancer Res.*, *11*: 543-551, 1951.

32. FURTH, J., GADSDEN, E. L., and UPTON, A. C.: Hyperplasia and cystic dilatation of extrahepatic biliary tracts in mice bearing grafted pituitary growths. *Cancer Res.*, *12*:739-743, 1952.

33. DERINGER, M. K., and DUNN, T. B.: Mast cell neoplasia in mice. *J. Nat. Cancer Inst.*, *7*:289-298, 1947.

34. SORSBY, A., KOLLER, P. C., ATTFIELD, M., DAVEY, J. B., and LUCAS, D. R.: Retinal dystrophy in the mouse: Histological and genetical aspects. *J. Exp. Zool.*, *125*:171-197, 1954.

35. DUNN, T. B.: Normal and pathologic anatomy of the reticular tissue in laboratory mice, with a classification and discussion of neoplasms. *J. Nat. Cancer Inst.*, *14*:1281-1433, 1954.

36. GREEN, E. U.: On the occurrence of crystalline material in lungs of normal and cancerous Swiss mice. *Cancer Res.*, *2*:210-217, 1942.

37. DUNN, T. B.: Relationship of amyloid infiltration and renal disease in mice. *J. Nat. Cancer Inst., 5*:17-28, 1944.
38. HESTON, W. E., and DERINGER, M. K.: Hereditary disease and amyloidosis in mice. *Arch. Path., 46*:49-58, 1948.
39. CHRISTENSEN, H. E., and RASK-NIELSEN, R.: Comparative morphologic, histochemical, and serologic studies on the pathogenesis of casein-induced and reticulosarcoma-induced amyloidosis in mice. *J. Nat. Cancer Inst., 28*:1-33, 1962.
40. CHRISTENSEN, H. E.: *Amyloidosestudier.* Doctoral thesis, Copenhagen, 1963.

DISCUSSION

Question: Would you comment further on the crystalline deposits in the lungs of aged mice?

Dr. Dunn: At the time we first noticed them Dr. William Ayres was especially interested in crystals. He studied some of the crystals from the mouse and concluded that they weren't Charcot-Leyden crystals. I am sure they don't occur except in old mice and I suspect, too, that they might very well be strain-related.

Question: Would you say more about the identification of the thymus within the thyroid.

Dr. Dunn: The Hassall's corpuscles in the mouse thymus are very indistinct. The presence or obviousness of Hassall's corpuscles are said to vary with strains but I have not observed this.

Frequently in these intra-thyroid masses we fail to see anything that we can identify as thymus reticulum or thymus medulla and occasionally all we recognize is a deposition of lymphocytic cells, but sometimes we find fairly large masses which completely replace the parathyroid, and are readily identified as thymus tissue.

Conversely, parathyroid tissue has been reported in the thymus, and certainly we find masses of epithelial cells in the thymus that could be parathyroid tissue.

In reference to pigmented parathyroids: We were able to remove them surgically with very little trouble because they were easily identified and we felt that we were not in any way disturbing the thyroid in the mouse. This avoided the complicating factor of a thyroidectomy. So far as I could see, the mice got along very well without a parathyroid, and we could not recognize any effect.

Question: What is the secret of identifying amyloid in the mouse kidney? I have seen specimens of some and if the lesion is not really obvious, and since the staining reactions are not characteristic, what can one do to be more or less sure one is dealing with amyloid in glomeruli?

Dr. Dunn: I identify some of these lesions by exclusion. No other substance is deposited in the same fashion around the vessels. Amyloid is usually a perivascular deposit, although it appears to be within cells in the adrenal cortex. We see it in amorphous masses within glomeruli. Even now many people insist upon calling this substance hyaline rather than amyloid. There is an English paper* in which a study was made of the various staining reactions, and the conclusion was reached that the proper term for it was "mouse" amyloid. We feel reasonably sure that this is the equivalent of amyloid in man.

Dr. Dunn: I would like to comment on a distinctly different condition. Twice since I have been at the National Cancer Institute I have encountered a curious condition among mice. I think the first time was about fifteen years or more ago—it was shortly after the war—and the animal attendants suddenly informed us that all the mice in our animal room were dying. We autopsied some and found that there was a tremendous amount of fluid in the pleural cavity and the lungs were compressed and atelectatic. A good many of the animal attendants looking after the mice, said they also felt sick, but whatever it was, it soon subsided. We had no further experience of this type of illness until about five years ago when we were asked to look at mice that were dying suddenly, in one of the animal rooms. At autopsy, these mice resembled those observed in the previous episode. At that time I wrote letters to ten or more people that I knew kept mice and asked if they had ever seen anything of this sort in any of their colonies. No one answered that he had.

In the interim we forgot all about these attacks because what-

---

*Turnbull, H. M.: The nature of the substance deposited in the spleen and liver of the mice in Dr. D. L. Parson's experiments. (Addendum to paper by Parson, D. L.: Tissue changes in experimental mice treated with pentose nucleotides. *J. Path. & Bact.*, 57:18-20, 1945.)

ever they are, they come and go very rapidly. I strongly suspect they are caused by some poison. We have even thought of the possibility that ANTU was being used in warehouses that supply the bedding. These episodes are not happening often enough to be a real hazard, but if anyone has seen such episodes in colonies of mice and could offer some explanation and propose a way of preventing them, we would be very grateful.

Dr. Stephen Sternberg: 6-mercaptopurine will produce similar pleural effusions in rats.

Dr. Leon Sokoloff: We had an unfortunate experience a year ago. Because the problem was so little known to the members of our staff, it might be of interest here. We had a large colony of DEA/2 mice supposed to be harvested at the age of sixteen months. Two weeks before they were to be sacrificed, the mice died spontaneously in large numbers. This came in the wake of a bout of Asiatic Flu, which our dedicated animal caretaker had. Five days after she came down with her illness, the mice suffered an acute necrotizing bronchitis, followed shortly by the usual sequence of reparative changes of metaplasia of the terminal bronchial epithelium and alveolar "adenomatosis." We did obtain from the caretaker's serum a high titer of antibody to the prevalent flu strain; unfortunately we did not recognize the problem in the animals in time to recover the virus from them. We know that mice are highly susceptible to influenza virus and it probably is worth while to keep away from mice while one has the flu.

Dr. Charles Harris: In the adrenal glands Dr. Dunn referred to the hypervolemic changes in the adrenals. In rats this has been associated by myself and others with some type of stressful situation and is considered a hemorrhagic and cystic degenerative change. I wonder whether the hemorrhagic cysts that we see in elderly rats or in rats that are subjected to stress are indeed hypervolemic and whether the type that Dr. Dunn showed are. Is this the same lesion in rats and mice?

Dr. Dunn: The hypervolemic change that we see in mice affects many organs. I happened to show the adrenal because that was convenient.

Question: Is this a distinctive lesion?

Dr. Dunn: All I depend upon ordinarily is a histologic section, but if one wanted to be accurate one should do tests for increased blood volume, which this lesion represents. Dr. Furth has done these tests, but we have depended only upon histological evidence, for we think that the appearance in the adrenal, the glomerulus, the liver, and in the spleen is characteristic, and these are the main organs in which it is seen.

Even without proven methods, if one bleeds these mice one gets much more blood than could be obtained in normal animals.

12

DISEASES OF THE RABBIT

HARRY S. N. GREENE

A WIDE VARIETY of spontaneous diseases have been encountered in the rabbit during the course of a long period of investigative work in which this species formed the principal laboratory animal. The diseases have been studied primarily from a point of view of pathogenesis and the object of this paper is to assemble pertinent observations for purposes of the present symposium. No attempt will be made to review the better known diseases or the field of rabbit disease in general.

Disorders based on hereditary variations have been noted with the greatest frequency. Many of these bear a close resemblance to well-recognized disorders in man and, because they can be reproduced at will, offer a unique opportunity for investigation. Such disorders as oxycephaly, brachydactylia, dwarfism and cretinism belong to this category. Other diseases with a definite but less clear-cut genetic background include hydrocephalus, toxemia of pregnancy, and neoplasia. There are, in addition, a large number of disorders of comparatively rare occurrence with a questionable genetic relationship and with little or no resemblance to human disease, such as bow-legs, accessory patellar groove, renal aplasia, cryptorchidism, walrus teeth, etc. Finally, there are a number of infectious diseases, only one of which, rabbit pox, will be discussed in the present report.

Oxycephaly (1). This is a craniosynostotic deformity in man often associated with blindness and a distortion of features so pronounced as to lead to the French name of Malade de Thersites, derived from Homer's description of Thersites as "the ugliest man who ever came to Ilium." It also occurs in rabbits as an heredity variation based on a premature fusion of the sagittal and coronal sutures. Compensatory growth occurs at other suture lines, and, as a result, the bregma is pushed up in a peak, the facial bones distorted, and the base of the skull deformed.

Injuries in embryonic life, diseases of the cranial bones, and meningitis have been considered as etiological factors in the human disease, and tuberculosis and syphilis have been emphasized in the theories supporting an inflammatory origin. The possibility of a genetic origin has been suggested by the frequency of the deformity among the inbred Greeks during the Golden Age of Athens. It is of interest to note in this connection that the common habit of portraying Pericles and other ancient heroes wearing crowns has been thought to derive from an attempt to cover the disfigurement of craniosynostotic skulls. However, a study of the literature concerning the inheritance of the condition in man shows its occurrence in more than one generation of a family to be relatively uncommon, and although more frequent in members of the same generation, the majority of cases are found as isolated instances.

In the rabbit, on the other hand, there is no questions of its hereditary character. Further, it has been possible by breeding experiments to separate the oxycephalic deformity into its component parts and to produce other craniosynostotic conditions found in man, such as trigonocephaly, bilateral coronal fusion without sagittal fusion, plagiocephaly, unilateral coronal fusion alone, and scaphiocephaly, sagittal without coronal fusion. And, then, by selective mating, these parts can be recombined into the original oxycephaly. In addition, a second calvarial anomaly, a bilateral bregmatic accessory bone, has been introduced into the craniosynostotic complex by appropriate breeding. The incorporation of the accessory bone is expressed anatomically by fusion of its anterior or coronal border with the adjacent frontal bone while its posterior border remains unfused and patent to constitute a diagonal suture line. Growth occurs at this suture line, and the gross cranial deformity of oxycephaly is prevented.

A detailed study of the development of the craniosynostotic abnormality during embryonic life showed that its anatomical basis lies in a division and displacement of ossification centers. The displacement of centers of adjacent bones to occupy peripheral positions in close proximity to each other resulted in the fusion of their radiating ossific fibers with the production of bone in a region normally traversed by a suture line. Growth of the bones was inhibited at their fused border and compensatory overgrowth at patent sutures in different planes produced the characteristic cranial distortion. The incorporation of an accessory bone provided an accessory suture so directed that compensatory growth was accomplished without gross cranial distortion.

Two additional points with reference to the rabbit's calvarium, not related to the deformity discussed but of possible anatomical interest, may be mentioned here. The coronal sutures of the adult rabbit assume a complex pattern of angles and curves but the configuration is highly characteristic in different pure breeds. In fact, the suture constitutes a fingerprint of breed for the rabbit and actually forms a better criterion of breed than does coat color. The second point concerns the interparietal bone. This is a small oval element situated in the mid-line between the two perietals and the occipital bone, and interest relates to the fact that, like the guinea pig's fourth hind toe, it is in the process of evolutionary disappearance. The bone is usually present in normal relations but may be represented by numerous small specules, a single unilateral fragment, or may be entirely absent.

Brachydactylia (2). The deformities considered under this title are characterized by a shortening or absence of the component parts of the feet. Extreme variations in the degree of malformation occur in the rabbit giving rise to a series of abnormalities ranging from minor brachydactylia to complete acheiropodia. Abnormalities of the ear may be associated with malformations of the feet and, like these deformities, are characterized by the absence of a constituent part.

The ratios of animals with deformities in F_2 and backross generations approximate those expected in the inheritance of a simple recessive character. It should be emphasized, however, that, although the deformities "breed true" and the presence of some degree of abnormality in one or other of the feet is regularly transmitted from parents to progeny, the distribution and extent of the malformations are subject to extreme variation in succeeding generations. In any case, the fact that "true breeding" occurs offers a unique opportunity for study of the pathogenesis of the disorder.

Such an investigation was carried out, and it was found that, during the latter half of gestation, feti derived from the interbreeding of brachydactylous animals showed pathological changes at sites corresponding to the deformities observed at birth. The sequence of alterations began on the sixteenth day and terminated in the complete deformity on the twenty-fifth day.

No changes were found in the developing foot buds prior to the sixteenth day, and at this time, sections showed no other abnormality than a dilatation of thin-walled blood vessels with occasional small areas of extravasated blood. By the eighteenth day, minute areas of red discoloration appeared on the surface of developing buds and, on microscopic examination, these were found to consist of hemorrhages, the largest of which were associated with necrosis. On the nineteenth day, involved areas were sharply outlined, swollen, and deep red in color and, microscopically, necrosis dominated the picture. A line of demarcation separating normal and abnormal tissues appeared on the twentieth or twenty-first day, and this was followed by an annular constriction and sloughing of the part. The remaining stub was invariably completely healed by the twenty-fifth day.

It has been generally assumed in abnormalities of this type that the defect arises on a basis of inferior or faulty tissues, but there is no evidence in the present instance that the involved tissues were morphologicaly different from adjacent issues which remained unaffected. In fact, available data suggests that the local tissues were not at fault. Transplantation of many toe buds prior to the development of a pathological change was carried out in the anterior chamber of the eyes of normal rabbits, and the fact that all of the buds developed in a normal fashion was taken as evidence that the somatic variation responsible for the deformity was not resident in the local tissue but was rather of systemic nature.

A determination of the primary fault is not possible from the evidence at hand, but the suggestion is offered that it is situated in vascular or nervous tissues. Vascular dilatation has not been observed in other parts of affected feti, and the constancy of the finding in involved regions is highly suggestive of a causal relationship. In view of the absence of any demonstrable lesion to account for the dilatation, the possibilty of an abnormal vaso-motor condition warrants consideration. The absence of local vasoconstrictor nerve fibers or the continued stimulation of existing fibers, giving rise to paralysis, would result in dilatation of the vascular segment and, conceivably, to stasis of the blood with subsequent hemorrhage and necrosis of the part supplied by the segment. In any case, it is clear that the expressed deformity in this disorder is a secondary effect of the genetic variation.

Dwarfism (3). An hereditary type of dwarfism occurs in the rabbit. In contrast to the dwarfs described in other animals, this type is evident at birth and conforms to the classification, nanosomia premordialis, as used in human pathology. In homozygous form, the variation is lethal and produces a miniature individual one-third the size of its normal sibs. Heterozygous animals are approximately two-thirds the size of normal sibs at birth and never attain an equal stature.

In addition to their small size, the dwarfs are distinguished by an abnormally bombose configuration of the head, resulting from a disproportionate reduction in the size of the brain, and this characteristic serves to distinguish affected individuals from runts and diminutive forms due to other causes. The actual weights of all organs are decreased in heterozygotes and lowest in dwarfs, but a comparison based on the relation to net body weight shows that in a number of cases the decrease is not proportionate and that in others the relative weight is actually increased. The amount of thyroid, adrenal, pituitary, liver and spleen substance per gram of net body weight is reduced in transmitters and least in dwarfs, while the relative amounts of thymus, kidney, heart, lung, and brain substance are increased in transmitters and largest in dwarfs. The decrease in relative weight of organs in dwarfs is most pronounced in the case of thyroid, pituitary and adrenal while the increase is greatest in the case of the brain.

At a rule, the dwarfs are born alive and are capable of nursing but die within forty-eight hours. Treatment of the mother with thyroid extracts or growth hormone during the last days of gestation is without effect in prolonging life. On the other hand, the implantation of whole pituitary glands obtained from normal litter mates into the subcutaneous tissues of dwarfs has maintained life for as long as five days in several cases.

At birth, dwarfs show no gross abnormality other than a reduction in size and histological changes are not striking. Both acidophils and basophils are present in the pituitary and their proportion is not significantly different from that found in normal sibs. Sections of the thyroid and adrenal are normal in appearance. The liver and spleen show an excess of hematopoietic tissue, but are otherwise unremarkable. The animals surviving for four or five days frequently show a unilateral or bilateral hydronephrosis, in such cases, the ureters are imperfectly developed. In other instances, no organic lesions are found, the stomach contains milk, and there are abundant deposits of pinkish fat throughout the body.

Transmitters of the dwarf variation generally present no external physical alteration other than that of size, with the exception of an unusual variation in the calvarium consisting of symmetrically placed defects in the frontal bones. The defects often persist throughout life as sharply circumscribed oval areas completely devoid of bone. In other cases, healing occurs, but a persistent fissure marks the site of the defect.

The majority of female transmitters become overfat at maturity, and the fat accumulates both in normal regions and in unusual depots, particularly in the anterior triangle of the neck and about the shoulder girdle. Despite this manifestation, the animals remain alert and active. Males do not become overfat, but continue vigorous and thrifty and are frequently characterized by a pugnacious disposition.

Females are particularly susceptible to toxemia of pregnancy in their third or fourth gestation. The incidence of deaths due to this disorder is 30 per cent in contrast to an incidence of 19 per cent in non-transmitters of the same derivation. Animals that survive toxemia of pregnancy for four years almost invariably develop adenocarcinoma of the uterine fundus. There is no evidence that males are susceptible to endocrine disturbances in later life, and the incidence of tumors is no greater than in the general male population.

Discussion of the pathogenesis of dwarfism will be postponed pending description of a second pituitary disorder in the rabbit with manifestations suggestive of cretinism.

Cretinism (4). This disorder is a complex of composite character and its different features may be transmitted and inherited independently, while the variation is expressed in typical form only when certain component parts are recombined in one individual.

In typical form, the distinctive features of the disorder usually developed toward the end of the first or second week of life. A faint redness with an edematous thickening of the skin appears first in the nape of the neck, spreads rapidly over the whole surface of the body, and becomes particularly prominent about the genital and anal regions. The edematous thickened skin is thrown into loose, transverse folds, at first red in color, but later stiff and endurated and covered with fine white scales and thick crusts. Growth of affected animals ceases within a few days of the development of signs and the disease progresses to a lethal temination in the course of a week or ten days.

At death, the animals present a characteristic wizened appearance highly suggestive of cretinism. However, autopsy and microscopic examination fail to show indicative changes in the thyroid or pituitary, and, thorough morphological study of all organs and tissues gives no clue to the etiology or pathogenesis of the disorder. However, as a result of breeding experiments, this disorder and the previously described dwarf variation were successfully combined in a new genetic complex and the fact that they could be combined is strong evidence of a common organic origin.

Dwarf-cretin Complex. The dwarfs derived from matings between animals carrying admixtures of the genetic factors concerned in the two hereditary variations were generally several grams heavier at birth and survived for periods up to fifty-five days. Their growth rate paralleled that of normal animals for approximately three-fourths of the survival period, but then reached a plateau, and the animals died immediately after a loss of weight became evident.

The appearance of the survivors was characteristic, and, if found in the wild at the end of a month, their species identification might be in doubt. The bombose configuration of the calvarium persisted and the ears remained small, resembling those of a kitten. The abdomen was full and rounded, and there were large deposits of fat in the region of the shoulder girdle. The hair was soft and silky. During the period of active growth, the animals were vigorous and playful, but with cessation of growth, they became apathetic and sat hunched in one position throughout the day.

The single significant gross finding at autopsy was a complete absence of gonads. The gonads are present and of normal appearance in dwarfs of this strain at the time of birth, and it must be assumed that survival was associated with atrophy of the gonads. Histological findings of interest were limited to the pituitary, and the striking alteration here was the pronounced increase in the size and number of acidophils. The increase was generalized throughout the anterior lobe and in many areas no other elements could be found. Scattered foci of basophils were present in other regions, and these cells were also greatly enlarged.

Apparently, the factor responsible for the longer survival of dwarfs obtained from the cretinoid cross results in a greater activity of the acidophilic cells and thus supplies growth-stimulating substances which are absent in ordinary dwarfs. Functioning basophils secrete thyrotropic hormone and prevent the myxodematous alteration of the cretinoid parent line. However, gonadotropic hormone is not available and gonadal atrophy occurs.

The data available, however, warrants no more than conjecture on such points. It can only be said that the evidence at hand indicates that the primary effect of the dwarfing gene is an inhibition of the secretory function of the pituitary. In homozygous individuals, the inhibition is complete, and the variation is expressed as a lethal dwarf. In heterozygous animals, the function of the organ is altered, producing an undersized individual. The modifying factors of the cretinoid line act either to partially remove the inhibition or to so alter the constitution of the animal that life is possible for a short time without the full complement of pituitary hormone.

Hydrocephalus. Internal hydrocephalus occurs in two forms in the rabbit. One form is present at birth and is rapidly lethal; the other develops during the first month of life and is not lethal. The former arises from a deficiency of Vitamin A-containing substances in the mother's diet and occurs without relationship to genetic constitution. The latter possesses certain familial or hereditary characteristics, but the mode of inheritance is complicated and obscure. It also arises on the basis of Vitamin A deficiency, but in this case the avitaminosis is due to an hereditary inability of the animal to convert the precursors in the plant material of its food into active vitamin.

The former type is apt to occur in epidemic form in a colony of breeding rabbits following a period of dietary deficiency. In one such experience of my own, the incidence of hydrocephalus in newborn young increased from 0.2 per cent at the beginning of breeding in September to 100 per cent during December of the same year. The administration of Vitamin A to pregnant animals during the latter part of gestation resulted in the complete disappearance of the abnormality in the ensuing litter while its withdrawal in subsequent pregnancies was associated with recurrence of the disorder. The incidence of hydrocephalus in the colony returned to a normal figure with the institution of an adequate diet.

The mechanics of the development of hydrocephalus is not apparent from morphological study in either case. There is no evidence of blockage and, although marked gliosis is present in older brains, it is clearly effect rather than cause.

Toxemia of Pregnancy (5, 6). Toxemia of pregnancy in the rabbit may occur as a rapidly fatal disease or as a comparatively mild, frequently asymptomatic disorder followed by recovery. In typical cases, the clinical manifestations are those of a sudden and severe intoxication. The signs of acidosis dominate the attack. Air hunger, dyspnea, and acetone breath are apparent. Thirst is an early manifestation, and there is a total suppression of urine. Convulsions occur in many cases, but in others the animals remain lethargic, and in all instances a comatose stage precedes death. The period of obvious illness may not exceed a few hours in duration.

Blood chemical findings are in general agreement with those obtained in human toxemia of pregnancy and, with several additional alterations in the rabbit, the pathological changes are the same. The principal organs affected are the liver, kidneys, heart, and brain. The most distinctive hepatic lesion is focal necrosis, but widespread fatty degeneration is also common. Intense fatty degeneration is also found in the kidneys and heart, and the brain is the site of edema and congestion. The rabbit also shows endocrine lesions consisting of fatty degeneration and necrosis of the adrenal, hypoplasia of the thyroid and hyperplasia of the pituitary with pronounced alteration of the pars intermedia.

The disorder occurs with highest incidence in animals of Polish and Dutch breeds and is most common in transmitters of the dwarf and cretinoid abnormalities described above. There were eighteen cases of the disorder among sixty-eight Polish rabbits known to be transmitters of dwarfism, an incidence of 26.4 per cent in contrast to an incidence of 19 per cent in forty-seven non-transmitters or of 9.2 in the remainder of the colony. A similar situation obtained in the Dutch breed with reference to cretin transmitters. Although the influence of the genetic factors concerned in these endocrinological abnormalities on susceptibility to toxemia of pregnancy is apparent, the relatively high incidence among non-transmitters of Polish and Dutch breed shows that other factors unrelated to the variations and associated with breed were also of importance in this respect. In any case, it is a point of interest that the incidence of a disease related to pituitary dysfunction is highest among animals known to transmit hereditary variations of pituitary origin.

The histological changes in the pituitary are productive in nature whereas the alterations in other bodily organs are degenerative. There is a marked hyperplasia of the cells of the anterior lobe with evidence of irregular secretion. Alterations of the intermediate lobe are also a constant feature. The cells of this lobe are markedly increased in number and frequently show adenomatous proliferation or invasion of the posterior lobe. In addition, there is a large amount of interstitial colloid substance, and cysts containing similar material are common both in the intermediate lobe and in the posterior lobe where Herring bodies are also unusually distinct and numerous.

Neoplasia. Tumors occur in rabbits with rapidly increasing frequency after the third year of life. The most common in my experience, in order of decreasing incidence, have been adenocarcinoma of the uterus (7, 8, 9) and breast (10), epidermoid carcinoma of the vaginal squamous-columnar junction (11), embryonal nephroma (12), epidermoid carcinoma of the skin (13), and leiomyosarcoma of the uterus. Leiomyosarcomas of the stomach and intestine, generalized lymphosarcomas, granulosa cell tumors of the ovary, and thymomas have also been observed, but with much less frequency (14). Only the more common tumors will be considered in the present context.

Adenocarcinoma of the Uterus. A systematic study of this tumor was carried out some years ago with particular reference to incidence and development. The study involved a colony of 849 female rabbits of various breeds and extended over a nine-year period.

The incidence was 16.7 per cent but varied widely in relation to age, breed and other constitutional factors. The frequency increased from 4.2 per cent in animals two to three years old to 79.1 per cent in animals five to six years old. No instances of the tumor occurred in the Belgian or Rex breeds, and the arrangement of breeds in order of increasing incidence is as follows: Polish, Himalayan, Sable, Beveran, Chinchilla, English, Marten, Dutch, Havana, French Silver, and Tan. It is significant that, with few variations in position, the standing of various breeds in a scale of susceptibility to toxemia of pregnancy was identical. It is also indicative that the high incidence of toxemia of pregnancy in transmitters of the dwarf and cretinoid abnormalities was mirrored in their susceptibility to uterine tumors. The incidence among transmitters of dwarfism was 48.2 per cent and of cretinism 33.7 per cent in contrast to an incidence of 14 per cent in the remainder of the population.

Disorders of pregnancy were known to characterize the breeding history of animals that subsequently developed uterine tumors and the close parallelism between the incidence of the tumors and that of toxemia of pregnancy suggested a possible relationship between these milder disorders and fatal toxemia. An investigation was instituted, and, in brief, it was found that the disorders under consideration represented less acute disturbances of the same nature. Accordingly, a group of animals, selected on a basis of recovery from toxemia, was subjected to special study, including monthly endometrial biopsy. It is significant that all of the animals followed for eighteen months developed uterine tumors, and that, in all instances, the development of the tumor was preceded by cystic endometrial hyperplasia.

Monthly biopsies were continued throughout the course of the tumors and tissue fragments so obtained were subjected to morphological as well as other studies. Very early tumors were polypoid and were usually situated in the mucosal folds adjacent to the mesometrial insertion. In the majority of cases, they were multiple and regularly spaced throughout both horns. Histologically they consisted of glandular elements embedded in a richly vascular, myxoid stroma. Advanced growth were associated with deep muscular invasion and extension laterally in the endometrium. Coalescence of adjacent growth was common and frequently the entire uterus was converted into a mass of tumor tissue. Diffuse infiltration of the pelvis and adbomen usually antedated metastasis by several months. Eventually, metastasis was widespread, involving all organs of the body.

At autopsy, characteristic changes were found in the adrenal and thyroid. The thyroid was small and made up of tissue resembling the fetal adenomas found in man. The alteration in the adrenal resembled that found in toxemia of pregnancy and consisted of a lipoid accumulation in the zona fasciculata so pronounced in many cases that the cortex and medulla appeared separated by a wide zone of this material. The pituitary changes were not consistent but generally there was a diminution in the number of chromophils and a hyperplasia of the intermediate zone.

Such endocrinological changes are characteristic of those induced by estrogenic hormone, and it is suggested that they are incident to an excessive concentration of this hormone resulting from an impairment of liver function relative to inactivation. It has been shown experimentally that the liver is the principal organ of the body concerned with the inactivation of estrogenic hormone and that damage renders it incapable of performing this function. Extensive liver damage occurs in toxemia of pregnancy, and there is evidence from chemical blood study as well as from histological examination that damage may persist for as long as a year after clinical recovery. In view of the known carcinogenic action of estrogenic hormone, it is not unreasonable to suggest further that the uterine tumors may arise on this basis and represent a natural analogue to the experimental induction of neoplasia with this substance.

Adenocarcinoma of the Breast. Two types of mammary cancer have been found in the rabbit. One type is distinguished by characteristic antecedent mammary changes similar to those found in chronic cystic mastitis in women and by a distinctive papillary structure. The other originates in the absence of antecedent breast disease and is characterized by an adenomatous pattern. These two types of neoplasia occur almost exclusively in two family groups and heredity plays a fundamental role both in the occurrence of the tumors and in the determination of tumor type.

Papillary tumors are by far the more common. They arise as uni-radicular papillomata from the epithelial lining of walls of dilated acini and ducts. They rapidly become multi-radicular and their branches unite with each other and with those of adjacent growths to form a complicated structure comparable to the duct papillomas of women. Anaplastic cellular changes are present from early stages of development, but the growths remain confined to normal boundaries for long periods of time. Local invasion is usually delayed for six or eight months, and metastasis rarely occurs in less than a year after the appearance of invasion.

The early stages of tumors of the adenomatous class consist of numerous small but otherwise normal appearing acini divided by fibrous bands into large lobules. Sections from adjacent breast show a normal, non-cystic structure. Growth proceeds through a multiplication of acini and the epithelium is confined to a single layer for long periods of time. Eventually, however, after a course that may extend as long as sixteen months, this compact, circumscribed arrangement gives way to invasive growth and groups of cells, still in aberrant acinar formation, extend throughout the surrounding tissue. Metastasis follows rapidly.

While the dominating gross lesion in these animals is the mammary tumor, pathological changes found in other organs at autopsy suggest that the presence of neoplasia in the breast forms only a local manifestation of a generalized constitutional disorder. Such changes are generally more pronounced in animals bearing papillary tumors, but, with the exception of the pituitary, comparable endocrine alterations are also found in the group with adenomatous tumors.

The adrenals contain small, pale gray areas made up of clusters of large, washed cells with pyknotic nuclei and numerous small vacuoles. Such areas are found scattered throughout the cortex but tend to be concentrated in the inner portion of the zona reticularis, and their presence in the gross is indicated by a distinct yellowish ring in this region. In later stages, cell boundaries become indistinct, and the areas appear more or less homogeneous. The thyroid is consistently involved, but the changes are less spectacular. Follicles are dilated, and the epithelium flattened. Septal walls are thin and rupture to form macroscopic cysts. The stroma is hyaline and appears infiltrated with colloid.

The pituitary is greatly enlarged and may weigh as much as 300 mg., representing a five-fold increase based on an average normal weight of 60 mg. The enlargement is due to a chromophobic hyperplasia which is usually generalized but may occur in the form of adenoma-like masses.

The endometrium is invariably hyperplastic and both adenomatous polyps and adenocarcinomas are common coexistent tumors.

The changes in the endocrine organs of animals bearing mammary tumors are comparable to those found to be associated with endometrial tumors, and it is suggested that, as in the latter case, the tumors represent a natural counterpart to the experimental production of neoplasia with estrogenic hormone.

Carcinoma of the Vaginal Wall. Despite the high incidence of fundic cancer in the rabbit, cervical cancer has not been observed. The absence of a squamo-columnar junction in the rabbit's cervix suggests an anatomical basis for the species' variation. Unlike the situation in man where columnar and squamous epithelium meet in the region of the external os, the columnar epithelium of the rabbit's fundus continues uninterruptedly over the cervix and down the vaginal wall to a junction with squamous epithelium at about the level of the urethral meatus. The occurrence of cancer at this junction despite its different location in the two species emphasizes its significance as a predisposing factor in carcinogenesis.

The tumor is uncommon, occurring in only three of approximately 1100 females over two years of age that came to autopsy during a sixteen-year period of observation. It is of interest, however, that these represent one-half of all the epidermoid carcinomas found in the rabbits in this period. One originated in the skin of the cheek, another in the skin of the tail, and the third in a nipple. It is suggested, therefore, that the vaginal squamocolumnar junction possesses an increased susceptibility over other bodily regions with reference to such tumors.

It is also of interest that all three animals bore adenocarcinomas of the uterine fundus in addition to the epidermoid cancers, and that all three had recovered from attacks of toxemia of pregnancy. Further, two of the animals showed breast changes comparable with those found in early stages of mammary cancer. All of the animals died of metastasis and all of the metastasis were epidermoid in type and derived from the vaginal carcinoma. No metastasis from the fundic or mammary tumors were found.

Embryonal Nephroma. Embryonal nephromas or Wilm's tumors occur in the rabbit as accidental autopsy findings in old animals. This is in sharp contrast to the situation in man when the tumors are unusually malignant diseases of childhood. Morphologically, all grades of admixtures or sarcomatous and carcinomatous tissues are found. In no instance has metastasis been observed.

Bow-legs. Genu varum occurs as a characteristic deformity in the Rex breed and in the author's experience is limited to this breed. It is clearly hereditary in nature but the manner of inheritance is complicated and obscure. The clinical appearance of the deformity is highly suggestive of rickets, but morphological study fails to show the distinctive bony changes of this disorder, and pertinent therapy does not prevent its occurrence.

Accessory Patellar Groove. This curious anomaly is limited in occurrence to the Martens, Sables, and Tans. It is hereditary in nature but its expression appears dependent on adverse environmental conditions. The primary defect lies in a relaxation or weakening of the patellar tendon with dislocation of the tendon from the patellar groove to a medial position, and with the passage of time, an accessory groove develops in the end of the femur to house the tendon. Affected animals are able to ambulate but the gait is abnormal and characteristic.

Renal Aplasia. This variation occurs with some frequency in one strain of the Havana breed and results in complete unilateral absence of the kidney. In males, the testicle is frequently absent on the affected side while in females the ovary is intact but the ipsilateral uterine horn is often shortened or completely missing.

Two other anomalies are found in this strain and may occur either independently or in association with renal aplasia. The genetic relationship, if any, has not been clarified.

One of these is aplastic in nature and consists in a unilateral or bilateral absence of accessory incisor teeth. The two upper incisors of the rabbit are normally provided with slender, peg-like, independently rooted structures occurring posteriorly at about the mid-line of the incisor and extending almost to the cutting edge. Their function is not apparent and their absence is not reflected in any disturbance of the animal's health.

The second variation is of greater pathological interest and is expressed as arteriosclerosis of Mönckeberg type involving the entire arterial system. It occurs in young adults, usually during the second year of life, and is of such severity that many arteries are pipe-stem in character. Death from hemorrhage following fracture of an iliac artery is a common occurrence.

Cryptorchism. Cryptorchism occurs with frequency in several strains of the Dutch breed. Bilaterally affected animals are, of course, sterile, but breeding experiments with unilaterally affected animals demonstrate the genetic nature of the anomaly. The undescended testicle usually persists in atrophic form throughout life but, in several instances, it has been the site of tumors resembling the embryonal carcinomas of man.

Walrus Teeth. The incisor teeth of the rabbit continue to grow throughout the animal's life, and their length is controlled by wear incident to contact of the cutting edges. Accordingly, malocclusion is associated with persistent growth. The lower incisors protrude while the uppers grow in curved fashion inside of the mouth and may fill the greater part of the cavity. Affected animals are unable to eat and, unless the incisors are trimmed with cutting pliers, the abnormality is lethal.

In any case, the disorder is an hereditary variation. However, its expression is dependent on environmental circumstances, and homozygous animals maintained under optimal conditions appear normal throughout life. On the other hand, when such animals are subjected to continued stress, such as repeated pregnancy and lactation or to an inadequate diet, malocclusion follows and the abnormality gains expression. It should be emphasized that this disorder is not a consequence of adverse environmental factors in the general population.

Rabbit Pox (15). Rabbit pox is a highly contagious, rapidly fatal disease in the rabbit. Clinically, the disease resembles smallpox in man, and evidence derived from the study of an epidemic indicates that it is produced by a virus originating from vaccine virus.

The general symptomatology of the infection varies within wide limits, and diagnosis rests on the occurrence of certain characteristic lesions. The most distinctive sign is a pock-like eruption which is often outspoken and widespread over the body, but is sometimes poorly defined and detectable only after careful physical examination. As a rule, the incubation period of the epidemic infection varies between five and seven days.

The dominant gross lesion in all organs and tissues is a small nodule or papule consisting of a mononuclear infiltration and necrosis. Diffuse lesions are also found in which the infiltration and widespread and accompanied by edema, hemorrhage, and extensive necrosis of affected tissues. An intimate relationship exists between the lesions and small blood vessels showing primary endothelial damage.

Death may occur within a few hours after infection or be delayed for days or weeks. In the epidemic noted above, 610 animals in a population of 1303 died of the disease - a mortality of

46.4 per cent. However, there were wide variations in different age groups and breeds. Among animals less than fourteen weeks of age, 71.8 per cent of cases of infection died; the mortality rate being highest among those four to eight weeks old. The mortality in adults was 14.7 per cent but there were marked differences related to breed. The death rate was highest in the American Blue, Belgian and Rex breeds, and lowest in the Sables, English, Martens, and Himalayans, with other breeds assuming an intermediate position.

REFERENCES

1. Greene, H. S. N.: Oxycephaly and allied conditions in man and in the rabbit. *J. Exp. Med., 57:*967, 1933.
2. Greene, H. S. N., and Saxton, J. A., Jr.: Hereditary brachydactylia and allied abnormalities in the rabbit. *J. Exp. Med., 69:*301, 1939.
3. Greene, H. S. N.: A dwarf mutation in the rabbit. *J. Exp. Med., 71:*839, 1940.
4. Hu, C. K., and Greene, H. S. N.: A lethal mutation in the rabbit with stigmata of an acromegalic disorder. *Science, 81:*25, 1935.
5. Greene, H. S. N.: Toxemia of pregnancy in the rabbit. I. Clinical manifestations and pathology. *J. Exp. Med., 65:*809, 1937.
6. Greene, H. S. N.: Toxemia of pregnancy in the rabbit. II. Etiological considerations with especial reference to hereditary factors. *J. Exp. Med., 67:*369, 1938.
7. Greene, H. S. N., and Saxton, J. A., Jr.: Uterine adenomata in the rabbit. *J. Exp. Med., 67:*691, 1938.
8. Greene, H. S. N.: Adenocarcinoma of the uterine fundus in the rabbit. *Ann. N. Y. Acad. Aci., 75:*535, 1959.
9. Greene, H. S. N., and Newton, B. L.: Evolution of cancer of the uterine fundus in the rabbit. *Cancer, 1:*82, 1948.
10. Greene, H. S. N.: Familial mammary tumors in the rabbit: I. Clinical history. *J. Exp. Med., 70:*147, 1939. II. Gross and microscopic pathology. *J. Exp. Med., 70:*159, 1939. III. Factors concerned in their genesis and development. *J. Exp. Med., 70:*167, 1939.
11. Greene, H. S. N., Newton, B. L., and Fisk, A. A.: Carcinoma of the vaginal wall in the rabbit. *Cancer Res., 7:*502, 1943.
12. Greene, H. S. N.: The occurrence and transplantation of embryonal nephromas in the rabbit. *Cancer Res., 3:*434, 1943.

13. GREENE, H. S. N., and BROWN, W. H.: A transplantable squamous cell carcinoma in the rabbit. *Cancer Res., 3*:53, 1943.
14. GREENE, H. S. N., and STRAUSS, J. S.: Multiple primary tumors in the rabbit. *Cancer, 2*:673, 1949.
15. GREENE, H. S. N.: Rabbit Pox: I. Clinical considerations and course of the disease, *J. Exp. Med., 60*:427, 1934. II. Pathology of the epidemic disease. *J. Exp. Med., 60*:441, 1934. III. Report of an epidemic with especial reference to epidemiological factors. *J. Exp. Med., 61*:807, 1935. IV. Susceptibility as a function of constitutional factors. *J. Exp. Med., 62*:305, 1935.

DISCUSSION

Question: Could you say a little more about the pathogenesis of the hydrocephalus which you describe?

Dr. Greene: The hydrocephalus is present at birth and is internal in character. There is no anatomical evidence of an obstacle to the flow of cerebrospinal fluid, but an abnormality in the base of the skull, obvious at birth, may bring about a functional blockage. The animals live to adult life, and the hydrocephalus is only lethal when associated with a craniosynastitic deformity prohibiting cranial expansion.

Dr. T. C. Jones: May I comment on this? Apparently it is the same situation that occurs in the dog, even in fairly old animals. We have been unable to demonstrate any obvious cause. We think there is increased cranial pressure but there is no obvious conclusion that we can reach.

Question: Is it possible to produce the toxemia of pregnancy syndrome followed by carcinoma of the uterus?

Dr. Greene: The productive lesions in toxemia of pregnancy are limited to the intermediate lobe of the pituitary and attempts to reproduce the disease have been based on this finding. Extracts of the intermediate lobe of beef pituitaries administered to pregnant rabbits do induce a disorder with an identical clinical and pathological picture. The severity of the experimental disorder depends on the dosage of pituitary extract and, at low dose levels, many recoveries occur. Such animals eventually develop chronic cystic endometritis and carcinoma of the uterine fundus. The development of these lesions can be accelerated by estrogenic hormone given in small doses at frequent intervals. Further, carbon tetrachloride may be substituted for pituitary extract as a liver-damaging agent and the same results obtained.

Question: Doctor Greene, have there been any studies in regard to women that have had toxemia of pregnancy and endometrial changes?

Dr. Greene: As far as I am aware, there have been no formal studies of the fate of women after recovery from an attack of toxemia of pregnancy. I have examined many hospital records myself and have been unable to discover what happened to such individuals.

However, I have traced the past histories of women with adenocarcinomas of the uterus, and in all instances, there has been evidence of some gestational disorder. In some instances, it has been frank eclampsia, in others pernicious vomiting - but some disturbance in pregnancy distinguished the past history of all cases.

Question: Would you care to discuss diarrheal, mucoid, or hemorrhagic enteritis?

Dr. Greene: I have purposely omitted reference to the parasitic and inflammatory diseases of the rabbit. They are abundant but beyond the scope of the present paper. It may be of interest, however, to note that coccidiosis in the rabbit may be controlled by the addition of trypansomids to the drinking water.

Dr. J. M. King: Would you care to comment on the similarity of pregnancy disease in sheep with pregnancy toxemia in rabbits.

Dr. Greene: I know nothing about pregnancy disease in sheep except what I have read.

Dr. King: The liver lesion is the same but the disease can be produced in wethers, which are castrated sheep, if one gives them a high carbohydrate diet. This is thought partially responsible for pregnancy disease in sheep, possibly, as you say, because of the liver damage.

Dr. Greene: It is noteworthy in this connection that toxemia of pregnancy sometimes occurs in pseudo-pregnant rabbits, emphasizing the point that the disease is dependent on the endocrinological state of the animal rather than on the products of conception.

Dr. Thelma Dunn: I would like to ask a question of the group here relating, again, to amyloidosis. We find it so clearly related to strain in the mouse, and I wondered if observation in any other species indicated this.

Dr. Greene: I haven't seen it in rabbits, and I have worked with some eighteen different pure breeds.

13

SPONTANEOUS LESIONS IN MONKEYS

JEAN K. WESTON

ALTHOUGH THE term "spontaneous lesions" is a misnomer, strictly speaking, in the context of this paper it encompasses the lesions which occurred in the monkey before its use as an experimental animal. It also includes any lesions which occur during the animal's existence in the laboratory not resulting directly or indirectly from the experimental maneuvers to which the animal was subjected.

My first encounter with "spontaneous lesions" was in pound dogs used in studies designed to evaluate the effects of varying doses of experimental drugs administered over relatively long periods. Obviously the total number of dogs subjected to each dose of an experimental drug under such circumstances has practical limits, even in the pharmaceutical industry. In such studies, all too frequently when final gross and histopathological data were coordinated, there seemed no relationship of certain lesions encountered to the doses of drug administered, even though they did not occur in the control animals or, if they did, they varied greatly in their degree of development. At times such spontaneous lesions so clouded the issue that it was necessary to repeat the study. In an attempt to minimize such difficulties we developed a technique of taking preliminary biopsies of liver, kidney, spleen and bone marrow in dogs, which at least produced a histological picture of these important organs as a base line against which to equate any consistent, observable changes related to administration of drugs at varying doses subsequently. Later this procedure was extended to monkeys when these became available to us as experimental animals. Biopsy of such organs is a thoroughly practical procedure still not adopted widely enough to exploit its potentialities, at least in my opinion. Briefly, it involved intermittent, intravenous anesthesia with a short-acting barbiturate,

Surital, at repeated anesthetic doses small enough to interfere with normal physiological processes as little as possible for as short a time as necessary while the desired biopsy specimens were obtained. The biopsy specimens of intra-abdominal organs were obtained by open laparatomy and the use of scissors, scalpel, biopsy forceps or loop cautery with as little trauma as possible. Stainless steel wire was used routinely for all sutures. Bone marrow was obtained by resecting a short segment of rib or by opening the marrow cavity of the proximal end of the tibia or the distal end of the femur and removing a marrow sample with a curette. In this fashion a sufficient specimen of each organ can be obtained, which, by utilizing appropriate histological techniques, can supply much data to the pathologist. Not only does this technique permit more intelligent selection of animals to be put on chronic studies, but, utilized serially after animals have been given various doses of drugs, it produces a great deal of useful information concerning the effects of these drugs at various doses and times as compared with control animals and for these particular organs, each animal also serves as its own control. Properly carried out it is well tolerated by the animal.

The information to be subsequently reported here* is the result of information the author has obtained primarily in Macacus monkeys by serial biopsy of control animals, preliminary biopsies of animals subsequently subjected to varying doses of a variety of drugs, control animals without biopsy, control animals for a variety of safety tests, safety test animals demonstrating unusual findings which, in all likelihood could not have been the result of the test administered, animals which died after receipt and before they could be experimentally utilized, animals sacrificed for

---

*The data presented here was collected during a six year tenure as Laboratory Director of Pathological Research, Parke, Davis & Co. Research Laboratories and, more vicariously during a subsequent period of about equal length while the author was Director of Clinical Investigation of the same firm. The author wishes to express his sincere appreciation to Dr. Donald H. Kaump and Douglas Roll of the Parke, Davis Research Laboratories for selecting, photographing, and furnishing color slides and diagnoses of the illustrative material used in the oral presentation of this paper. He regrets that because much of this material was in the form of Kodachromes the expense precluded all of its reproduction to accompany this paper.

kidneys used in virus vaccine production which demonstrated unusual gross findings, etc. When one views retrospectively his experience with "spontaneous lesions" in monkeys, one is impressed with its resemblance to human pathology excepting in the tumor area. However, when it is realized that the total number of monkeys reported on here is probably not more than an estimated four to five thousand, which is still a lot of monkeys, one cannot help but wonder whether if one examined a number of monkeys comparable to the total number of autopsied humans and at comparable ages, the total range of pathology would not be equally extensive. The fact that these were chiefly young monkeys (3-12 Kg.) probably explains the relative absence of tumors.

With the foregoing in mind and considering the matter from the practical aspect of what people using the monkey as an experimental animal are most apt to see in the way of spontaneous lesions, we can most readily classify these as lesions associated with: (a) bacterial infection; (b) viral infection; (c) parasitic infection, and (d) miscellaneous lesions.

Whatever may be the situation of the monkey in his natural state so far as his exposure to bacteria, viruses and parasites is concerned, once he is in contact with man his exposure to *both* monkey and human infectious agents in these categories is a function of the various human and monkey populations he encounters. From his capture in the wild to his delivery to the research scientist the monkey encounters many unnatural situations—holding areas, caging, changes in food, water and climate, handling and a variety of transportation facilities. Hence it is understandable that monkeys on delivery (excepting when delivered by plane direct from their area of capture) have been exposed to a variety of both monkey and human infectious disease and that the stress of travel may well have worsened such endemic disease as they may have had when captured.

A. SPONTANEOUS LESIONS ASSOCIATED WITH BACTERIAL INFECTIONS

After a considerable experience with monkey histopathology, one will have encountered histopathological evidence of infection, either chronic or acute, in almost every major organ or tissue as "spontaneous lesions." The most common infection encountered is in the respiratory system. Histopathologically, radiologically and clinically such infections resemble closely the human situation. In our experience, respiratory infections are most responsible for most deaths of monkeys soon after arrival, regardless of what may be the situation in their natural state. Likewise, properly handled soon enough, no monkey disease is more susceptible to proper and adequate therapy. Interstitial pneumonitis and acute, subacute and chronic lobular or lobar pneumonias are the types of diagnoses applicable to the monkeys that die within a few weeks of receipt. The lesions are histologically comparable to what one sees in man with respiratory infections. Aspiration pneumonia has been observed with sawdust shavings or food particles recognizable in the exudate. A further complication here is that monkeys are very susceptible to tuberculosis. Regardless of the controversy as to the incidence of this disease in the natural state versus after contact with humans, unmistakable tuberculosis lesions will crop up with reasonable frequency in any sustained monkey experience. Tuberculin testing and x-ray or fluoroscope checking with this in mind is a must for anyone who pretends to operate a first class monkey colony, if for no other reason than to protect those who contact the monkeys directly. Tuberculosis, when encountered, most usually has the characteristics of the acute hematogenous or childhood variety, if compared with human. Whether this is associated with the fact that most monkeys we have used are young or that they have recently acquired the disease from man, or other monkeys, or both is not known. We have seen a small number of cases where the adult caseating type of lesion appeared. We suspected the exporter was covering the monkeys in his holding areas with a tuberculostatic antibiotic but could never verify this.

Gastrointestinal infections are also very common in newly arrived monkeys and run a close second to pulmonary infections (and are often associated with them) as a cause of mortality in newly arrived animals.

Both liver and kidney also frequently show evidence of preceding bacterial (or viral) infection. This is most commonly characterized by varying amounts of infiltration of predominantly mononuclear type cells. To a lesser degree this type of infiltration has also been seen in almost every organ, but particularly in pancreas, gut, salivary glands and brain. It is frequently restricted to the area adjacent to blood vessels.

B. SPONTANEOUS LESIONS ASSOCIATED WITH VIRUS INFECTIONS

While it is entirely probable that virus infection may have played a part in some of the lesions noted above, spontaneous CNS lesions, undoubtedly of viral origin, still plague the pathologist who deals with safety test histopathology in the virus vaccine area. Dr. Bodian, working closely with the National Institutes of Health and pharmaceutical industry pathologists, has done much to characterize "spontaneous lesions" of the monkey CNS due to a variety of viruses, largely on the basis of their distribution, correlated to some extent with serological data. Until this had been accomplished, "spontaneous lesions" which even remotely resembled poliomyelitis were sufficient cause for rejecting any lot of vaccine being tested since, with a few notable exceptions, viral infections of the CNS produced essentially similar types of inflammatory lesions with similar distributions, at least in the brain stem and spinal cord.

Perivascular and diffuse mononuclear cell infiltration, especially in the dorsolateral medulla in proximity to the V, VII, IX and X cranial nerve components within the medulla were the most commonly encountered "spontaneous lesions." Such lesions, when confined chiefly to this distribution, Bodian characterized as viral radiculoencephalitis. When a wider distribution in the forebrain was observed—and largely depending on the extent of this distribution—the diagnoses of subacute encephalomyelitis (virus type) or meningo-encephalitis were applied. All gradations of these lesions to glial scarring have been encountered in various parts of the brain or spinal cord.

Perivascular infiltration of similar type but confined to the meninges was also frequently encountered, more often in some shipments of monkeys than others.

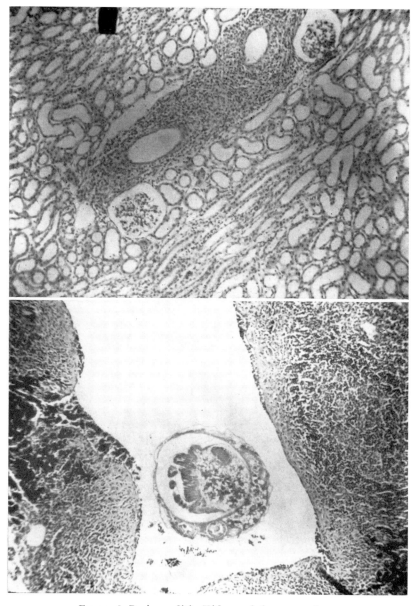

FIGURE 1. Perivasculitis. Kidney of rhesus monkey.

FIGURE 2. Lung mite in bronchus. Rhesus monkey. Note dark pigment excreted by the mite in the tissue.

Rarely lesions due to B virus infection were observed and verified by serological studies. The lesions were similar to the above in many respects but more widespread in distribution and with the admixture of a more acute type of cellular infiltrate in the few cases seen.

A case tentatively diagnosed as leucocytic choriomenigitis has been encountered.

C. SPONTANEOUS LESIONS ASSOCIATED WITH PARASITIC INFECTIONS

From the standpoint of their relative frequency, "spontaneous lesions" due to the lung mite, the esophagostomum worm and filariasis are fairly common.

The lung mite inhabits the lungs, as its name suggests. Due to its presence and the irritation resulting therefrom, localized chronic granulomatous lesions develop, varying in number and extent. They have been misdiagnosed as tuberculosis. The infection can be transmitted from monkey to monkey, since young born in the laboratory have demonstrated the infection at autopsy. How it is transmitted is not clear. Although no case has been reported in man, so far as I know, the possibility of transmission from monkey to man should be kept in mind. It is interesting that some monkey shipments were relatively free of this parasite and others were 100 per cent infected.

Lesions due to the esophagostomum worm may be encountered almost anywhere along the gastrointestinal tract but particularly along the large intestine. Many are grossly easily recognizable as cysts attached to the peritoneal surface. Histologically, as with most worm parasites, the surrounding tissue exhibits a varying degree of acute, subacute, or chronic inflammatory reaction with frequently some part of the worm being sectioned and recognizable.

In filariasis the parasites may be recognized both in tissues and in blood smears. This infection should be suspected in granulomatous lesions not otherwise accounted for.

In addition to "spontaneous lesions" due to the foregoing, spontaneous lesions associated with the following parasitic diseases have been encountered—though much less frequently:

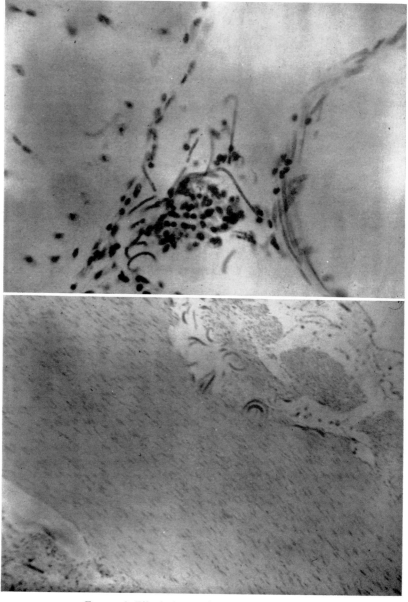

FIGURE 3. Filaria in meninges. Vervet monkey.

FIGURE 4. *Strongyloides sp.* Colon of rhesus monkey.

1. Myiasis
2. Gall bladder fluke infection
3. Strongyloidiasis
4. *Nochtia nochti* infection
5. Cysticercosis
6. Gongylonemiasis
7. Echinococcosis

No doubt the monkey has many other parasites. To diagnose these usually requires the cooperation and interest of an expert parasitologist.

D. MISCELLANEOUS SPONTANEOUS LESIONS

1. Traumatic

In monkeys, as in man, almost any kind and degree of mechanical trauma may be encountered. Lacerations and contusions frequently due to biting, scratching, or caused by sharp

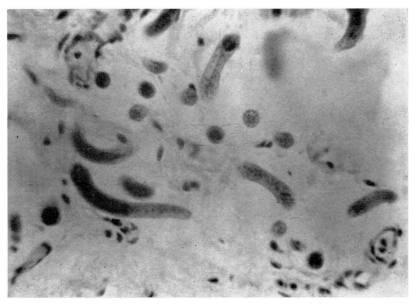

FIGURE 5. *Strongyloides sp.* Colon of rhesus monkey. Higher magnification of Figure 4.

protrusions of cage or runway are common. A case of liver herniated into the thorax has been observed.

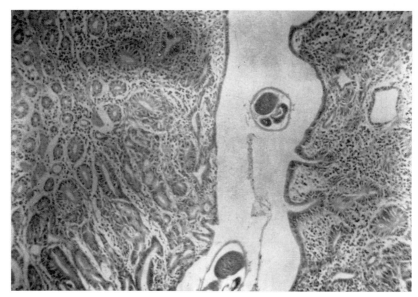

FIGURE 6. Nochtia nochti. Stomach of rhesus monkey.

2. Developmental Anomalies

The two possible examples which have been seen are a thyroglossal cyst and a case of syringomyelia. Others probably occur but have not been encountered in our experience.

3. Vascular Lesions

Perivasculitis is encountered from time to time in different organs. Likewise, isolated examples of varying degrees of intimal arterial thickening have not been uncommon, the reason for which is obscure.

4. Tumors

A thecoma and a fibroma are the only two tumors encountered. This may well be because most of the monkeys used were young animals. Both were incidental findings at autopsy.

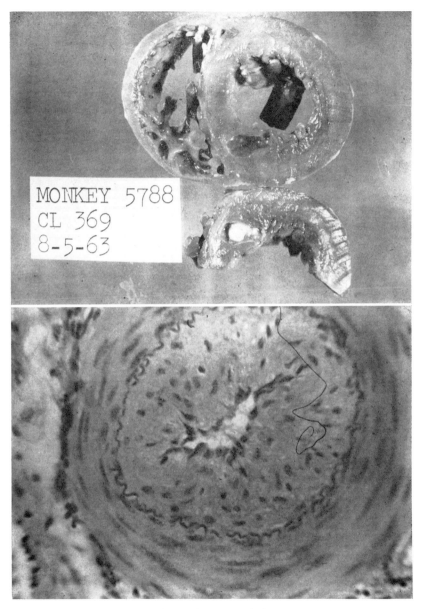

FIGURE 7. Cysticercosis. Heart of rhesus monkey.
FIGURE 8. Artery in mesentery of colon. Note intimal thickening. Rhesus monkey.

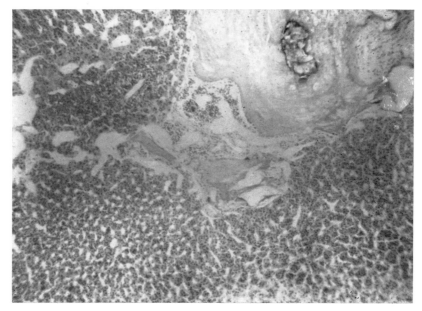

FIGURE 9. Adrenal. Calcification with adjacent bone marrow formation.
*Black and white copies of color slides shown at conference.

5. Calcification and Bone Marrow Nests in the Adrenal Gland

This was an incidental finding of unknown etiology.

6. Collagen Disease

This is a questionable diagnosis in an animal which underwent a six month progressive deterioration, apparently unrelated to any experimental maneuver. At autopsy it had rheumatoid-like nodules in the tail and fingers, atrophy of extremities with flexion contractures, and mesenteric arteritis with intimal thickening and mononuclear cellular infiltration of the adventitia of many arteries.

7. Cystic Degeneration of the Choroid Plexus

Discussion and Conclusion

From the kinds and variety of spontaneous lesions encountered in monkeys it would appear that many human disease entities may also occur in monkeys. Possibly if our total experience with monkeys of any species were sufficiently great, we would find them demonstrating all the types and variants of human pathology. The degree to which human disease is accepted by monkeys and vice versa is relatively unknown excepting for tuberculosis and some of the parasitic and virus diseases.

A knowledge of the lesions commonly encountered in the monkey is essential for scientific workers who are utilizing, increasingly, this species in the laboratory. Unfortunately, all too commonly this is not knowledge that is readily available to them. It is to be hoped that the various primate centers now in existence and planned will give adequate consideration to this aspect of the monkey, record such data carefully, and share their knowledge with others who use the monkey as an experimental animal.

BIBLIOGRAPHY

1. BODIAN, DAVID: The monkey safety test for poliomyelitis vaccine. *American Journal of Hygiene, 64*:104, 1956.
2. BONNE, C., SANGROUND, J. H.: On the production of gastric tumors bordering on malignancy in Javanese monkeys through the agency of *Nochtia nochti*, a parasitic nematode. *American Journal of Cancer, 37*:173, 1939.

DISCUSSION

Question: Dr. Weston, I was wondering if you would comment a little bit on cage paralysis.

Dr. Weston: Cage paralysis in monkeys is something that I have seen very rarely. I think the reason for this is that we did not keep monkeys chained in any way. We followed Dr. Herbert Schmidt's technique of having them in groups in a cage, letting them out in a runway, and catching them in the runway. Now, this makes a little more trouble for your attendants, true, but as far as I recall I can think of no case of true cage paralysis in our monkey colony.

I would suggest it might have much to do with the amount of restraint used on the monkey.

Dr. K. M. Das: I would like to make a comment on the subject of cage paralysis in monkeys. I think this name is somewhat a misnomer and usually denotes a specific disease of monkeys, which is known as simian bone disease. When one follows the pattern of the disease from the clinical stage to the lethal stage, one can observe several stages of progression of disease from painful limbs to almost paralysis. The bones are rather soft. The animal has pain when he tries to get up; he therefore crawls, not walks. On radiological examination one sees a honeycomb-like appearance of bones, typical of osteoporosis. When followed progressively it is seen to become a state of osteodystrophia fibrosa; with a knife one can cut the bones. The etiology is perhaps metabolic and a complex of nutrition and metabolism of the bone. It is possibly an imbalance between Vitamin A and D.

It is commonly found in the New World monkeys, not with the Rhesus monkeys, but mostly among the woolly monkey and spider monkey.

The common parasites of monkeys would also include the pinworms. They are not exactly the same pinworm as is found in the human, but similar. They belong to two genera: (1) *Enterobius*, and (2) *Syphacia*. One can frequently find a good number of these in the colon of the monkeys. These are short, pointed, white, glistening round worms. The animals suffering from this infection are bad actors due to pruritus of the perianal region. This would be comparable to signs of human pinworm infection.

Then there is one parasite of the heart, *Dirofilaria*, which causes heartworm disease in the dog. It causes a pericarditis in monkeys. It usually lodges in the pericardium and epicardium in monkeys.

Dr. Robert M. Sauer: I would like to make a few comments on the monkey.

The first of these is on cage paralysis. I think probably this term should go right along with "wet tail" of hamsters, i.e., somewhere down the drain. This is a particular syndrome associated with South American monkeys and it should not be confused with the stiffness that nutritionally sound monkeys will get after long periods of close confinement. The stiffness will usually wear off within a very short period of time, within ten minutes to half an hour or so.

Now, as regards this cage paralysis of South American monkeys. This is a very specific syndrome and is a nutritional osteodystrophy. It probably involves a good many factors, including calcium, parathyroid response, Vitamin A, Vitamin C, but the critical factor is Vitamin D and I venture to say that if these monkeys have ten days of life left to them when you are able to see them, an injection of Vitamin D will start on their way to recovery. Many of these animals will not respond to oral Vitamin D and what we usually use here is 100,000 to 200,000 units of Vitamin D every two weeks for three injections and then monthly thereafter.

The disease can be acute. If this is the case it will probably show up within two or three months. On the other hand, it can be chronic. I have seen it take up to three or four years to develop. If it is acute the response to the Vitamin D is very rapid, in as short a time as ten days. Otherwise the clinical response may take upwards of six weeks or more.

Most monkeys at this time are not eating and as the clinical response occurs the animals will begin to eat, then the diet can be adjusted to include proper amounts of protein and of the other vitamins that I have mentioned. This can be followed with a radiograph taken at monthly intervals—and the radiographs are not indicative of the clinical response. If you take monthly radiographs over a period of six months you can see the difference between the first one and the one a half year later. However, as I say, the clinical response is more rapid—a prostrate monkey in the acute stage may be up walking around in ten days, or at the most six weeks, if it is chronic.

The other comment that I wanted to make is on *pneumonyssus simicola,* the lung mite. As far as its transmission is concerned, this mite is viviparous and by taking sections you can probably see both the eggs and the developing larvae. Inasmuch as they do inhabit the lumen of the bronchial tree I think the method of its spread becomes suggestive if not obvious.

Dr. E. C. Melby: On this problem of cage paralysis, I think the term should be specifically defined. I have found that many people will find an animal showing symptoms of paresis, or paralysis and if it is a monkey they term it cage paralysis. As brought out here, the problem of nutritional deficiency, particularly in the South American monkey, may be one type. I have also seen recently two cases diagnosed clinically as cage paralysis and these turned out to be tuberculous meningitis and tuberculous spondylitis.

In general injuries have been indicated as being a form of cage paralysis.

This is just another instance, where we have to define our terms more explicitly. In working with monkeys I have found it important to tell what species of monkeys one is working with rather than lumping them all together as Old or New World monkeys. I think this will be extremely important as we progress in working with some of these more obscure species.

Dr. Sauer: Dr. Melby said that it is important to mention species. I agree with this. The woolly monkey, for instance, in addition to having disease, shows an extreme parathyroid reaction to low serum calcium and the parathyroids of these animals may be twice the size of the thyroid and these are the monkeys where one encounters the typical softening, the osteofibrosis, of the bone, and almost complete lack of calcification.

The other species, such as squirrel monkey, the Rhesus, the spider monkey, don't seem to show this.

Again, so far as treatment with injections of calcium, I think it is a well established fact that animals, even on very low calcium diets, if they have adequate Vitamin D will make the utmost use of extremely small amounts of calcium, whereas if Vitamin D is lacking or limited, then even larger amounts of calcium are of little value.

Dr. J. R. McCoy: We have some monkey adrenals which have shown a considerable fibrosis of the cortico-medullary junction and I wonder if anyone could enlighten us on whether or not there is a variation in the amount of connective tissue in this location in the monkey adrenals.

Dr. Weston: In trying to think back over several years I would say that I cannot recall having encountered any significant number of monkeys where this connective tissue impressed me.

Dr. Gerald Cosgrove: I have two slides of parasites from our monkeys. Could I show them?

Chairman: Yes, of course.

Dr. Cosgrove: (showing slides). Dr. Bill Nelson, the pathologist at the Oak Ridge Institute of Nuclear Studies, has autopsied several hundred South American marmosets, genus *Tamarinus,* and they have a very different spectrum of parasites than the Old World monkeys do.

One is a linguatulid, or tongue worm, genus *Porocephalus,* and occurs encysted in many different tissues in the marmoset. The final host of this parasite is probably a large snake, such as the boa, which eats the monkey. Digestion releases the parasite, which then migrates to the lung. The head of this worm has a series of four hooklets and a small mouth. The worm gives an appearance of annulation and it lies in a cyst in a U-shaped curl.

When released from the cyst it is about one inch long.

Another is an acanthocephalan parasite (thorny-headed worm) which is classified in a phylum between the nematodes and the flatworms. They have a spiny proboscis with numerous hooks on it. The proboscis is embedded in the mucosa of the intestine. The mature worms lie in the ileo-cecal area, usually in the terminal ileum with a few of them in the cecum if the infestation is heavy. The immature worms attach higher in the intestinal tract, perhaps in the mid-jejunal area. These worms are very important as a cause of mortality and morbidity in the marmoset. The head imbedded in the intestinal mucosa causes a severe lesion and often leads to intestinal perforation and abdominal abscess. This worm is also an inch to an inch-and-a-half long and is of a fairly characteristic shape with a small round proboscis at the anterior end.

J. Russell Lindsey: I would like to discuss a condition encountered in white-lipped marmosets.

There had been continued losses in the marmoset colony since the summer of 1962, that is, over a period of six to nine months. Some of the animals had been replaced with additions to the colony and the losses continued. We did a few autopsies on animals from this group. One case in particular was of concern to us. This particular animal had rather a large ulcer covering about half of the dorsum of the tongue, and there were a few pale foci in the adrenals. These were the only lesions noticed grossly.

On microscopic examination of the tongue the large ulcer in the center of this area consisted of massive coagulation necrosis, there were intranuclear inclusions around the margin of the ulcer, with the syncytosis, which has been described for B Virus infection. There were a few questionable inclusions in some of the superior cervical lymph nodes and the adrenal had a very striking focal necrosis with intranuclear inclusions in the cortex. There were a few very small areas of acute inflammation in the brain stem and in the ileum in the region surrounding the attached acanthocephala, examples of which you saw earlier. There were intranuclear inclusions in some of the epithelial cells.

This concerned us a great deal because it resembled B Virus infection, even though this has not been reported in marmosets, and on questioning the attendant we found out that he had been scratched on the face just a few days previously when working with this colony. At the time, as best we could analyze the situation we felt that it could be one of three possibilities. We thought of B Virus, of the possibility of herpes simplex infection even though we found out this had been tried in the early thirties with marmosets and there were no takes, and thirdly we thought this might be a herpes infection natural to marmosets.

About this time the Federation proceedings appeared and we found out that Dr. A. V. Holmes, at the University of Chicago, had been working with such an agent like ours and later we found that people at Baylor had also worked with it. It appears that Dr. Holmes has done rather extensive immunological studies and he feels very strongly that it is a new herpes virus. From this information, and putting the fragments of information together, it does appear as if this is true and that it is a natural infection of marmosets and not the usual herpes infection.

We don't know how many of the deaths were due to this agent because only one of the two or three cases seen at autopsy had the lesion described.

Dr. Robert M. Sauer: In this connection, if we are talking about the same thing, in the next *Laboratory Animal Journal,* I published a very short paper on six red mantle marmosets that were received from California and the day after they arrived one of the animals died. The caretaker autopsied it and sent in a small section of liver that contained focal areas of necrosis. In the younger lesions there was cytomegaly—the liver cells appeared to join together—and these very large typical type A inclusion bodies, quite typical of herpes, were quite prominent. Within the week the other five marmosets died and one of these was autopsied. The same lesions were found. We took some of the lesion material and ground it up and injected it into rabbits in the hope of isolating herpes B virus, but were unsuccessful.

Just last June I was in California and Dr. Kennedy asked me to look at a couple of slides of a South American monkey. It was the same lesion. Then he showed me two more. I bet him this came from a marmoset. He didn't know, but he called up the contributor and sure enough it was. So I am glad to see that somebody is working on this condition. I think this is probably the same lesion that you are talking about.

Question: How significant is filariasis as a cause of death in monkeys?

Dr. Weston: I am not a filariasis expert but the lesions which have occurred we have found in the spleen as widespread perivascular cell infiltration with chronic granulomatous lesions. I would think that with as much chronic granuloma as we have seen in the spleen that the spleen probably does not function too well as a result of infection. I do not recall having seen any other vital organ with anywhere near the degree of gross involvement as the spleen.

From the standpoint of the distribution of the parasites and their numbers, I personally have seen many of them in blood vessels in some animals. Almost wherever in a section you would have a blood vessel, you would see considerable numbers of filaria.

The most severely affected animals were animals that had died rather than been killed in the course of a study. Whether filariasis was the primary cause of death I wouldn't know because they went through a stage when they got droopy, wouldn't eat, were malnourished and skinny, and died. So I can't answer your question as to whether this is a significant and primary cause of death in monkeys. I would suggest that when the infection is there in large numbers it isn't doing the monkey very much good and it may well push him over the divide.

Question: Dr. Weston, did you see any rise in blood platelet counts in monkeys with pronounced involvement of the spleen?

Dr. Weston: I don't recall that we studied this particular parameter. I think sometime earlier we had decided to limit our blood studies except when we had something particular to study, thus we restricted ourselves to a hemoglobin and a hematocrit, and only when we had some reason, for going into the other parameters did we do so. Practically, this was necessary because we preferred to do biopsies that gave us more information with the time allotted than we would otherwise have spent getting additional blood parameters.

Dr. Gerald Cosgrove: In the marmosets at Oak Ridge, which incidentally are *Tamarinus nigricollis,* there also has been a problem with filariasis. A number of the animals that are heavily infected have had the parasite in the peritoneal cavity and it is accompanied by a turbid ascitic fluid and a marked thickening of the serosal lining and the mesentery. When you examine the peritoneum histologically it turns out to be very edematous and to be heavily infiltrated with inflammatory cells. Sometimes worms have died and been encapsulated in this kind of tissue with the usual type of foreign body reaction around them.

I don't know whether Dr. Weston considers filariasis the primary cause of death in his monkeys but certainly there are definite tissue lesions.

On the other hand we haven't noticed any tissue lesions around the microfilaria, which are widely distributed in the circulation and sometimes in fantastic numbers.

I haven't seen any filarial-induced nodules in the spleen, as were described earlier from other monkey colonies.

Dr. E. L. Jungherr: In continuation of Dr. Weston's presentation I should like to make a few remarks on nonspecific diseases in the central nervous system of common laboratory monkeys, especially rhesus and cynomolgus. These species are used extensively for the preparation of kidney tissue cultures and for neurovirulence tests of live oral polio vaccines and other vaccines such as measles and adenoviruses. The neurovirulence test for live polio vaccine is the only instance in biologic production where a major characterization of a vaccine strain is based upon large scale neuropathologic examination. Unlike the all-or-none test for the inactivated Salk vaccine, it is based upon quantitative evaluation of the residual neurovirulence of the vaccine strains. It is obvious that the occurrence of nonspecific lesions in the central nervous system could interfere with conducting and reading the tests and every effort must be bent to differentiating pre-existing lesions from specific ones caused by the inoculum.

Among the nonspecific lesions there are four general categories, namely those caused by malformations, injuries, inflammatory processes, and tumors. I should like to show you some examples of these various conditions. All of them but one were found in young, healthy appearing rhesus and cynomolgus monkeys which had been conditioned in the plant for at least six weeks. Stock monkeys are watched carefully, and if they display any neurologic signs they are killed immediately for pathologic analysis. We have less experience with African Green monkeys, *Cercopithecus aethiops,* because so far they are used primarily for kidney tissue culture work, but this situation may change. We know already that each species has its own set of nonspecific lesions and that generalizations are not warranted.

Figure 10 is an example of malformation. Doctor Weston mentioned syringomyelia. This slide shows the less developed stage of

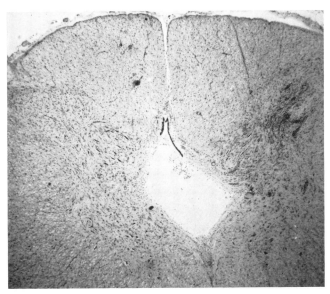

FIGURE 10. Syringomyelus in lumbar cord.

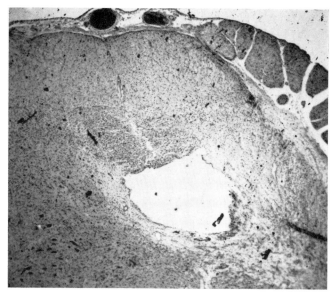

FIGURE 11. Syringomyelia in lumbar cord.

the same process, syringomyelus, a congenital dilatation of the central canal in the lumbar cord. It is relatively common, but varies in intensity, and may occur in the very same region where an intraspinal test inoculum is placed between L_1 and L_2.

Figure 11 is a typical example of syringomyelia. You see the tubular cavitation in the lumbar cord just above the central canal accompanied by intense glial reaction.

Figure 12 is an example of spina bifida. It is a section through the lumbar cord of an intrathalamically inoculated rhesus. The lumbar cord is completely divided by the herniation of the meningi during the developmental period. There are two central canals, the lateral hemisections are fairly well developed, the medial ones are degenerated. Duplication of the central canal in the lumbar cord is quite common but complete division of the cord is rare.

Figure 13 shows an old injury in the motor cortex of the cerebrum. This is the region which is often traversed on intrathalamic inoculation. The resulting tracks are usually represented by linear, cellular scars whereas here we see a deep indentation of the outer three layers of the cerebrum associated with an intense, blood-pigmented, glial reaction at its floor and disturbance in lamellation. Although the lesion has the appearance of a direct local injury, contrecoup injury can not be ruled out in such cases.

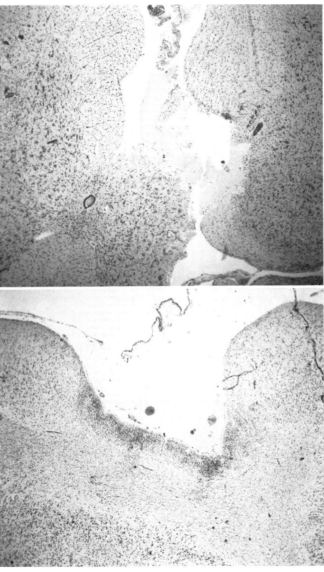

FIGURE 12. Spina bifida occulta in lumbar cord.
FIGURE 13. Old injury in motor cortex of cerebrum.

Figure 14 represents the lumbar cord of a rhesus which received an intrathalamic inoculum. The right lateral white column shows an old injury not unlike a track produced by a misplaced (because of not hitting the motor horn) intraspinal inoculation. In the lesion there is some foreign body giant cell reaction which serves as a clue to its origin.

Figure 15 shows focal degeneration in the dorsal white column of the lumbar cord or myelosis, not unlike tabes dorsalis in human syphilis. Myelosis has been considered a condition of old monkeys but we find it quite frequently in young laboratory monkeys, without associated neurologic signs.

Figure 16 shows cysticercosis which has already been mentioned by Dr. Weston. The slide is from an intrathalamically inoculated rhesus with multiple cysts in the sensory cortex. The adjacent motor cortex is not affected but there is cellular infiltration in the leptomeningi of the sulcus centralis.

Figure 17 represents the lumbar cord of a Aotus monkey which received an intrathalamic inoculum of polio vaccine. Although otherwise free from lesions this level of the lumbar cord is normal on the right side but has in the left ventral horn a definite lesion characterized by loss of neurons and replacement gliosis, probably the result of a pre-existing mild viral infection.

Figure 18 is a section through the brain stem, at the level of the nucleus locus coeruleus, of a rhesus inoculated intrathalamically with SV_{40}. In the anterior velum and the periventricular substance there are glial and perivascular foci with involvement of the ependyma as in granular ependymitis.

These alterations are representative of encephalomyelitic lesions which one may find in both inoculated and in non-inoculated monkeys. They are believed to be caused by clinically inapparent simian virus infections of which over forty types have been described. The "spontaneous" lesions are similar in type, but vary in extent, and tend to occur in the regions washed by the cerebrospinal fluid. If they occur together with lesions caused by the inoculum they may present a real problem for differential diagnosis. In the evaluation of lesions caused by attenuated polio vaccine strains emphasis must be placed upon the examination of the

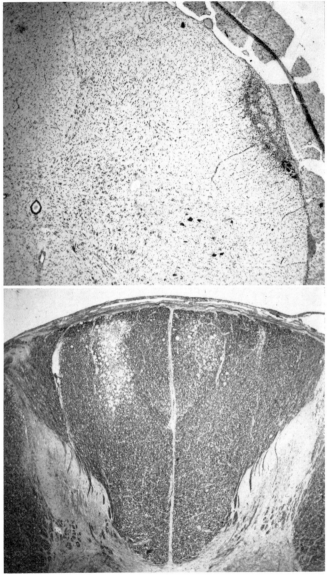

FIGURE 14. Old inoculation-track-like injury in lumbar cord of intrathalamically inoculated monkey.

FIGURE 15. Myelosis of dorsal white columns in lumbar cord.

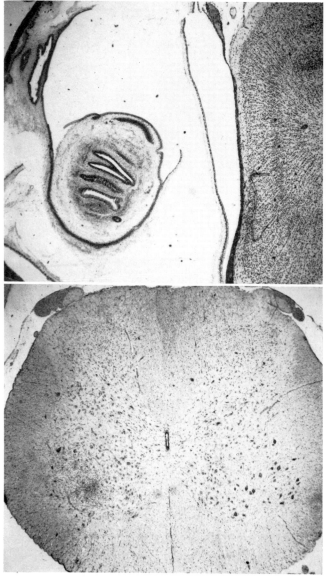

Figure 16. Cysticercosis in sensory cortex of cerebrum, adjacent motor cortex intact.

Figure 17. Nonspecific encephalomyelitic focus in left ventral horn of lumbar cord from polio vaccine intrathalamically-inoculated Aotus monkey, otherwise without lesions.

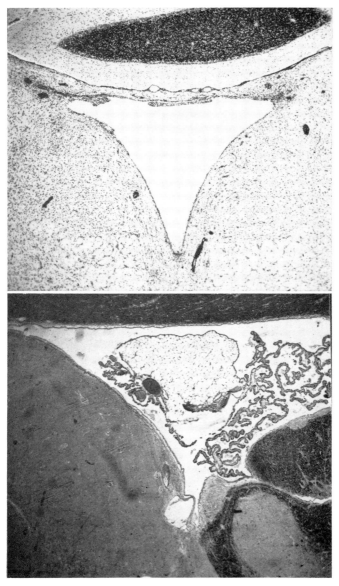

FIGURE 18. Brain stem lesions in rhesus, intrathalamically inoculated with simian virus 40, representative of clinically inapparent, spontaneous simian virus infections (Courtesy *J. Neuropath. Exp. Neurol.,* Jungherr *et al.,* 1963) .

FIGURE 19. Lipoma in choroid plexus of anterior horn of lateral ventricle. Incidental finding in intrathalamically inoculated monkey.

known anatomic target areas such as the nucleus ruber and the nucleus vestibularis lateralis. Focal periventricular or periaqueductal lesions without involvement of the known target areas, may be nonspecific in character. In several instances it was actually possible to confirm this suspicion by isolation of SV_{40} and not of polio virus from the central nervous system of monkeys inoculated with attenuated polio vaccine strains.

Figure 19 represents a lipoma in the choroid plexus of the lateral ventricle, incidentally found in an intrathalamically inoculated rhesus.

Figures 20 and 21 represent a vertebral endothelioma in a stock rhesus which suddenly became paralyzed in the hind legs and had a small intravertebral tumor in the lumbar region. Pressure on the dorsal roots of the regional spinal nerves was believed responsible for the clinical syndrome. Under high power (Fig. 21) the tumor was found attached to the periosteum, and to consist of closely spaced capillary channels lined by hyperplastic endothelial cells. There was no definite evidence of malignancy.

Figures 22 and 23 are from a case of meningiomatosis of the lumbar cord in a rhesus which had received an intrathalamic inoculation of attenuated polio virus. The monkey became paralyzed in the hind legs on day twenty post-inoculation. While there were no significant polio lesions in the brain, the lumbar cord showed an intense meningeal thickening, accompanied by pressure distortion of the cord, which at first was suspected to represent a localized lumbar meningitis. Under high power (Fig. 23) the mass was found to consist of proliferated arachnoidal cells which almost encircled the cord at some levels and had undergone extensive necrosis in the center. While finding this neoplastic disease of long standing ruled out the possibility of polio induced paralysis, the late onset of the clinical signs remained unexplained.

On the whole, these examples of diseases in the central nervous system of common laboratory monkeys emphasize the importance of differentiating between specific lesions caused by the inoculum and nonspecific, pre-existing lesions. With the increased use of laboratory monkeys for neurovirulence tests there is an acute need for awareness of this problem and for detailed cataloguing of observations.

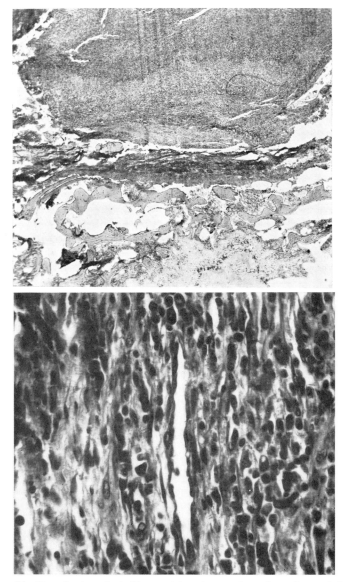

FIGURE 20. Vertebral endothelioma *(above)* on visceral surface of lumbar vertebra *(below)* in paralyzed stock monkey (courtesy *Ann. N. Y. Acad. Sci.,* Jungherr, 1963).

FIGURE 21. High power of Figure 20 showing capillary channels with hyperplastic endothelial cells (courtesy *Ann. N. Y. Acad. Sci.,* Jungherr, 1963).

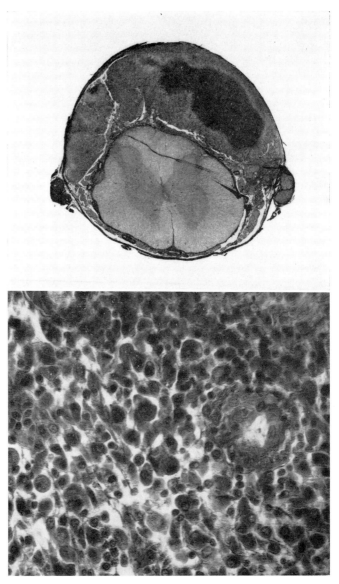

FIGURE 22. Preexisting lumbar meningiomatosis and cord compression in polio vaccine intrathalamically-inoculated monkey paralyzed on day twenty (courtesy *Ann. N. Y. Acad. Sci.,* Junkherr, 1963).

FIGURE 23. High power of Figure 22 showing masses of proliferated arachnoidal cells (courtesy *Ann. N. Y. Acad. Sci.,* Jungherr, 1963).

REFERENCES

JUNGHERR, E. L., CABASSO, V. J. and STEBBINS, M.: Comparative pathology of attenuated poliovirus and simian viruses 12 and 40 in monkeys and mice. *J. Neuropath. Exp. Neurol., 22:*512–527, 1963.

JUNGHERR, E.: Tumors and tumor-like conditions in monkeys. *Ann. N. Y. Acad. Sci., 108:*777–792, 1963.

14

THE INTERPRETATION OF
PATHOLOGY DATA

G. E. PAGET AND PHYLLIS G. LEMON

AN ANALYSIS OF THE PATHOLOGICAL LESIONS
ENCOUNTERED IN SPECIFIC PATHOGEN FREE RATS

THE INTERPRETATION of pathology data from experiments with animals presents many difficulties, but in long-continued experiments no sources of confusion are more important in assessment of the results than are lesions due to diseases unrelated to the variable that the experimenter has studied. The ordinary laboratory animals that have been used in the past have, in fact, been extremely unhealthy and consequently, even over quite short periods, a high proportion of them became ill and many died because of intercurrent diseases. Such diseases included the almost universal viral pneumonia of rats, ectromelia of mice, and innumerable internal and external protozoan and metazoan parasites of both species, as well as less frequent viral and bacteriological infections, often of epizootic proportions. It is not, therefore, surprising that in recent years many units and individuals concerned with provision of animals for experiments have studied ways in which this unsatisfactory situation might be improved.

Broadly, there are two main approaches to this problem. The most radical approach is that pioneered by workers at Notre Dame, in which animals are reared in an environment entirely free from all live biological contamination. Such animals are spoken of as "germ-free" or gnotobiotic. For several reasons, such animals have not been widely used for routine experimentation and are probably not suitable for this purpose. Without expensive facilities, the number of animals available at any one time is small and it seems probable that the germ-free animal differs in many important physiological respects from his more conventionally reared cousins.

The other approach is to rear the animals in an environment freed of biological agents known to be pathogenic to the species concerned, but in other respects bearing a normal bacteriological flora. Such animals are referred to as "specific-pathogen-free" (SPF) and several units throughout the world are now producing such animals in moderate or large numbers. The SPF animals can be handled with far fewer precautions against the outside environment than are required with the germ-free animals, and there seem to be no reasons to suppose that these animals' biological responses have been modified in any important respect by freeing them from the major pathogens affecting the species. The SPF animal may be thought of as resembling the healthy individual of a highly developed community, whereas the animals used in the past may be thought of as resembling the disease-ridden individual of mediaeval times or of a backward modern community.

The advent of the SPF animals is so recent that no data are available on the life span or on the causes of morbidity and mortality which may be expected, although those using such animals realize that the life span is longer and that the major infective causes of morbidity and mortality are less important than with the conventional "dirty" animal. This paper, therefore, considers an experiment which has now been in progress for four years in which two populations of rats have been compared for incidence of disease and the causes and times of death. One population was born and reared under SPF conditions, the other under dirty conditions, but both came from a Wistar-derived stock, bred in our laboratories for over eighteen years. The SPF rats were from the then-recently-inaugurated SPF breeding unit at I.C.I. Pharmaceuticals Division, Alderly Park, Macclesfield, and this strain is now called Alderly Park Strain 1. The details of this unit have been described by Davey (1959) and a brief preliminary account of the lesions of the animals derived from it has been given by one of us (Paget, 1962).

Table I shows the distribution of animals as between SPF and dirty conditions at the beginning of the experiment.

The only major difference in numbers is between the two groups of breeding males. The original intention was to have

TABLE I
THE DISTRIBUTION OF DIRTY AND CLEAN RATS

	Breeding		Non Breeding		Totals
	♂	♀	♂	♀	
SPF Conditions	42	151	152	137	482
Dirty Conditions	149	145	137	141	572

equal numbers of breeding males and females and keep them in permanent pairs. This was done in the dirty unit, but in the SPF unit the necessity of fitting the experiment in with the routine work resulted in the breeding animals being kept in harem conditions, the number of males being thereby greatly reduced. In all cases, the diet of the animals was similar whether within or outside the unit and consisted of a pelleted diet made to our own specification. The diet taken into the breeding unit was sterilised by autoclaving, whereas that used outside was not so treated. The conditions of caging and density of population were roughly similar in the two areas. The animals were inspected frequently. Sick or moribund animals were killed and a full post-mortem was performed on all animals killed or dying, except where autolysis was advanced or where cannibalism had occurred. When possible, sections of the lungs were taken, even if a full post-mortem was not practicable. Table II shows the proportion of animals autopsied. This table is only concerned with the death so far fully analysed, and includes all deaths in animals up to thirty months of age.

TABLE II
PROPORTIONS OF ANIMALS AUTOPSIED

	Deaths (% of Animals in Expt.)		Full P.M. (% of Deaths)		Partial P.M. (% of Deaths)		No P.M. (% of Deaths)	
SPF Conditions	275	(57%)	208	(76%)	41	(14%)	26	(9%)
Dirty Conditions	492	(86%)	380	(77%)	83	(17%)	29	(6%)

Results

Table III shows the cumulative mortality in all the animals of both groups. Certain features of the mortality curves are of interest. The last surviving animals kept under dirty conditions died

at thirty-nine months, whereas a handful of survivors under SPF
conditions lived to forty-seven months and one of these animals
achieved the remarkable age of fifty-one months. The general
shape of the mortality curves, as might be expected, is similar between the two groups. It will be noted, however, that the mortality
commenced early in the dirty group and that 5.7 per cent of the
dirty animals were dead at twelve months, compared with 1 per
cent of the SPF animals and, perhaps the most striking difference,
42 per cent of the dirty animals were dead at two years, compared
with only 21 per cent of the SPF animals. The median mortality
for dirty animals was at twenty-five and one-half months and for
SPF animals at twenty-nine months.

TABLE III
CUMULATIVE MORTALITY OF DIRTY AND SPF RATS

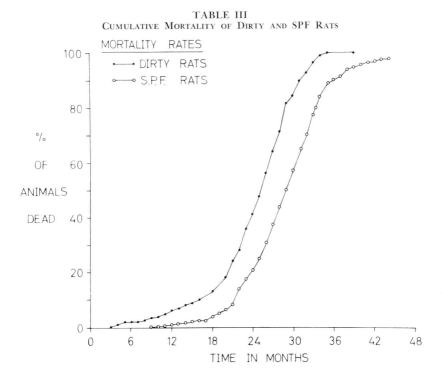

Table IV compares the mortality rates of breeding females with
non-breeding females in the two conditions. The general difference between dirty and clean animals is preserved; however, the
mortality curve for breeding SPF animals is almost coincident

with that for stock dirty animals. It would thus appear that the strain of repeated pregnancy imposes a similar burden to that of intercurrent disease. Table V shows the difference in mortality between males. The small group of breeding SPF animals is excluded.

TABLE IV
Non-Breeding Females Under Dirty and SPF Conditions

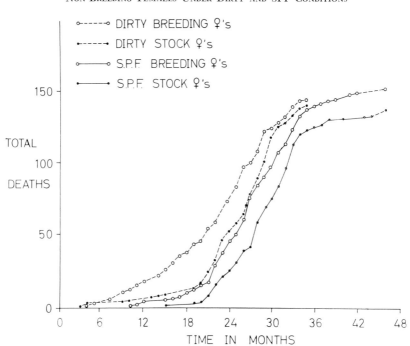

A striking feature of the mortality curves, both of the various comparable groups and of all the animals kept in one or other condition, is the marked shift to the right of the mortality of the SPF animals. This is due to a far smaller number of early deaths in this group. When the causes of mortality are considered it is clear that the early deaths in the dirty group are largely due to infective diseases and highest on this list is chronic murine pneumonia which, in a greater or lesser degree, affects virtually all rats not reared in germ-free or SPF conditions. Table VI compares the incidence of lung disease by age groups in SPF and dirty animals.

TABLE V
MORTALITY RATES OF BREEDING AND NON-BREEDING
MALES UNDER DIRTY AND SPF CONDITIONS

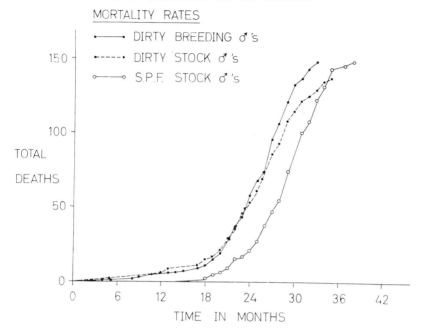

MORTALITY RATES

●——→ DIRTY BREEDING ♂'s

●-----● DIRTY STOCK ♂'s

○——○ S.P.F. STOCK ♂'s

TABLE VI
INCIDENCE OF LUNG DISEASE IN DIRTY AND S.P.F. RATS

Age in Months	Normal Lungs		Infected Lungs		Lungs with Abscesses		Lymphosarcoma of Lungs	
	Dirty	SPF	Dirty	SPF	Dirty	SPF	Dirty	SPF
0-6	2	–	1	–	0	–		–
7-12	7	0	10	1	2	0		
13-18	8	10	22	1	3	0		
19-24	0	66	34	2	7	0	3	1*
25-30	1	127	247	12	87	1	12+4*	
TOTAL	18	203	314	16	99	1	15+4*	1*
TOTAL DEATHS	463	249						
%	3.9%	82%	68%	6.4%	21%	1%	3.2%	

*Lymphosarcoma found in lungs but probably secondary to tumours elsewhere, e.g., mediastinum.

Eighty-one per cent of the SPF animals had healthy, normal lungs (Fig. 1a) whereas only 3.9 per cent of the dirty animals fell in this class. The majority of dirty animals, especially with advancing age, have evidence of infection in the lungs. The characteristic histological picture (Fig. 1b) of chronic pneumonia is that most commonly observed. The small number of infected lungs seen in the SPF animals show a somewhat varied histological picture (Fig. 2) and it is thought that these infections are probably of various origins and are often secondary to other illnesses. A high proportion of the dirty animals show the characteristic progression of chronic murine pneumonia to bronchiectatic abscesses (Fig. 3) whereas only one lung abscess was seen in a clean animal. We believe that our clean animals have been, and remain, free of the virus causing chronic respiratory disease of rats. This belief is

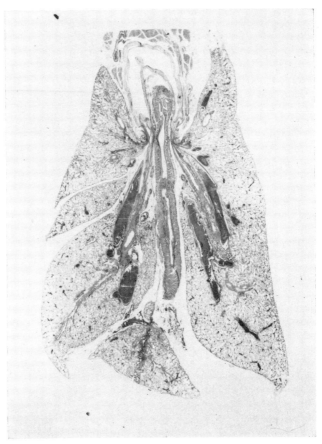

FIGURE 1a. Normal lungs from an SPF rat. (Non-breeding female, age 27 months.)

supported by consistently negative Nelson tests on lungs from our SPF animals. This freedom from chronic lung disease is of itself sufficient to account for a considerable improvement in health. Cases of primary lymphosarcoma of the lungs are included in Table VI since they are confined to the dirty animals and we be-

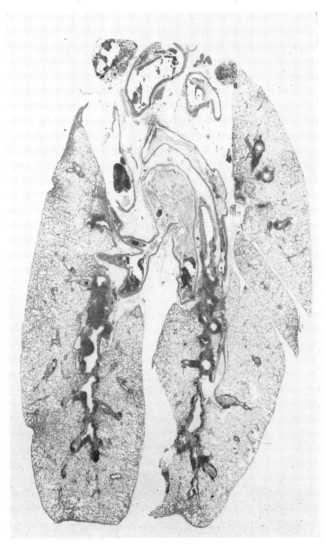

FIGURE 1b. Murine pneumonia in a dirty rat. Lymphoid hyperplasia is evident along the bronchi. (Breeding female, age 27 months.)

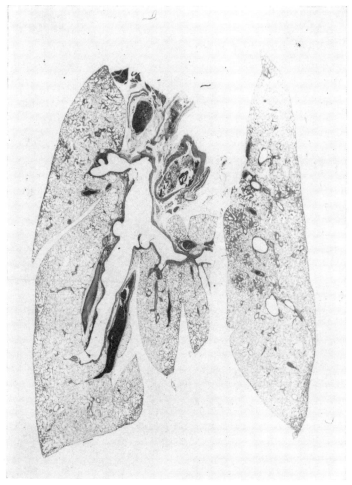

FIGURE 2. Mild bronchopneumonia in an SPF rat. (Non-breeding female, age 26 months.)

lieve that this is related to the enormous accumulation of lymphocytes which occurs as a feature of chronic murine pneumonia, and
possibly the chronic inflammatory process itself may play a part.

Kidney disease is another common cause of morbidity in rats.
The classification of diseases of the kidney in the rat, as in humans,
leaves much to be desired. In assessing the importance of kidney
disease, we originally used three categories: animals with complete-

ly normal kidneys, those with mild or moderate nephropathy, and those showing severe kidney disease (Figs. 4 and 5). Figure 4 shows an example of moderate nephropathy, and Figure 5 a severe case. An arterial disease similar to periarteritis nodosa in humans occurs in rats (Fig. 6) and can be produced experimentally by damage to kidney tissue (Koletsky, 1955). Table VII analyses the incidence of normal kidneys, severe kidney disease, total cases of periarteritis and the cases associated with severe nephropathy. It

TABLE VII

INCIDENCE OF NEPHROPATHY AND POLYARTERITIS IN DIRTY AND S.P.F. RATS

Age In Months	Normal Kidneys		Severe Nephropathy		Polyarteritis All Cases		Polyarteritis c Severe Nephropathy	
	Dirty	SPF	Dirty	SPF	Dirty	SPF	Dirty	SPF
0-6	2	–	0	–	0	–	0	–
7-12	7	4	0	0	0	0	0	0
13-18	9	6	1	0	0	1	0	0
19-24	12	11	15	4	11	2	5	2
25-30	6	7	52	22	52	16	37	11
Totals	36(10)	28(12)	68(62)	26(17)	63(55)	19(14)	42(38)	13(10)
Total P.M.'s	380	208						
% Age Incidence	9.5%	13%	18%	12.5%	16.5%	9.1%	11%	6.2%

Figures in brackets denote number of ♂'s in the group.

can be seen that a somewhat higher proportion of SPF animals have normal kidneys than of dirty animals, and that the incidence of all varieties of severe nephropathy and arterial disease is lower in the SPF group. There is a marked difference in incidence of all types of nephropathy between the sexes in both SPF animals and dirty animals, males being more severely affected in each case. We are unable to say whether any of the animals were hypertensive or whether any of them died from renal failure, although from the severity of the lesions seen in some cases it is reasonable to suppose that renal failure represents an important cause of death.

Table VIII analyses the incidence of severe infections leading to abscess formation in the two groups. Such infections include pyometra, subcutaneous and perioral abscesses, and various other infections. Here again, it can be seen that the SPF animals has a far lower incidence of infection than does the dirty animal. We

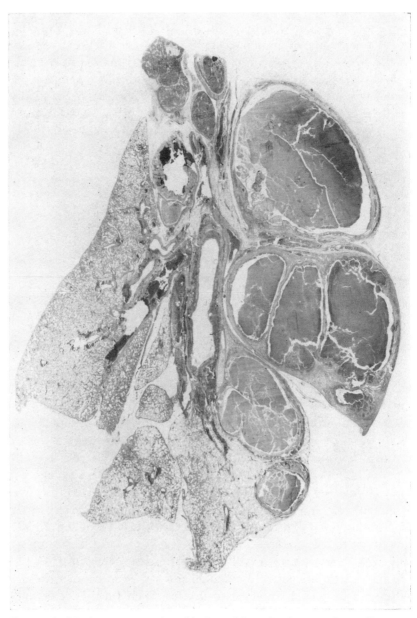

FIGURE 3. Murine pneumonia with bronchiectatic abscesses in a dirty rat. (Non-breeding female, age 22 months.)

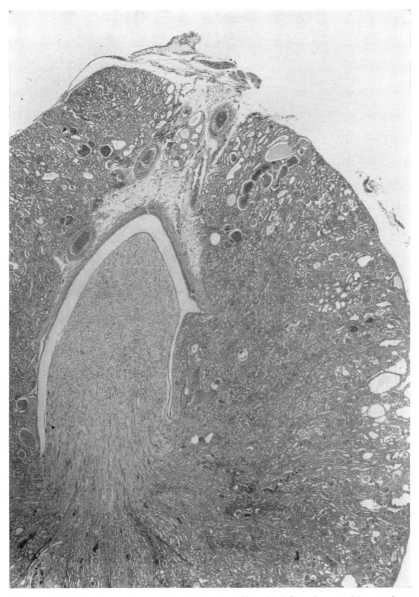

FIGURE 4. Moderate nephropathy. (Non-breeding SPF female, age 30 months.)

TABLE VIII
INCIDENCE OF ABSCESSES IN DIRTY AND S.P.F. RATS..
(EXCLUDING LUNG ABSCESSES)

Age in Months	Dirty Rats	S.P.F. Rats
0-6	1/3	–
7-12	3/11	1/4
13-18	3/20	0/9
19-24	34/126	2/62
25-30	23/223	8/133
TOTAL INCIDENCE	64/380 = 17%	11/208 = 5.5%

have not, unfortunately, made bacteriological investigations of these infections. However, by analogy with mice kept in SPF conditions, in which it has been shown in our unit that "spontaneous" abscesses may arise from human type staphylococci that are not normally pathogenic to the mouse, it may be supposed that there would be bacteriological differences between the abscesses in the dirty and SPF groups.

Routine parasitological surveys have not been carried out on either group of animals. However, intestinal worms and the bladder worm *Trichosomoides crassicauda* have been noted in histological sections from 15 per cent of the dirty animals in this study, while no case of a metazoan parasite has been noted in the SPF group.

The remaining important cause of death which we wish to analyse is neoplasia. Table IX analyses the incidence of neoplasia in the two groups of animals. The figures given are for total numbers of tumours, rather than numbers of tumour-bearing animals, although this distinction is only of importance in the older age

TABLE IX
INCIDENCE OF NEOPLASMS IN DIRTY AND S.P.F. RATS (1)

Age in Months	Dirty Rats		S.P.F. Rats	
	Benign	Malignant	Benign	Malignant
0-6	0	0	–	–
7-12	2	0	1	0
13-18	3	2	3	9
19-24	18	18	15	11
25-30	119	37	98	23
Total	142	57	117	43
No. of Animals P.M.'d	380	380	208	208
% Incidence	37%	15%	56%	21%

groups. Table IX shows that there is a greater total number of tumours in the SPF animals, especially in the later stages of the experiment. However, when the figures are corrected for numbers of animals at risk, it is apparent that the difference occurs because

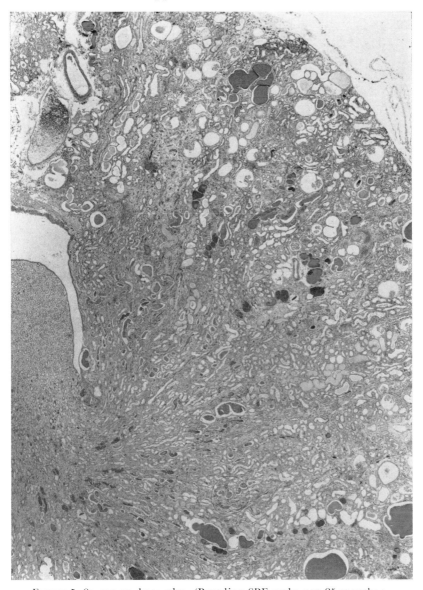

FIGURE 5. Severe nephropathy. (Breeding SPF male, age 25 months.)

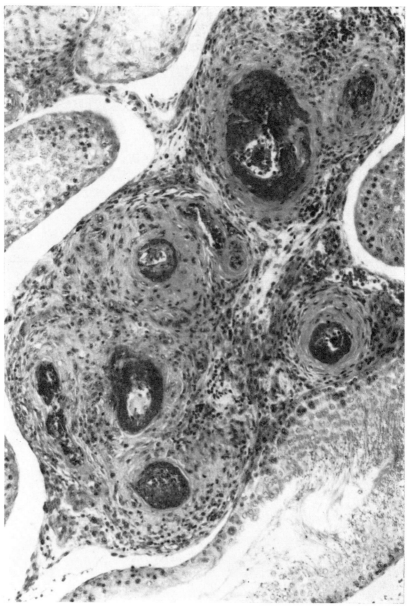

Figure 6. Periarteritis nodosa in the testis. (Dirty male rat, non-breeder, age 26 months.)

larger numbers of SPF animals survive into the tumour-bearing age group. Table X shows this analysis and the incidence of tumours in the two groups is seen to be almost identical.

TABLE X
INCIDENCE OF NEOPLASMS IN DIRTY AND S.P.F. RATS (2)

| | Dirty Rats | | S.P.F. Rats | |
	Benign	Malignant	Benign	Malignant
TOTAL NEOPLASMS IN 30 MONTHS	142	57	117	43
NO. OF ANIMALS RECEIVING FULL P.M.'S	380	380	208	208
% INCIDENCE IN THESE ANIMALS	37%	15%	56%	21%
NO. OF ANIMALS IN EXPERIMENT	572	572	482	482
% INCIDENCE TO 30 MONTHS IN ALL ANIMALS	24.5%	10%	24%	9%
INCIDENCE IN ALL ANIMALS EXCLUDING PRIMARY LUNG LYMPHOSARCOMATA		7.4%		

It is reasonable to enquire whether the histological types of tumour seen are similar in the two groups. Table XI shows such an analysis and, if lymphosarcoma of the lung be excluded as we believe it reasonable to do, it can be seen that there is no significant difference between the clean and dirty animals in this respect.

TABLE XI
COMPARISON OF THE INCIDENCE OF VARIOUS COMMON NEOPLASMS
IN DIRTY AND S.P.F. RATS

	Dirty Rats	S.P.F. Rats
FIBROADENOMA MAMMA	19	17
PITUITARY ADENOMAS (24 - 30 MONTHS)	56	52
THYROID ADENOMAS	8	7
PHAEOCHROMOCYTOMAS	14 (9 ♂ 5 ♀)	8 (5 ♂ 3 ♀)
ISLET CELL ADENOMAS	3	5
LEYDIG CELL TUMOURS	11	9
LYMPHOSARCOMA LUNGS	15 + 4*	1*
OTHER LUNG TUMOURS	7	6
FIBROSARCOMAS & ANAPLASTIC SARCOMAS	7	6
OTHER TUMOURS NOT ACCOUNTED FOR ABOVE	53	42

*Lymphosarcomas present in lungs but probably not arising there.

The commonest varieties of tumours noted were mammary fibro-adenoma of the young age groups and, in the older animals, tumours of the endocrine organs, particularly pituitary adenomas (Fig. 7), thyroid adenocarcinomas (Fig. 8), Leydig cell tumours

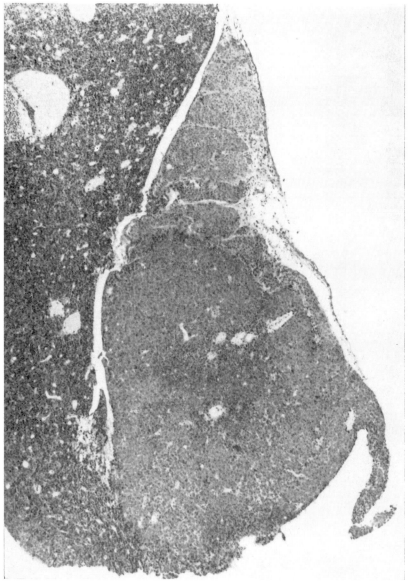

FIGURE 7. Pituitary adenoma. (Non-breeding SPF male, age 24 months.)

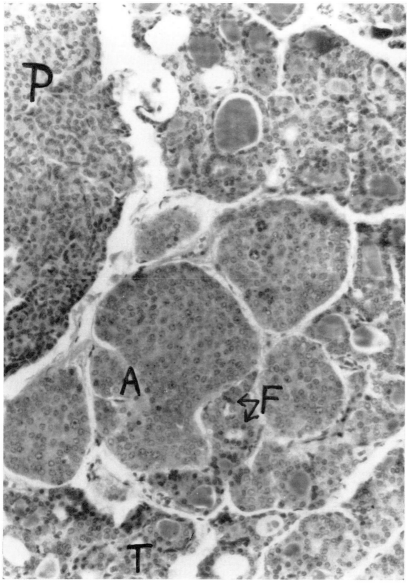

FIGURE 8. Early adenocarcinoma of the thyroid. (Non-breeding SPF male, age 30 months.)

P = parathyroid
A = adenocarcinoma
F = thyroid follicles surrounded by neoplasm
T = normal thyroid

(Fig. 9), phaeochromocytoma, and tumours of the pancreatic islets.
It is interesting to note that the tumours of the pancreatic islets
all occur in animals with other tumours. Numbers are unfortu-

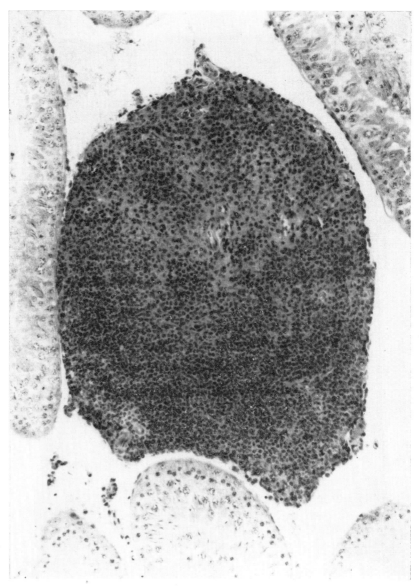

FIGURE 9. Small Leydig cell tumor of the testis. (Non-breeding SPF male,
age 24 months.)

nately too small to be sure whether this represents a fundamental feature of such tumours. Altogether, some forty-nine histological varieties of tumours were observed.

DISCUSSION

The experiments reported in this paper are not complete; although all the dirty animals have died, some of the SPF animals survived until a few weeks ago and some of these animals had a life span of nearly four years. Despite the incomplete data, it has been thought worthwhile to present them at the present time, rather than to await the completion of the analysis of the experiment, which may take some considerable time. There are several reasons for publishing the data at this time. The most important reason is that many institutions and individuals must be contemplating the establishment of SPF colonies and will wish to know what sort of animal may be produced. The second reason for presenting the results now is the attitude of certain authorities who, as a part of their legal obligations, have to consider the results of a variety of animal experiments. In at least some cases, doubts have been expressed about the worth of SPF animals, particularly in toxicity experiments. There can be no doubt that the SPF animal is different in many respects from his dirty brother. Some of these differences are readily observed by individuals used to handling experimental animals. The general condition of the SPF animal is strikingly better than the dirty animal of a similar strain. However, their pharmacological reactions are similar to those of the dirty animal, although quantitative differences appear in the reactions to stress. Relevant figures are given by Davey (1962).

The most striking difference between SPF and dirty animals is the virtually complete absence of early mortality in the SPF animal. Most people who work with dirty experimental animals have had the frustrating experience of a complete failure of an experiment lasting perhaps only a few weeks or months because of massive mortality unrelated to the variable studied in the experiment. Such massive mortality is most commonly due to chronic murine pneumonia and it is now completely feasible to produce, as a routine, animals in which this disease is unknown. A further corollary to this point is related to the use of rats in studies of pulmonary diseases. The histology of the normal rat lung is so different from that commonly seen in dirty animals carrying pneumonia virus that it would not be too much to say that most studies of the reactions of the rat lung to experiment are of no value whatsoever unless they have been carried out on rats shown to be free of the disease.

As well as freeing the stock from chronic pneumonia, SPF rearing markedly reduces the incidence of other infections and completely, or almost completely, abolishes metazoan parasites. Although metazoan parasites are not an important cause of death in experimental animals, there can be no doubt that a heavy parasite burden must materially detract from the general well-being of the animal. In certain circumstances such parasites may determine the onset of a fatal disease, for example the fibrosarcoma of the liver which is commonly associated with encysted worms.

It is noteworthy that, despite the major change produced by SPF conditions in the incidence of infection in animals reared in such conditions the incidence of neoplasia remains unaffected. It is perhaps disappointing that some effect on the incidence of neoplasia does not occur. However, it is convenient, since it would have been a major difficulty had SPF conditions so modified the incidence or the nature of neoplasia as to cause doubts about all work done on this subject in the past.

In summary, therefore, it can be said that the SPF animal represents a more reliable and consistent basis for the study of any pathological process or pharmacological reaction than the disease-ridden animal reared in conventional dirty conditions.

The objections to the use of such animals do not really support examination. It is sometimes argued that, as far as toxicity tests on drugs are concerned, the dirty animal carrying occult infections is a more realistic subject for study than the SPF animal. This view is, of course, nonsense. Drugs are used in human beings to treat a specific disease and it is unusual for more than one major specific disease to be present and to require treatment in the same individual at any one time. If it is thought that the presence of the disease in man might modify the reaction to the drug, then the experimental animals used for the study of the action of the drug in the laboratory should be directly modified by some specific experimental procedure, so as to resemble the human subjects of the ultimate experiment as closely as possible. It is irrational to believe that a rat in the later stages of chronic murine pneumonia resembles a human suffering from any disease whatsoever more closely than does a healthy rat. The only possible result of using animals in which such burdens of disease are present is the total confusion of the experiment and the accumulation of a series of uninterpretable pathology data.

The duration of chronic toxicity tests is the subject of considerable debate at the present time. It is perhaps not appropriate to discuss this subject here, except to state our personal belief that very long studies never produce information that could not have been obtained or predicted from the results of adequately conducted short studies, the exception of course being information about carcinogenesis. However, the health and longevity of the strain of animal used clearly has an important bearing on the length of toxicity studies, and the natural incidence of tumours has a bearing on studies of carcinogenesis.

Experiments of two years' duration in rats are commonly piously called "life-time" studies. Our figures make it clear that this is a misnomer. Two years is only a life time study in the rat when the animals are so debilitated by parasitic infections and bacterial and viral illnesses that they die prematurely. Experiments of two years' duration, therefore, represent at best an expediency imposed by the inferior quality of most experimental animals used in them. Since the hallowed "two-year experiment" can be seen to be based only on a misconception of the natural life span of the rat, the whole question of the correct duration of a chronic toxicity study should be examined from a basis of scientific principle.

Our figures make it clear that SPF rearing does not affect the age at which tumours become an important cause of mortality and morbidity, nor the types of tumour encountered. Since a higher proportion of animals survive into the tumour-bearing age, SPF animals are clearly more satisfactory for studies of carcinogenesis than are dirty animals. We do not know whether the incidence of induced tumours will be similar in the SPF animal to that in the dirty animal, but the virtual identity of the true incidence of tumours between the two stocks suggests that SPF rearing will not affect the response of the animal to administered carcinogens.

It is our belief that the SPF animal is superior to the dirty animal for virtually every experimental procedure, and that it is indispensible for experiments that must be interpreted by the pathologist. Indeed we would perhaps go further and say that the interpretation of most pathology experiments lasting more than a day or two is open to grave doubts unless SPF animals have been used.

SUMMARY

The morbidity and mortality of two groups of rats are compared. One group was reared in conventional dirty conditions and the other was reared in SPF conditions. It is shown that the SPF animals live longer and show fewer infections that do dirty animals. The incidence of neoplasia is identical in the two groups. The significance of these findings is discussed from the point of view of the interpretation of pathology data.

ACKNOWLEDGMENTS

A large number of individuals took part in the work reported here. We wish particularly to thank Mr. G. W. Ash, who has been in general charge of the husbandry of all the animals in the experiment, and Miss Mary Tucker, who has done much of the routine histological examination involved in the experiment.

REFERENCES

DAVEY, D. B.: *Lab. Anim. Centre.* coll papers, *8*:17, 1959.
DAVEY, D. G.: *Proc. Roy. Soc. Med.,* 55:256–9, 1962.
KOLETSKY, S.: *Arch. Path.,* 59:312, 1955.
PAGET, G. E.: *Proc. Roy. Soc. Med.,* 55:262–3, 1962.

DISCUSSION

Question: I wonder whether you could predict, if one maintained a dirty colony over a period of years whether there would be a diminution of the incidence of disease and an improvement in the general health of the animals.

Dr. Lemon: The dirty colony has in fact been maintained for a great many years, so I don't think that the incidence of disease would have lessened, without drastic changes in the conditions under which the rats were kept.

Question: You mentioned the Nelson test. Does this include PPLO cultures and mouse inoculations?

Dr. Lemon: It included mouse inoculations. At that time we weren't very clever at growing PPLO's. We have since learned how to grow them properly.

Question: Is your SPF colony cared for by conventional methods? I mean, these rats weren't kept in isolation, were they?

Dr. Lemon: They are kept in a unit in which everybody who cares for the animals is kept spotless. The animal technicians undress, they have a shower, they get into autoclaved clothes, and then they go into the animal rooms. They don't wear masks. The food is autoclaved. The water supply is not sterilized nor is the air, but there are ultra-violet barriers. We attempt to prevent outside infections getting in as much as we possibly can without imposing too great a strain on everybody concerned.

Dr. Berg: In a series of papers by Dr. H. S. Simms and myself published in the *Journal of Nutrition* (1960-63), observations on several subjects discussed here were reported. Included in the various publications were observations on the effect of endemic respiratory tract infection on nutrition and growth in the rat; data on body weight and skeletal size of uninfected rats from weaning to time of death; the nature of the non-infectious diseases that developed with age; longevity and the onset of lesions; nutrition in relation to longevity with particular reference to the accelerating effect of overfeeding on onset of lesions and longevity; and weaning weight in relation to adult body size and onset of disease.

The lesions described by Dr. Lemon were similar to those observed in our Sprague-Dawley rat strain.

15

THE RECORDING AND REPORTING OF PATHOLOGY DATA

ARTHUR A. NELSON

T HE DIVISION of Pharmacology of the Food and Drug Administration receives a great mass of submitted animal experimental material, including pathology studies, in food additive petitions, new drug applications, investigational new drug data, etc. Many people such as physicians, chemists, pharmacologists, and pathologists, must consider and reconsider these data. The total professional man-hours expended per new food additive, pesticide or drug in the FDA is at least dozens, usually hundreds, and sometimes thousands. You can see, therefore, why a good presentation of data is important. At the least, many man-hours are saved for both sides, and at the most it can mean the difference between life and death to at least a few people.

The first suggestion seems obvious—good organization of the material; consecutive numbering of the pages, if reasonable and possible; an index, or table of contents; a clearly written summary and evaluation; tables that stand by themselves. Yet, a rather high percentage of individual reports and of volumes of data fails in one or more of these respects.

In the histopathology report on a given experiment, one should state what tissues were examined and from how many animals. These important points are often omitted. Knowing what was looked at microscopically and was negative is important to us. Gross examination, if negative, may mean little; we have too often seen severe microscopic changes with an essentially normal gross appearance, even in large organs.

In an individual animal report or in a table, one should not simply identify an animal by a number, leaving the reader to ferret from elsewhere the dosage, the duration, the route, etc. On the other hand, for normal organs excess verbiage in the ritualized autopsy protocol style such as "the capsule strips with ease," or "the testicle has a normal tunica albuginea," are a waste of time and space. There is a happy medium between this type of report and a mere statement that for a group of animals "microscopic study was negative."

Use and present data on proper control animals. "Proper" means concurrently run and under the same conditions, except for the test chemical, and use of littermates if possible. If the test animals are dosed by tubing or injection, the controls should be given the vehicle and not merely be untreated. We have seen some bad examples of the lack of control animals. At worst, it allows the assumption that all abnormalities are a result of treatment, whereas they may be incidental. Last year's controls will not do, because animals vary too much from one time to another.

Derived figures or values (e.g., "Drug intake at this dosage level was calculated to be 100 times the suggested human dose"; or "The level of 1000 ppm in the diet represents a daily dose of 38 mg./kg."; etc.) should be accompanied by the bases, that is, the actual numbers used for their derivation. For instance, what particular version of the suggested human dose is being used? The maximum one given in the labeling is the one that counts, yet the laboratory man may have another in mind. What food consumption figure for the animals is being used? That figure may be unrealistic because of uncalculated spillage, the use of only a selected period of time, etc.

Mention of some very practical items in determining the course of an experiment may be omitted in reports. For example, animals dosed "daily" by capsules may receive them five, six, or seven days per week. A seven-day week means 40 per cent more dosing than does a five-day week. Which one was it? As another example, animals may receive medication in addition to their test chemical if some communicable disease attacks the colony. As yet another, administration of a test chemical may be temporarily suspended, or special supplementation of the diet may be temporarily made, in the face of what appears to be excessive toxicity. Without discussing the pros and cons of such practices, it is reasonable to expect that they will be mentioned and discussed.

Brief references to the methods used for blood chemistry, enzyme, etc., determinations should be given. Certain of these methods give different numerical values and have different reliability than others. No more than one line is needed for such reference, and once gathered, the list will need infrequent changing.

For organ weights, one should give relative ones (i.e., on a per cent of body weight basis) if you wish, but also give the absolute ones in any event, and also include the arithmetic averages for groups. Relative weights alone, like the term "significant difference," can be deceptive. The reader generally likes to see the actual weights, from which he can draw his own conclusions as to significance. Too often in reports a summarized collection of significances uncritically mixes everything from mountains to molehills. I personally would rather see a careful evaluation in plain English.

Similarly, in tumor or other pathology tables incidence is sometimes given as a percentage. But percentage of what? Of microscopically sectioned animals, or of all animals in that group? The table doesn't tell. And is the percentage of rats with, e.g., mammary tumor those with tumor of any kind, or of the whole group? When actual numbers are small, percentages become misleading. This emphasizes two points; (1) the reader should be allowed to see actual numbers (how many out of how many?), and (2) tables should "stand on their own," that is, be self-explanatory. In tumor induction studies, tables or graphs should show the time of appearance of the tumors and their incidence at a given time.

As for the question of whether to include individual animal pathology reports, it is difficult to discuss these in any arbitrary manner. In general, we like to see individual reports for monkeys, dogs, and larger animals unless there can be a uniting of a group because of uniformity of response. Individual reports can be short yet complete if the writing is compact. Well-organized tables can often supplement or even suffice for the data on a group of animals. Regardless of what has been presented up to this point, there is then needed a written summary and evaluation of the pathology data, signed and dated by the pathologist. The pathologist is such a key person in helping the FDA that for good or bad his work should stand unadorned. Furthermore, any paraphrasing of his work should be checked by and be acceptable to him. Too often the pathologist is anonymous, and he should not be so.

One important point in summarization and discussion is to focus on the no-effect versus beginning-effect area. Some other facet than the pathology may have shown a beginning effect at a lower dosage level, but pathologists can certainly discuss it for the pathological material. The pathology area is of course more important in subacute and chronic studies than in acute ones, because time has allowed tissue changes to develop, and because the relative dosage is nearer that of the human. It becomes particularly important where mass consumers have no choice about being dosed chronically with small amounts of pesticide residues and food additives, and safety factors have to be set up.

Tabulation is very important. I would recommend the reading of pages 319-381 of the recent book *Introduction to Dynamic Morphology* by Dr. Edmund Mayer. The pathologist's workup of the individual animal data into a report to his employer or to an agency such as the FDA is made much easier if, no matter how the individual animal pathology is or not recorded up to this point, the details for an entire group of animals (say twenty-five rats) are listed on tabulating sheets under appropriate gross and microscopic column headings. Please do not misunderstand; I am not saying that these detailed tabulations should go to the reader, but that such tables are an excellent basis for what he does get. Comparison among groups for any given item is then simply a matter of running the eye down a column for each group, which can be done much faster than going through individual animal sheets. Extraction of data for less detailed reports and tables, such as for the FDA, is greatly facilitated. Of course, if you have a system whereby all bits of raw data are fed into a computer and an accurate comparative report on several large groups of animals comes out in finished form, that is another matter. Until then, the "secret word" for easy comparison and good reporting is "tabulate," not forgetting that clearly written general descriptions and summaries are also necessary.

Among tables that we receive, it would be easy to pick out examples of poor ones; that is, those that are difficult to understand. Time does not permit comment on many examples, and furthermore most tables are large enough so that lantern slide reproduction would show their printing type size below the point of readability. Therefore, I will limit the examples to three, one each of a portion of a poor, a middling, and a good sort of table, for one purpose or another.

Table I is an example of a portion of a poorly designed table of pathology findings, though satisfactory enough for one's own rough evaluations. For this sort of table, put yourself in the place of the reader or reviewer. A full page of explanation was necessary to decipher the meaning of the symbols for the microscopic lesions, and there was no summing up of the incidence and grades of the different lesions.

TABLE I

Rabbit Number	Gross Lesions	Organ or Tissue	Microscopic Lesions
0048	x	liver	pli ±
	x	kidney	ff 1, fli 1
0052	sp	kidney	ff 2, fli 2
	x	liver	fli ±
	x	brain	mg 1, pvlc 1
	x	pitu'y	cy
	x	skin	flppd ±
0068	m ±	lungs	fpn 1
	x	testes	asp

Table II is an example of a portion of a fairly satisfactory type of table of pathology findings. It will be noted that the lesions are named, not given in code. Its main defect is that if the average grade varies much among groups in leaning toward one or the other extreme, misinterpretation occurs. Such trends should either be stated or better yet shown in the table by actual numbers for

TABLE II

Diagnoses	Control			10,000 PPM		
	Male	Fem.	Grade Range	Male	Fem.	Grade Range
Spleen—Normal.......	1/5	—		1/5	—	
" —Hematopoiesis	4/5	5/5	+-+++	4/5	4/4	+-+++
" —Hemosiderosis.	3/5	4/5	+-+++	3/5	3/4	+++
" —Lym. atrophy.		1/5		1/5	1/4	+/o-++
Kidney—Normal......	—	2/5		—	—	
" —Chr. Nephritis	4/5	1/5	+/o-+++	5/5	3/5	+-++
" —Pigment......	2/5		+-+++	2/5	4/5	+-++
" —Tub. protein.	3/5	2/5	+-+++	3/5	2/5	+-+++++
" —Focal regen'n.	2/5	1/5	+-++	1/5	4/5	+-++

each grade. Recording the degree (intensity) of a given lesion is as important as recording the incidence, because tissues generally react in only so many ways, and if (with no greater incidence) the increase in degree of a lesion is beyond the reasonable bounds of chance, it should, if not must, be considered an effect of the substance being tested.

Table III is a somewhat idealized version of a different type of table. It is a summarized toxicology (this includes pathology) table as a sort of capstone to the summaries and the other tables. Let us assume that a chemical is fed to three species of animals; then a rough sketch of such a table could be as follows. In some studies, of course, data will not be available on all of the situations provided for by this type of table, but even an incomplete one is helpful in starting a review of data.

TABLE III
In PPM of Diet (or MG./KG./DAY)

Days of Dosing	No Effect			Sl't Effect			Strong Eff.		
	Rat	Dog	Mky	Rat	Dog	Mky	Rat	Dog	Mky
One Dose......	200	50	100	400	100	200	1100	200	500
1 Week........	100	25	50	200	50	100	600	120	300
2 Months......	60	25	40	100	40	60	400	80	200
1 Year........	25	10	10	50	20	25	100	40	80

"Strong Effect" for single dose is the LD50; for other dosages it means significant mortality or high grade pathological changes.

From a table such as this the reviewer can quickly get his first impression of several important criteria, namely:

(1) The relative sensitivity of the different animals species.
(2) The no-effect level for each species after varying dosage times.
(3) The change in degree of toxicity of a fixed dose with increasing time.
(4) The probable margin of safety with respect to the human dose.

It is then easier to work backward to the details and the verification of critical points than it is to work up to such an overall view in its absence.

The problem of gross pathology data, particularly on the smaller and more numerous animals, is one of both recording and reporting of pathology data. Sometimes the gross examination may not be performed by the professional pathologist who studies the microscopic slides, but by relatively untrained help. In such instances, either nothing or little will be said about gross pathology in what we receive, or else there may be relatively meaningless observations, often suggesting non-existent pathological changes. It is a matter of available qualified help.

We have this problem too, and our way of dealing with it is as follows.

(1) Less trained personnel do the rodent (not dog or other larger animal) autopsies with supervisors who, although not trained in pathology, have by experience become fairly well able to detect abnormalities. Their observations are recorded in their own language, and they also record organ weights.

(2) If anything unusual shows up, a pathologist checks on the fresh tissues from time to time. This gives him the pre-fixation appearance of the lesion in question; he makes notes, and his observations aid the less trained personnel in their further autopsies.

(3) The fixed tissues are then given their definitive gross examination by a pathologist. Since some changes are best seen in fresh tissues (color, presence of fluid, etc.) and other in fixed tissues, I feel that some type of a combined approach, such as the example given, is about the best that can be done in the usual circumstances. It is based on the concept that good notes on gross lesions are very helpful in the study of the microscopic changes.

(4) There is some further discussion of this question on pages 87-88 of *Appraisal of the Safety of Chemicals in Foods, Drugs and Cosmetics,* 1959, Association of Food and Drug Officials of the United States.

This paper is essentially not on how to perform one's pathology studies, yet inevitably the way one does them in reflected in what one reports. I will mention just one thing that is not good practice. That is the sending of pieces of tissue for microscopic examination to a pathologist (who probably has not seen the autopsy and may not even be given treatment data, perhaps for supposedly greater objectivity) who is supposed to write down what he sees in that piece of tissue, and that's it. Then someone else may put together what the pathologist has said about the individual pieces of tissue. This type of pathology study should be avoided if possible. The pathologist needs the treatment data for an accurate evaluation of what he sees. The pathologist who could not be depended on for an accurate opinion if he were given the treatment data would probably give a worse one without them. This is my personal opinion, but a pharmacologist in the FDA (one of the four persons who were asked to comment on this paper) has a different opinion. I believe that the proper sort of a pathologist will, in a borderline situation, use his own method of insuring objectivity even when he has identifying data. Many of us have done this. Then, after a "blind" comparison, the treatment data are valuable to the pathologist in picking up minor degrees of effect in a given dosage group, whereas if he were merely "reading" pieces of tissue in a scattered order, without knowledge of what was done to the animals, he might well consider such minor (and sometimes not so minor) effects as "within normal limits."

Changing the subject a little, let us take up briefly the presentation of informal data. Pathologists, among others, not only present data to FDA in completed form and from a distance, but often have conferences with FDA people prior to this—on the planning of the experiment, interim reports, what residue tolerance might reasonably be asked for, etc. The presentation of toxicology and pathology data at such conferences should ordinarily be guided by one major rule (beyond having, of course, data of good quality to start with) —come to the critical points quickly, and then as becomes necessary work backward from there.

Why? Because often in the animal data gathered together for a new drug or pesticide there is one critical or difficult area—is or isn't there an effect at a certain level; what does this increased organ weight without histological change mean; does or doesn't this compound produce a few additional tumors; is the animals' thyroid hyperplasia insignificant because man will get relatively so much less of the compound? In verbal discussions such points should be an early order of business, and come to grips with by both sides. In written presentations they should be singled out for special and frank discussion, without shading of words to minimize them. With these difficult points out of the way, the rest is less difficult. Also, and we all realize time pressure, let the discussants if possible have the data for study before the moment of the conference.

The easiest, and I believe often neglected, way to the good presentation of data, either written or verbal, to one's employer, to the FDA or to a scientific journal, is to put oneself in the reader's or hearer's place. Failure to do that is usually not unwillingness, just human nature. Specifically, then—after having put together the data on pathology, toxicology, or whatever subject, one should look for lack of clearness and smoothness and orderly organization, for tables that don't stand by themselves (having to go back and forth through the text to understand abbreviations, symbols, dosage, time), for failure to deal critically with the troublesome points, and for lack of indexing and page numbering. Then, when one is satisfied, try it on a critical co-worker who will try to find flaws.

Lastly, a few items upon which I can only briefly touch. We are frequently asked, "Will the FDA accept data from a *foreign source,* or from some unorthodox source in this country?" The answer is "Yes, the data stand by themselves." It is of course more difficult to settle uncertainties about foreign than domestic data. English translations of foreign language material are appreciated. With regard to *statistical treatment,* how much should be included? Generally speaking, about as much as you wish. The data on which the statistical values are based should be furnished in any event, and depending upon the experimental situation, statistical treatment of data may be helpful in some instances and unnecessary in others. *Photomicrographs* are occasionally included with pathology data. It is always a pleasure to see good ones, and for items where individual pathologists have considerably differing standards of grading (e.g., thyroid hyperplasia) they are useful. *Photocopying* of typewritten or similar size tables to get more data on a page is satisfactory, down to about a 50 per cent reduction.

SUMMARY AND CONCLUSIONS

In this paper on "The Recording and Reporting of Pathology Data," there have been mentioned some aspects of the reporting of pathology and allied data to the Food and Drug Administration which make their evaluating of it more difficult than needs to be.

The majority of data received do represent high class work, carefully presented, but as in almost any similar endeavor, a considerable minority could stand improvement. I realize that time pressure may well be a factor, but the following principles should aid in an improvement:

(1) Keep reviewers and future readers in mind, and write with the answers to their questions in mind.

(2) Tables should "stand on their own" and be truly informative by themselves.

(3) Come to grips with, and clearly present, the effect versus no-effect area.

(4) Make every big and little bit of data easy to find.

(5) Include the pathologist's own signed summarizing report and evaluation, no matter what further coordinating and interpreting there may be.

DISCUSSION

Question: I would like to ask Dr. Nelson a hypothetical question:

Assuming that you had a superior pharmacologist and toxicologist setting up an experiment and an excellent pathologist for gross and microscopic examinations, do you think anything would be missed in this particular experiment if organ weights were not included?

Dr. Nelson: I would feel that some things would be missed.

Dr. Stephen Sternberg: Would you comment on the not too uncommon increase of liver weight with no difference in histology. It occasionally occurs with humans that we encounter a large liver, especially in cases with leukemia. We find to our surprise that the liver does not have leukemic infiltration and is otherwise normal and we are stuck with a heavy liver for which we have no explanation.

Dr. Nelson: Industry folks and Food and Drug folks have been discussing this for some time and I don't think that there is any agreement on it. Biochemical determinations of fat, water, glycogen, etc., content might give clues. What did liver function tests show? Perhaps the heavier liver was simply reacting well to a greater physiological work load.

I do feel that in rodents the smaller organs—thyroid, adrenal, and what have you—can vary significantly in weight without any particular histological difference, at least by the routine methods we use.

Question: Dr. Nelson, do you feel that there should be standardization of autopsy conditions such as withholding feed before autopsy and so forth, with regard as to possible effects on organ weights and certain other changes, perhaps, in the liver?

Dr. Nelson: We fast rats overnight that are to be sacrificed and I imagine many places do that. It avoids the mess of a full stomach, variations in liver glycogen, and so forth.

I am not one for too much standardization as long as reasonable sense is followed, but again, this is one of the details of the experiment that should be put into reports so it is in the record.

Dr. Edmund Mayer: May I make a comment?

In view of the difficulties of including morphologic descriptions into reports alongside of other non-morphologic data I think it is gratifying if morphologic findings can be expressed in numbers. The trend toward such participation seems to be quite important in morphology, if a morphologist is to keep abreast of the biochemist and the pharmacologist in presenting interpretable data.

Dr. Charlie Barron: I have never been able to get very much useful information out of organ weights. I think that this organ weight search can be overdone, particularly with a number of persons who are studying wild animals. They run around weighing adrenals; they want to find out why the animal died so they weigh the adrenal.

I think much of the time and money could be spent on studying some other aspect of the disease rather than weighing organs.

Dr. Nelson: Dr. Barron is certainly entitled to his opinion. I think the majority of workers in chronic toxicity experiments would feel that there should be at least the major organs weighed— heart, liver, kidneys, spleen, gonads and perhaps the endocrines. I am not one for going overboard in the most minute and comprehensive weighing including very detailed weights and fine statistics, but I think a reasonable compromise is necessary until there is a specific mass of data available to be argued and discussed as to the merits of organ weights. Until that time it is simply one opinion against another.

Question: I would like to ask a question concerning attempts to objectively read slides and not to identify them at that time as to "treated" or "control" (i.e., blind reading). I wonder if they have done this and whether they would advise this sort of procedure.

Dr. Phyllis Lemon: We very often do this.

Dr. Nelson: I think that sending out pieces of tissue to a pathologist who has not seen the autopsy and does not have adequate gross notes, and then just having him read those pieces of tissue blind and putting down "Here it is, this is what is in it."—I think this is to be condemned.

This present paper was read by four pharmacologists in the Division of Pharmacology and one of them agreed with the questioner, but my own feeling is that a person that couldn't give a reliable opinion if he had the data would give a worse one without it and that there should be a combination. The data should be available and if it looks like it is going to be a close decision then certainly the pathologist could read the groups of slides, not knowing which group was which, but at least have them collected to that extent and then he can be given the data. The truly blind and random reading, I think, will result in the pathologist having wider limits of normality than he otherwise would have, and eventually what is actually a mild but definite effect will be passed off as within those broad normal limits.

Dr. Ernest Feenstra: May I respond?

My own opinion would be close to what Dr. Nelson has stated in that it would be the exception rather than the rule that slides be read blind. They ought to be first read with an understanding of the gross changes. If a problem arises in interpretation perhaps it would be helpful to try and distinguish control from treated in a blind fashion or to ask a colleague if he can distinguish one slide from another. It is only the exception rather than the rule that I would add the blind reading.

Dr. Phyllis Lemon: On important slides I think two people might be needed. I think this really covers what has been said. The second person doesn't necessarily know what is being shown to them at any particular moment.

Dr. Charlie Barron: I am not very much in favor of the blind reading of slides. On something as important as toxicity experiments I find that I have many times to go back and check the normal features carefully, back and forth, when I feel that I may have a lesion, in order to determine whether I do or do not have a lesion. I feel strongly about this and it causes some trouble in my company since I have just about reached the point where I refuse to read any slide on an experiment wherein I didn't enter into the planning of the experiment.

Dr. Nelson: On Dr. Barron's remarks about his thoughts on slide reading, I think we pretty much agree. It is simply a matter of terminology. There have been a number of occasions where I will have a suspicion of some lesion and will be looking for quite small differences, but mental fatigue comes in and one just isn't sure, but then I will take a pack of slides and shuffle them and go at it blind and straighten myself out that way.

Question: If you are doing a toxicity experiment you ordinarily prepare curves of the growth rate. If an animal's curve shows a plateau or even a loss of weight but the liver shows nothing histologically how do you interpret that?

Dr. Nelson: Would you repeat those conditions, please?

Question: In a fairly long-term toxicity experiment, I assume that you make frequent weight determinations so that you have a good curve. If during the course of that experiment the growth curve for a treated rat plateaus, whereas with control rats the weight still increases constantly, and you secure that treated animal at that time and find nothing in the liver or kidneys or anywhere that is pathological, would you then interpret that as a toxic effect?

Dr. Nelson: It would depend upon the amount of that weight difference. I think we need specific data to get very good answers to questions.

Dr. Barron: On the question that has been proposed, one would also have to take into consideration the food consumption of the animal. If this animal has reduced its food intake just be- cause a drug may have an effect on its appetite, this is not neces- sarily a toxic effect of the drug.

Dr. Nelson: That is a very good point. I would agree.

INDEX

421